Beacham's Guide to International Endangered Species

Volume 2

Mammals Listed
1970 to July 1997

Edited by
Walton Beacham
Kirk H. Beetz

BEACHAM PUBLISHING CORP.
OSPREY, FLORIDA

Beacham's Guide to International Endangered Species

Editors
Walton·Beacham
Kirk H. Beetz

Photo Editor
Deborah Beacham

Book and Cover Design
Amanda Mott

Species Accounts
All of the gibbon entries and introduction were written by Lori K. Sheran and Allan Mootnick of the International Center for Gibbon Studies. Most of the other articles were compiled by the editors; some material was contributed by the Threatened and Endangered Species Information Institute, Golden Colorado.

Spine and Cover Photo Credits
Howler Monkey, Art Wolfe
Wild Bactrian Camel, Rich Block
Black Rhinoceros,
   Rick Weyerhaeuser
Douc Langur, Noel Rowe
Mhorr's Gazelle, Art Wolfe

Title Page Photo Credits
Vol. 1, Ring-tailed Lemur
   Noel Rowe
Vol. 2, Long-tailed Marsupial Mouse
   Babs & Bert Wells, NPIAW

Library of Congress Cataloging-in-Publication Data

Beacham's guide to international endangered species,
    volumes 1-2: mammals / edited by Walton
    Beacham, Kirk H. Beetz.
    Includes bibliographical references and indexes.
    Contents: v. 1-2. Mammals listed 1970 to July 1997

    Describes all international endangered or threat-
ened species listed by the U.S. Fish and Wildlife
Service through July 1997, and some other species
listed by IUCN or included in CITES Appendices.

    ISBN 0-933833-34-2 (alk. Paper)

1. Endangered species. 2. Wildlife conservation. I.
    Beacham, Walton, 1943- . Beetz, Kirk H., 1952- .
    QL82.B435 1997   97-35751
    333.95'42--dc21   CIP

Printed in Singapore
10 9 8 7 6 5 4 3 2

Contents
Volume 2

Beacham's Guide to
International Endangered Species

Wild Cattle, Pronghorns, Antelopes, Duikers, Oryx, Sheep, Goat Antelopes, Gazelles, Chamois
Family: Bovidae

Nubian Ibex

Philadelphia Zoo

General Characteristics of the *Bovidae*

The Bovidae family includes pronghorns, wild cattle and spiral-horned antelopes, duikers, grazing antelopes, oryx, gazelles, dwarf antelopes, gerenuk, goat antelopes and chamois. It is one of the most diverse and prolific of all species, and has greatly influenced the dispersal and culture of humankind.

Pronghorns

Pronghorns are among the swiftest and most graceful of mammals, attaining speeds of up to 55 miles per hour. They have long, slim legs and long, pointed hooves that are cushioned and serve as shock absorbers. Both sexes have horns: the buck's horns have forward-pointing prongs and backward-pointed hooks. The rather chunky body is tan and white, providing camouflage against their open prairie habitat, and to facilitate communication. The upper body is tan; the underbody, inner limbs, throat and rump are white. The black face masks of the bucks are used in courtship and in establishing dominance.

Pronghorns occur in the Western United States and Canada, and parts of Mexico. Although they are exceptionally agile, pronghorns are curious and will closely approach moving objects. This characteristic has made them easy prey for humans and natural predators, and their numbers declined from 50 million in the 1850s to 13,000 by the 1920s. On the verge of extinction, pronghorns were the recipient of early conservation efforts, and their numbers have rebounded to 450,000.

Spiral-horned Antelopes

Modern day domestic cattle and water buffalo evolved from the tribe Boselaphini, of which the four horned antelope and the nilgai survive in their Pliocene form. The subfamilies evolved into yaks and bisons on the cold Eurasian plains 3 to 5 million years ago. Having developed a strong tolerance for severe cold, as well as the ability to withstand moderate heat, bovine species were able to adapt well to diverse habitats. And because of their economic value to people, bovine species have generally fared well. The American bison, hunted to near extinction to support the economy of westward expansion, has responded well to conservation efforts.

Unlike the more solitary social behavior of their ancestors, the four-horned antelope and the nilgai, bovines evolved into herd animals. Using their horns and in the safety of numbers, buffalos and other bovines can repel predators, such as lions, that would prevail in one-to-one combat. Using their keen sense of smell to detect enemies, the herd instinct developed into cohesive herd activities so that all individuals respond to threats and opportunities together.

Of the wild cattle species, the lowland and mountain anoas, tamarau, yak, kouprey, and western giant eland are listed as endangered, while the wild water buffalo, banteng, and gaur are listed as vulnerable by IUCN.

Duikers

Duikers are medium-sized antelope named for their ability to "dive" into thickets. Their short forelegs and arched body shape allow them to easily maneuver through dense underbrush. Both sexes usually possess short, conical horns with long hair between; horns are sometimes absent in the female. The coat is reddish to blueish gray and may be striped.

Duikers are difficult to study because they are so well able to hide within their dense, impenetrable habitat. Some species are active only at night, some are active only during the day, and some are diurnal. They require high quality food sources comprised of leaves, fruits, shoots, buds, seeds and bark. They sometimes stalk birds and rodents, and will eat insects and carrion.

Duikers usually live alone or in pairs and pairs seem to mate for life. They defend 5-10 acre territories against intrusion by all other duikers. Female duikers produce one calf; the young reach sexual maturity at about one year of age and leave the parents during their second year, before the birth of the next young. Duikers possess large scent glands beneath each eye from which a clear or blue liquid is secreted. This liquid is used by both sexes to mark territories, by males to mark other males as a prelude to fighting, and by both sexes to mark their partner.

Of the seventeen species of duikers, Jentink's duiker is endangered.

Gazelles

Gazelles are graceful, swift animals with beautiful fur that inhabit open grasslands and semideserts. They can tolerate harsh temperatures, can go long periods (months or years) without drinking water (they obtain moisture from their vegetative food supply), and will migrate to the most suitable habitat. Because of their adaptability and strong reproductive capability, gazelles are one of the most successful animals in Africa and the Middle East, but they are also easy prey for natural predators and have been hunted ruthlessly by humans. As a result, some gazelle species are near extinction.

Gazelles have excellent sight, hearing and smell, which allow them to detect danger in their open habitat. They are also swift runners and in a foot race can outdistance most of their predators. Gazelles run with an unusual gait that easily distinguishes them from antelopes. They bounce stiff-legged with all four feet landing at the same time. These leaps propel the animal high in the air, giving it an aerial perspective on impending danger and making it more difficult to attack.

Physically, the various species of gazelles resemble each other. They have long legs and necks, slender bodies and ringed horns. Unlike many mammals, the females of most species possess horns that are only slightly smaller than the males. It is thought that female gazelles developed horns to defend food resources in their generally under abundant habitats. With the exception of the black buck of India, gazelles are reddish to fawn colored above with lighter underparts. It is thought that this coloration provides some camouflage in the open, semiarid habitat of most gazelles. Some species have dark brown or black lateral bands that divide the upper and lower parts. It is thought that these bands provide a visual marker for keeping the herd together when fleeing. All species have white rumps and the tails are fringed with some black.

Gazelles mark territory with secretions from their preorbital glands, with scratch marks, dung and urine. The function of marking territories is more for identifying and protecting food resources than for monopolizing females. Gazelles are mainly browsers but also graze on grass when it is available. Generally, they eat the greenest vegetation, which might include young shoots, twigs, leaves, grass and even berries. Because food is scarce throughout the gazelles' ranges, it is advantageous for individuals to know the growing seasons and patterns within a territory, and to exclude gazelles that are not part of the group from feeding there.

Gazelles form four types of groups: single territorial males, females with their recent offspring, bachelor groups of non-breeding, non-territorial males, and mixed groups of all ages and sexes outside the breeding season. Males usually mate with the same female or with a small number of the same females from year to year. Breeding males will tolerate a subordinate male entering his territory as long as the subordinate male makes no advances toward the female. Males often spar by locking horns, but these bouts are not intended to change the status of an individual. Serious fights do occur between neighboring territorial males for the right to establish a territory and breed. Because the availability of territories is limited, there are fewer territorial males than breeding females, and there are usually more females than males within a territory.

Although gazelles may breed year round, the conditions within the range may require them to breed seasonally. In harsher climates they breed so that births coincide with new growth in the spring or rainy season. Females retreat by themselves to give birth to one, seldom two, fawns. For a period of several days to a few weeks after birth, the young gazelle will lie hidden in the grass. The mother feeding nearby returns to the infant several times a day to nurse. Once the fawn can run well, it and the mother will rejoin the group.

The primary threat to gazelles is loss of suitable habitat. Increasing human populations have forced goat and cattle ranchers into the gazelles' territories. These livestock animals compete for the gazelles' food sources and cattle hooves degrade the sandy terrain. Goats can even climb trees and eat vegetation that normally can be reached only by gazelles. Additionally, if food resources are scarce, ranchers will exterminate gazelles so that they cannot compete with the livestock.

Goat Antelopes, Sheep, and Goats

The goat antelopes are stocky bovids with small horns, while the true sheep and goats have long, massive curving horns. Extremely adaptable to habitat, from hot deserts to snow-covered mountains, these animals evolved into many body types and markings, and in size, depending on how isolated the habitat was. The grazing antelopes, which occur in less productive, more severe terrain, roam wide areas in gregarious herds which provide a line of defense around the perimeter so that the individuals that are grazing inside are protected from predation.

As sheep and goats moved into higher, more isolated terrain, they developed larger horns and specialized feet. Goats specialized for cliff dwelling, while sheep specialized for open land close to cliffs. Sheep defend themselves against predators through herding tactics, while goats use inhospitable terrain to escape pursuers. The dependence of goats on a specific cliff habitat restricted their ability to disperse. Solitary in their self defense, goats developed larger and larger horns that could deal powerful blows to enemies, including competing males. Because of their ability to graze in sparse or harsh habitat, goats and sheep were domesticated by tribes in severe areas of the world, providing the staples of meat, dairy products, and clothing materials. Their wild ancestors, such as the argalis and the ibex, became the object of sport hunting, and a number of species are on the verge of extinction.

Black-faced Impala

Aepyceros melampus petersi

Art Wolfe

Status	Endangered
Listed	June 2, 1970
Family	Bovidae (Bovine)
Description	Upper body is reddish brown, underbody is pale, usually white; black along the front of its face.
Habitat	Open deciduous woodlands, brush lands, and savannahs.
Food	Grasses, leaves, flowers.
Reproduction	Gestation lasts 6.5 to 7 months, resulting in one young.
Threats	Overhunting; natural predation.
Range	Angola and Namibia

Description

The scarce black-faced impala, *Aepyceros melampus petersi*, is easily distinguished from other impala subspecies by the black coloration of its face. Its upper body is reddish brown, almost mahogany, and the legs are a lighter reddish brown. The underbody is pale, usually white, and the brushy tail is white on its underside, darker on top. The chin and upper lip are also white. Each side of the hindquarters has a prominent vertical black stripe. Overall, the hair is short and sleek.

Males are larger than females. An adult male black-faced impala has a head-and-body length of 4 feet eight inches, whereas an adult female has a head-and-body length of 4 feet 2 inches; an adult male stands 3 feet high at the shoulder, whereas an adult female stands 2 feet 10 inches at the shoulder; their tails are about a foot long. The greatest difference in size between adult males and females is in weight: An adult male weighs 180 pounds while an adult female weighs 100 pounds. Another significant difference between the genders are the horns: Males have them and females do not. The horns are wavy, reminiscent of the shape of a lyre, and they are ridged on the front. They grow up to 2 feet 6 inches long. The hooves of both genders lack clefts.

Behavior

When alarmed, black-faced impalas leap, sometimes several times in quick succession. Their leaps can top 8 feet in height and be over 30 feet long. A distinguishing behavioral trait is that they do not simply try to outrun their predators; instead, they seek out dense ground cover and hide within it.

Black-faced impalas are active all day and night, alternating periods of grazing with periods of rest. Females and their young live in herds 10 to (before their near extermination) 200 members. Bachelor males are sometimes solitary but usually would join into herds of up to 60 members. There are now too few to create such large groups. A herd's home range is 500 to 1500 acres in size. Fully mature males with long horns depart from bachelor herds and either establish a new territory for themselves or drive out another older male from its individual territory. These individual male territories are 50 to 225 acres in size. A territorial male will try to capture females from female herds as they wander through his territory, and he will keep them in a compact group. When male herds venture into his territory, he will keep the females separate from the males by charging between them, with vigorous wagging displays of his horns and loud roars. When a bachelor male challenges a territorial male, the conflict is usually resolved through display. The males will turn their head from side-to-side to display their horns and will slash the points of their horns into bushes. The male with the smaller horns will retreat. Sometimes displays are not enough; combat consists of the males locking horns and pushing and pulling. This is dangerous business because the horns are sharp and strong, capable of inflicting serious gashes; further, the horns may become so firmly locked that they cannot become unlocked, resulting in death for both males.

The black-faced impala differs from its southern impala relatives in having two breeding seasons that coincide with East Africa's two rainy seasons. The two mating seasons run from February to April and August to October. During these periods, the males grunt and roar frequently. The mating ritual begins with a territorial male staring at a mature female. She will then run away and he will chase her. The chase slows to a walk and eventually the female will stop. The male then approaches her with his head outstretched, and he will lick her genital region, and after that he mounts her. Gestation lasts 6 or 7 months, resulting in a single birth. The young are hidden in dense ground cover; even so, natural predators find them and half of the young born during a given season will be killed before they are three weeks old. Youngsters are weaned between four and six months of age. When a territorial male finds weaned young males in a female herd traversing his territory, he will force them out; these youngsters usually band together in bachelor herds. By one year of age, females are sexually mature. Black-faced impala males reach sexual maturity between thirteen and eighteen months of age.

Habitat

Black-faced impalas are found in both mountainous and flat terrain. They inhabit open woodlands, brushlands, and savannahs.

Distribution

Black-faced impalas occur in Angola and Namibia.

Threats

Overhunting the black-faced impalas by

humans for food has brought the subspecies to near extinction.

Conservation and Recovery

Namibia has been making progress in protecting its wildlife, including the black-faced impala. The Namibian government has been trying to both protect its natural heritage and meet the needs of its people, many of whom depend on hunting for their survival. Etosha National Park in northern Namibia has become a particularly promising refuge where several wild species, including the black-faced impala, may be able to recover their numbers.

Swayne's Hartebeest

Alcelaphus buselaphus swaynei

USFWS

Status	Endangered
Listed	June 2, 1970
Family	Bovidae (Bovine)
Description	Large antelope with chocolate brown, shortish hair with white ends; muzzle is black, with a clear stripe at the center.
Habitat	Open steppes to dry savannas, as well as bush regions in flat and hilly country.
Food	Grasses and herbs, loamy and salty earths, and rarely, leaves.
Reproduction	A single calf is born after a gestation period of 8 months.
Threats	Competition with domestic cattle for food; easily hunted.
Range	Ethiopia

Description

Swayne's hartebeest, *Alcelaphus buselaphus swaynei*, is a large antelope of the *Alcelaphinae* subfamily. It is about 79 inches long and 51 inches high at the withers; its weight is about 440 pounds, and its tail is 28 inches long. Because its back is sloped, the animal is higher at the withers than at the end of its body, a typical characteristic of the subfamily of the hartebeests.

Its color is a chocolate brown, with shortish hair with white ends that give its fur silvery reflections. The muzzle is black, with a clear stripe at the center. The upper parts of its legs have dark marks tending to black.

The shape of the horns is quite different from that of other hartebeests. They are very close at the base, then point forward, then inward, then outward.

Behavior

This is a gregarious animal that typically lives in herds; at one time these herds were very large. Adult males, particularly old bulls, are usually solitary.

A single calf is born after a gestation period of 8 months. Calves weigh 29 to 33 pounds at birth and wean after about 4 months. Sexual maturity is reached at about 1.5 to 2.5 years of age. The lifespan of the species in captivity has reached 19 years.

The name "hartebeest" comes from the Afrikaans, and is supposed to mean something like "tough beast." The Boers noted in the old days that the hartebeests were tireless runners which could not be run down with a good horse, as most other antelopes could. In addition, they were supposed to be able to tolerate a large amount of lead.

Swayne's hartebeest feeds on grasses and herbs, loamy and salty earths, and rarely, leaves. It can survive without water for long periods, but generally drinks daily when water is available. Swayne's hartebeest is diurnal, feeding in the early morning and late afternoon and resting in the shade during the heat of the day.

Habitat

Swayne's hartebeest is found in open steppes to dry savannas, as well as bush regions in flat and hilly country.

Distribution

In 1891, large herds of this animal could be seen on the plains of northern Somalia. However, by the beginning of the twentieth century the population in that area had been severely reduced and by the 1960s had been extirpated. The current distribution of Swayne's hartebeest is limited to Ethiopia, where it exists mainly in four distinct groups in the Rift Valley.

Threats

This once abundant animal has been greatly reduced in numbers due to indiscriminate killing and habitat modification. It probably has suffered the greatest contraction in range of all African ruminants, primarily because it must compete for food with domestic cattle, and it is easy to hunt.

Conservation and Recovery

The planned 700 square mile national park of Nachisar will help protect Swayne's hartebeest. Additionally, Senkele Sanctuary holds the largest population with the best reproductive success.

Tora Hartebeest

Alcelaphus buselaphus tora

A. b. jacksoni   Jim Tamarack, Wildlife Survival Center

Status	Endangered
Listed	March 30, 1972
Family	Bovidae (Bovine)
Description	High shoulders, sloping hindquarters, and a slender neck with a long, narrow head; uniformly colored dark chocolate brown coat.
Habitat	Open scrub and thorn bush country.
Food	Feeds on grasses and herbs, loamy and salty earths, and rarely, leaves.
Reproduction	Gestation of about eight months.
Threats	Introduction of domestic cattle, devastating spread of epizoites; some hunting.
Range	Sudan, Eritrea, and Ethiopia.

Description

The tora hartebeest, *Alcelaphus buselaphus tora*, like all hartebeests, has the body conformation of high shoulders, sloping hindquarters, and a slender neck with a long, narrow head. It measures 79 inches in length, with a maximum height at the withers of 53 inches and a weight of up to 400 pounds.

The tora hartebeest has a uniformly colored coat that is similar in color to other hartebeests of this group (such as Swayne's hartebeest, *A. b. swaynei*, which has a chocolate brown coat) but darker. The horns are robust and set very close together at the base. Initially they point upward and outward, then forward, and finally backward and somewhat inward. In the male, the maximum length of the horns is around 22 inches, whereas in the female they are less well developed.

This species is also known as the Ethiopian tora.

Behavior

The tora hartebeest habitually rubs its horns and forehead in the grass and damp earth, often covering its entire body with this mud.

The tora hartebeest is a gregarious animal, generally living in herds of 10 to 15 head. During the mating season, males will establish territory and defend it with force while trying to attract females. After these fierce fights, the participants will often have deep wounds, particularly in the areas of the neck, breast and shoulders, caused by the adversary's horns.

Females give birth to their young after a gestation lasting approximately eight months. Calves are born during the time of the spring rains and are strong enough to follow the mother within a short time.

The name "hartebeest" comes from the Afrikaans, and is supposed to mean something like "tough beast." The Boers noted in the old days that the hartebeests were tireless runners which could not be run down with a good horse, as most other antelopes could. In addition, they were supposed to be able to tolerate a large amount of lead.

The tora hartebeest feeds on grasses and herbs, loamy and salty earths, and rarely, leaves. It can survive without water for long periods, but generally drinks daily when water is available. The tora hartebeest is diurnal, feeding in the early morning and late afternoon and resting in the shade during the heat of the day.

Habitat

The tora hartebeest is found in the open scrub and thorn bush country of northwestern Ethiopia and eastern Sudan. It lives at altitudes between 4,103 and 6,564 feet.

Distribution

The tora hartebeest formerly occurred from southern Egypt to Somalia. It has been extirpated in southern Egypt, and in 1965 there were no more than 200 to 300 individuals surviving in Sudan. Reliable numbers for Eritrea and Ethiopia are not available.

Threats

A certain amount of blame for the decline of the tora hartebeest can be laid on hunting, although that does not appear to be the determining factor. In addition to human hunters, this animal is preyed upon by most local predators, including lions, leopards, and hyenas.

The main cause of the tora hartebeests's decline is the introduction of domestic stock into its range. In addition to competing for forage, the domestic cattle have caused a devastating spread of epizoites, which have decimated the herds of tora hartebeest.

Conservation and Recovery

The tora hartebeest has rarely been kept in captivity, and then only the occasional animal; therefore there has never been a sufficient number to establish a captive population. Since there is no captive reservoir, reestablishing a declining wild population is unlikely.

Clark's Gazelle (=Dibatag)

Ammodorcas clarkei

Philip Jones

Status	Endangered
Listed	June 2, 1970
Family	Bovidae (Bovine)
Description	Long-legged, long-necked gazelle with a head-body length of 59 to 67 inches and weighing 48.5 to 77.2 pounds; only the males have horns.
Habitat	Grassy plains with trees and bushes of the Somali Arid Zone.
Food	Grasses, herbs, leaves, buds and shoots.
Reproduction	Females give birth to 1 or 2 young after a gestation of 5-6 months.
Threats	Poaching and competition with domestic livestock for food.
Range	Somalia and Ethiopia

Description

Clark's gazelle, *Ammodorcas clarkei*, is a long-legged, long-necked gazelle. This graceful bovid has a head-body length of 59 to 67 inches and stands 31.5 to 34.7 inches tall. Its tail measures 11.8 to 14.2 inches. Clark's gazelle weighs 48.5 to 77.2 pounds, depending on sex. Only the males possess horns, which is a single thin horn that curves forward. The flexible pelvis allows this gazelle to stand fully upright on its hind legs, giving it access to vegetation that all other browsers, except giraffes and goats, cannot reach. The coat is a uniform, dark tan color with white patches on the ventral and caudal areas.

A. clarkei was formally described by Thomas in 1891. Another common name for this species is the Dibatag.

Behavior

Clarke's gazelle feeds on grasses, herbs, leaves, berries, buds and shoots especially species of *Commiphora*, *Acacia*, and *Solanum*.

Periodicity is unknown; most gazelles are active in the early morning and early evening hours.

Female Clark's gazelle form small groups, which occasionally may contain a few males. Males, however, are usually solitary except during breeding season.

Females give birth to 1 or 2 young after a gestation period of 180 to 210 days. For a period of several days to a few weeks, the young gazelle will lie hidden in the grass as its mother feeds. The mother returns to this hiding place several times a day to nurse. Clark's gazelle lives 10 to 12 years.

Habitat

Clark's gazelle inhabits grassy plains with trees and bushes scantily distributed throughout. This gazelle is endemic to the Somali Arid Zone, east of the Webe Shebeli River. This area is characteristically a tropical and subtropical desert dominated by broadleaf, deciduous shrub forms no taller than 3 feet. The most abundant tree form is the *Acacia* with grasses dominating the understory.

Distribution

Clark's gazelle ranges from east of the Webe Shebeli river in Somalia and extending to the eastern Ogaden region in Ethiopia, near the Somali border. The estimated population is 5,000 to 10,000 individuals.

Threats

Clark's gazelle has been nearly extirpated as a direct result of poaching and competition with domestic livestock for food. Additionally, grazing has reduced the amount of vegetation thus allowing the desert to expand into former grasslands. Even though Clark's gazelle has a tremendous height advantage for browsing, feral goats can climb trees and are fierce competitors for the sparse vegetation within the gazelle's range.

Natural predators include lions, leopards, cheetahs, wild dogs and hyenas.

Conservation and Recovery

Because of the recent upheavals in Somalia and Ethiopia, little conservation measures have been taken. The hunting bans that are in place are not being enforced.

There are no captive populations. The only attempt at captive breeding was in the Naples, Italy zoo, but it was largely unsuccessful.

Peninsular Pronghorn

Antilocapra americana peninsularis

Harvey Doerksen, USFWS

Status	Endangered
Listed	September 25, 1975
Family	Antilocapridae (Antelope)
Description	Long, slender legs with large eyes and thick, black lashes; the fur is reddish-brown to tan above with white underneath, on the rump, and on two bands across the neck; short black mane on the nape of the neck.
Habitat	Hot, open deserts and grasslands.
Food	Wide variety of shrubs, forbs, grasses, cacti, and other plants.
Reproduction	For the first pregnancy, usually one calf is born; subsequently, females usually produce twins.
Threats	Uncontrolled hunting.
Range	Mexico: Baja California peninsula

Description

As with the other subspecies of the pronghorn, *Antilocapra americana*, the peninsular pronghorn, *A. a. peninsularis*, is well-adapted for life in open country. This robust animal has relatively long, slender legs adapted for swift running to escape predators. The peninsular pronghorn can run and leap over hard ground, reaching speeds of up to 53 miles per hour. When running over long distances, the animal averages 30 miles per hour. The eyes are large in order to see movement over long distances. Heavy eye orbits and thick, black lashes protect the eyes from excessive sunlight.

The fur of the peninsular pronghorn is reddish-brown to tan above with white underneath, on the rump, and on two bands across the neck. It has a short black mane on the nape of the neck. The animal has two distinctive white rump patches that can be seen over great distances. The fairly long, straight, coarse, outer hairs overlay a woolly undercoat. By flexing its skin muscles, the peninsular pronghorn can move its hair to help regulate body temperature. In the hot desert sun, the hairs are erected to allow air to flow over the surface of the skin and keep it cool. The peninsular pronghorn molts in the spring. As the seasons progress, the fur changes from sleek and bright in late summer to pithy and dull by midwinter.

The horns of the peninsular pronghorn consist of a core of laterally flattened bone covered by a keratinous sheath. After the breeding season, the outer sheath is shed. The male's horns are 10 inches long and are dark colored with whitish tips with prongs in front. The female's horns, if present, are smaller, less than 5 inches long, and usually don't have prongs. Hornless females have a small button of horn, less than 1 inch high, covered by a whorl of hair.

In addition to the horn, males and females differ in other characteristics. The male's face and a patch on the side of the neck are black while the female does not have this mask. A male runs with his nose pointing slightly down. The female, however, runs with her nose more horizontal.

Many authorities consider *A. americana* to be the only species in the family *Antilocapridae*, with *Antilocapridae* placed with the family *Bovidae* in the superfamily *Cervidae*. However, other authorities, such as O'Gara and Matson and Honacki, Kimnan, and Koeppl, classified *Antilocaprinae* as a subfamily of the *Bovidae* family.

Thirteen now extinct genera of *Antilocapridae* existed during the Pliocene and Pleistocene, with *Antilocapra* the only living genus. *A. americana* is the single living species of the genus *Antilocapra* and contains 5 subspecies: *A. a. americana*, *A. a. mexicana*, *A. a. oregona*, *A. a. sonoriensis*, and *A. a. peninsularis*.

Behavior

A. americana are territorial, although territoriality in southern populations like the peninsular pronghorn has not been studied. In the populations that have been studied, males over 3 years old compete with each other to form territories between March and October. Some old males return to the same territory year after year. This territory usually has prominent physical borders, a permanent water source, and may be separated by a "no mans land" from other territories. Marking the territory with urine, feces, and glandular excretions, the male constantly attempts to keep groups of up to 23 females within and any other males out of the territory. The females, however, do not remain in a particular male's territory for long, preferring to move freely from territory to territory. Males too old to hold a territory may wander around alone. Young males form bachelor herds of up to 36 individuals.

After mating season, the separate herds come together to form larger groups containing members of both sexes and all ages.

Females usually reach maturity at 15 to 16 months of age. For the first pregnancy, they usually bear one calf. For all subsequent pregnancies, the female usually gives birth to twins or, rarely, triplets. The young are born after a gestation period of approximately 252 days and weigh 4 to 9 pounds. The newborn's fur is wavy and grayish, turning to the adult coloration by 3 months of age. The young grow quickly, outrunning humans by 4 days of age and eating vegetation by 3 weeks of age.

The peninsular pronghorn eats a wide variety of shrubs, forbs, grasses, cacti, and other plants. Southern pronghorns, such as *A. a. peninsularis*, eat more forbs than northern pronghorns. Plants provide a lot of the moisture needed by these animals, although they will drink water when it is available. During the rut, all territories used by does have open water.

The peninsular pronghorn is active both at night and during the day, with slight peaks just after sunset and before sunrise.

Habitat

The peninsular pronghorn lives in the hot, open deserts and grasslands in the Baja California peninsula of Mexico.

Distribution

The peninsular pronghorn currently exists in two areas of central Baja California, Mexico. On the west coast, it can be found from the head of Bolenas Bay in the south to about latitude 29 degrees North. On the gulf side, the animals can be found from a southern boundary beyond 32 degrees North to the southern end of the Colorado desert.

Threats

Centuries of uncontrolled hunting has reduced the populations of the peninsular pronghorn. Even today, illegal hunting continues to kill off the remaining pronghorn. Additionally, the human usurpation and modification of the animal's habitat contributed to the decline of the subspecies.

Conservation and Recovery

The peninsular pronghorn's habitat needs to be sheltered from human intrusion if it is to survive. Mexico has reserved some land, but it is threatened by intrusions of livestock and land development. Further, the peninsular pronghorn has been heavily hunted, but since the early 1980s, Mexico has tried to enforce laws that forbid the hunting. The cooperation between Mexico and the United States in the preservation of the Sonoran pronghorn may have the beneficial side effect of helping conservationists learn how to protect the peninsular pronghorn, as well.

Wood Bison

Bison bison athabascae

Charles R. Belinky

Status	Endangered
Listed	June 2, 1970
Family	Bovidae (Bovine)
Description	Large head, horns curving upwards; brown hair is long and shaggy on the shoulders and front legs, and a large shoulder hump.
Habitat	Prairie or open woodlands.
Food	Grass
Reproduction	Single offspring after 9 months gestation.
Threats	Hybridization; low numbers.
Range	Canada

Description

The wood bison, *Bison bison athabascae*, is one of two races of the American bison surviving to the present day. At the shoulder, it reaches a height of between 5 to 6 feet. In length, it grows to 11.5 feet and it weighs between 800 and 2,000 pounds. The species possesses a large head, horns curving upwards, hair that is long and shaggy on the shoulders and front legs, and a large shoulder hump. Adults are a brown color while juveniles are yellow.

The wood bison is distinguished from other races by their larger size and darker coat which is also denser and more silky. The horns are more slender. The subspecies is one of two races of the American bison, although *B. b. athabascae* is closer in description to the European bison, *B. bonasus* than other races in North America. It is distinguished from the plains race by its larger size, darker coat and longer horns.

Behavior

Bulls often fight during the mating season, leading to courtship rights with females that takes for several hours before mating. After gestation of about 9 months, offspring are produced which are protected by both parents and sometimes by the rest of the herd. Nursing ends after a year and the young will stay with the mother for up to 3 years. The young are born without horns and are reddish in color. Within 2 months of life, horns sprout from a lumpy hump atop the head.

The wood bison herds in sizes ranging from a single family to multiple family groups of a thousand or more. It can run up to 30 miles per hour if threatened despite being the heaviest land animal in North America. In winter, the coat becomes matted with woolly hair covering most of its body. In the spring, the animal rubs its body against trees, rocks, or other bison to remove the winter coat.

The wood bison feeds on grasses, herbs, leaves, shrubs, and twigs. Not chewing their food fully before swallowing, the bison will regurgitate clumps of food while resting and continue chewing. After thorough chewing, the food is again swallowed for digestion. The wood bison grazes in the morning and evening and rests during the day. Life span ranges from 18 to 22 years.

Habitat

The wood bison occurs on large tracts of open grassland and woodlands that are well vegetated. It occupied prairies, plains, forests, and woodlands in North America.

Distribution

This subspecies once ranged through central Saskatchewan and Alberta. It extended from the North Saskatchewan River northward to Lac la Martre and the Horn Mountains in the Northwest Territories, and westward to the eastern slope of the Rocky Mountains. The range ran south along the Rockies as far as Colorado.

The United States military encouraged and supported the slaughter of the wood bison. It was killed for trophies, tongues, and hides. It had been an unofficial policy to actually seek the bison's extinction. A Congressman said the buffalo must go. "They are

as uncivilized as the Indians," he said. At this same time, General Sheridan wrote:

> The Buffalo Hunters have done more in the last two years to settle the vexed Indian Question than the entire regular army in the last 30 years. They are destroying the Indians' commissary. Send them powder and lead, if you will, and let them kill, skin, and sell until they have exterminated the buffalo.

Indeed, Sheridan later told Congress a bronze coin should be minted for the skin hunters with a dead Bison on one side and a dead Indian on the other. Such attitudes prevalent at the time lead to the wholesale slaughter of the bison. Between 1850 and 1880, 75 million hides were sold on the open market. None of these animals was used for food as the Indians used them. 'Buffalo Bill' Cody once claimed to have killed 4,862 bison in one year which would have fed the entire population of San Francisco for two weeks at that time.

By 1893, about 500 wood bison were left.

Threats

When American expansion turned west, the early settlers viewed the wood bison as a nuisance that was in the way. During the period of initial contact with Europeans, herds were described as infinite. In 1839, Thomas Farham wrote that it took him 3 days to travel on horseback through a single herd. In 1871, the famous lawman, Wyatt Earp, wrote:

I could see, twenty or thirty miles in each direction. For all that distance the range seemed literally packed with grazing buffalo. . .the prairie appeared to be covered by a solid mass of huge, furry heads and humps, flowing along like a great muddy river. . . Clear to the horizon the herd was endless.

Today, a few wood bison survive in protected areas of northwest Canada and Alaska, and there are some individuals in zoos, but not enough to sustain a captive breeding program.

Conservation and Recovery

In 1893, the U.S. government began protection measures for the wood bison to save it from extinction. Laws were passed prohibiting hunting. Lands were also preserved for the animals to use. The remaining known numbers were moved to Wood Buffalo Park in Alberta, Canada. By 1922, the plains bison numbers grew to 2,000. It had been thought that the wood bison had disappeared through interbreeding with the plains bison. But in 1957, 200 were found in a remote section of the park. Since then, the subspecies has declined further and in 1965, estimates put it at fewer than 100. Disease caused this subsequent decline. A herd of plains bison transferred to the park introduced tuberculosis. Tuberculosis was the most significant cause of death to the wood bison herd and its numbers continued to decline due to an outbreak of anthrax. This resulted in the death of over 500 bison.

In the summer of 1964, an independent breeding herd was established which consisted of 18 individuals. By 1965, the herd increased to 25. A second herd has been established but the wood bison remains dangerously close to extinction.

Seledang [=Gaur]

Bos gaurus

Kenneth W. Fink

Status	Endangered
Listed	June 2, 1970
Family	Bovidae (Bovine)
Description	Largest of the wild cattle; coat varies from red-brown to purplish-black, with white stockings; tan-to-cream patch between the horns.
Habitat	Deep forests or bamboo jungles adjacent to grasslands or glades.
Food	Grasses, shoots, twigs, and bark.
Reproduction	One young after gestation of 9 months.
Threats	Hunting; habitat loss.
Range	Nepal, Bangladesh, Bhutan, Laos, Thailand, Vietnam, Indonesia (Borneo, Bali, and Java)

Description

The seledang, *Bos gaurus*, is the largest of the wild cattle, weighing up to 2,200 pounds and standing over 7 feet at the shoulders; males are much larger than females. The color of the coat varies from red-brown to purplish-black, with white stockings and a tan-to-cream patch between the horns. The legs are short and stocky and the head is large. Males have a hump between the shoulders that can be as high as 4 feet.

The three formerly recognized subspecies, the Indian gaur (*B. g. gaurus*), the Indochinese gaur (*B. g. readei*), and the Malayan gaur (*B. g. hubbacki*) have been consolidated into one species, *Bos gaurus.*

Behavior

Seledangs graze on grasses, bamboo shoots, twigs, and bark which they forage with their tongues. They feed in the late morning, the early afternoon, and the evening on their way to a resting place. They sleep from midnight until mid-morning when they slowly awaken.

In optimal conditions, seledangs spend the summer in lowland areas and cooler months in the mountains. They rest during the day in shady areas which may be turned into permanent resting sites that are used year after year.

Seledangs are shy and avoid humans. They signal danger by tossing their heads and emitting a high-pitched snort or a growling moo. When the herd is resting, some individuals remain standing to establish a guard against predators, which are usually large cats (tigers and leopards) and humans. Seledangs can detect danger at great distances and will flee all predators, but if cornered, the herd forms a protective ring with the adults on the perimeter and the young inside.

Old bulls are solitary, young bulls may form bachelor herds, and females are gregarious, traveling in herds of one mature bull, juveniles, and several adults cows and their young. Mating may occur year round but peaks between November and May. During the mating season, males may roar for hours, which stimulates the female's receptiveness. Females leave the herd to give birth to one young after gestation of 9 months; she nurses the calf for 9 months, after which she may breed again.

Habitat

Today, the seledang has been driven into high elevations (up to 6,000 feet) where it inhabits deep forests or bamboo jungles adjacent to grasslands or glades.

Distribution

The seledang is widely distributed throughout Bangladesh, Bhutan, Laos, Nepal, Thailand, and Vietnam, and the islands of Borneo, Bali, and Java.

Threats

The seledang's habitat has been rapidly destroyed throughout its range by logging and by conversion to agriculture. It has also been widely hunted for its meat and hide. During the Vietnam war, much habitat and many individuals became victims of the conflict. Today, the seledang is not only threatened by severe loss of habitat, but also by communal diseases, particularly hoof and mouth disease and rinderpest, that it contracts from domestic livestock that co-inhabits some of its grassland range. One field scientist, M. Krishnan, believes that the seledang is more susceptible to infection than any other wild mammal. Sport hunting remains a danger to the seledang.

Conservation and Recovery

The gaur (seledang) was domesticated thousands of years ago into an animal known as the gayal. Some taxonomists regard the gayal as a true, domesticated species originating from the gaur; others regard it as a cross between the gaur and the banteng.

The human population crisis throughout the seledang's range continues to pressure its habitat, and the host countries are doing little to prevent the wholesale destruction of forests, so the fate of the wild populations is uncertain. The captive population of gayals in European and North American zoos is large enough to sustain itself.

Wild Yak

Bos grunniens mutus

USFWS

Status	Endangered
Listed	June 2, 1970
Family	Bovidae (Bovine)
Description	Coat is dark brown, with a black underside and black fringes.
Habitat	Steppes, swamps, and moors with temperatures frequently below freezing.
Food	Grass, herbs, moss, and lichens.
Reproduction	Breeding season is in September and October. Gestation lasts 258 days, resulting in a single birth.
Threats	Human predation for the yak's meat and hide, as well as for sport.
Range	China, India, and Tibet.

Description

The wild yak, *Bos grunniens mutus*, also known as the grunting ox, is one of the least known members of the *Bovidae* family. Much of what is known about it dates back to scientific expeditions in the 1930s. It is a huge animal with a frightening appearance: a massive head sagging down from wide, humped shoulders, a long, straight back, and short, powerful legs. A bull stands as high as 6.75 feet at the shoulders, has a head-and-body length of 10.75 feet, and weighs 1,200 pounds. Cows are much smaller than bulls, standing 5.25 feet at the shoulders and weighing 675 pounds. The male is equipped with impressively large and long horns that are 20 inches in circumference and curve out and then up to the sides of the head, reaching 3 feet in length. The horns of cows are smaller than those of males, reaching about 20 inches in length.

Both genders have shaggy outer coats of hair, with bulls being somewhat shaggier under the lower jaw and neck, as well as along its coat's fringes. The outer coat is coarse, but the inner coat is soft and dense. The shagginess of the coat and the soft inner layer probably serve to help the wild yak conserve heat. The coat is dark brown, sometimes almost black, with a black underside;

The hair around the muzzle is white.

Yak's are good mountain climbers; their short legs help them maintain a low center of gravity which aids them in keeping their balance; their short legs may also help them conserve heat by exposing as little legs to the cold air as possible, while allowing the shaggy fringes of the wild yak's coat to cover much of them. Food is scarce, requiring the wild yak to travel far to find it; it has a keen sense of smell which may aid in its search for food, as well as helping to detect predators such as wolves. They have rough tongues that they use to lick lichens and moss from stones.

Behavior

Little is known of the wild yak's behavior; most of its encounters with humans have resulted in its being killed rather than studied. It does not care for the company of humans, and when it detects them the wild yak responds as it would to other predators: It snorts, holds its head high, and then stares directly at the source of danger. When the herd responds to the alarm, all run away. If, while fleeing, something gets in their way — for instance, a human being — they lower their heads and charge. This is said to be a very frightening sight, but the yaks nearly always pull up several feet short of their target and snort loudly. This would scare away most other animals, but humans often regard this behavior as a sign that the wild yak is a killer. Another aspect of the wild yak's behavior that disturbs people is its response to encountering the domesticated yak, a smaller animal that is descended from the wild yak: The wild yak will kill the domesticated yak.

The wild yak lives in herds, which seem to come in two types. One type has between 20 and 200 members and is composed of females, their young, and immature females. When three years of age, the males leave these herds and form all-male herds consisting of one or two old bulls and several young ones. These herds migrate throughout the year, reaching the lowest elevation of their range in July, when food is most plentiful at the lower elevations, then returning to the higher elevations in August, then to slowly work their way back down to the lowest elevations in July. These migrations usually traverse very harsh, cold, and rocky terrain, but the wild yak is a good, even agile climber that seems to handle even steep, rocky slopes with ease.

The role migration plays in reproduction is not clear, but the birthing of calves in June seems timed to take advantage of the relative abundance of food in July on the lower slopes of its habitat. A cow will give birth only once every two years, probably because it takes a year to wean a calf. During breeding season, a male will single out a female from a herd and focus his efforts on her to reproduce. Other males may contest for the opportunity to mate with the female, with the larger bull usually winning.

The wild yak is very tolerant of cold and even seems to prefer cold areas to warm ones. It will bathe in rivers and lakes even when they are nearly frozen over.

Habitat

The wild yak mostly lives in very cold, as much as 40 degrees Fahrenheit below freezing, highlands of 14,000 to 20,000 feet above sea level. It is found primarily on desert steppes, but also lives in swamps and on moors. These areas tend to be open lands, bare of trees or even tall bushes.

Distribution

The wild yak once ranged from far northern India to northern Siberia. Even in the 1890s, it was still common in central Asia and northwestern China. It now survives in patches, mostly on the Tibetan plateau. Some are to be found in northern India and possibly in Nepal; others live in southeastern Xinjiang, western Qinghai, and northwestern and northeastern Tibet.

Threats

Loss of habitat is a significant problem for the wild yak. Most of its ancient range has been taken over for the raising of domesticated animals such as cattle and sheep. Of greater significance is the hunting by humans of the wild yak for its meat, hide, and hair, each of which is much prized. The yak has been pressed out of its range primarily by extensive, constant hunting, with local populations being exterminated throughout most of central Asia. Although the twentieth century has seen the wild yak hunted relentlessly, the key period for the near extinction of the wild yak was the 1950s into the 1970s; yaks were nearly wiped out for their meat, to feed people who were starving because of government mismanagement of agriculture. At present, the wild yak is protected under Chinese law, but people still kill it for its meat and skin, and others hunt it for sport, sometimes as guests of government officials.

Conservation and Recovery

China's huge Arjin Shan Reserve is home to some wild yaks; the reserve's great size, 17,000 square miles, means that wild yaks have the space to continue their migratory way of life. The Arjin Shan Reserve needs to be well protected if the wild yak is to survive; it is likely to be exterminated from all other parts of its range. Zoos do not hold many wild yaks, making a captive breeding program unlikely. The wild yak is included in CITES, Appendix I: Trade Prohibited. This prohibition is unlikely to have an effect on the yak's survival because international demand for the animal is small; local law enforcement is the key to the wild yak's survival.

Banteng

Bos javanicus

Art Wolfe

Status	Endangered
Listed	June 2, 1970
Family	Bovidae (Cattle and oxen)
Description	Small hump and slender legs; short coat is reddish brown to black with white stocking feet.
Habitat	Open forests with dense vegetation.
Food	Leaves and grass.
Reproduction	1 to 2 young.
Threats	Diseases carried by domesticated cattle, competition for resources.
Range	Indonesia, Southeast Asia.

Description

The banteng, *Bos javanicus,* weighs 1,100 to 2,000 pounds, making it slightly smaller than its other oxen relatives. Part of its slighter build can be attributed to a smaller hump and slender legs. The short coat varies in color from reddish brown to black; both sexes have white stocking feet that reach above the knees. Males are darker than females and are much heavier. Males have a bald spot between the two horns, which have thick bases narrowing to points. The horns are strongly decurved; they are perpendicular to the head and curve in a long, almost half circle over the head.

Behavior

The banteng eats the tender leaves, flowers, and shoots of bushes and trees, and grazes on grass when these are unavailable.

Generally, bantengs herd in groups of a few individuals, no more than 40, led by a dominant bull. Older males become solitary and younger males may form bachelor groups. Mating occurs in May and June; birth occurs in 9 to 10 months, after which the female may mate again in 6 to 8 weeks. Calves are weaned at 9 months and become sexually mature at 2 to 3 years of age.

Bantengs often associate with other animals and live harmoniously with pigs and deer.

Habitat

The banteng lives in open forests and prairies of southeast Asia, and prefers dense vegetation with access to open grazing land. It rarely intrudes on cultivated land, and avoids human contact.

Distribution

As a domestic animal, the banteng was historically widely distributed throughout eastern Asia and Australia. The domesticated animals, known as Bali cattle, are not a pure strain, and these feral cattle breed with the wild animals and contaminate the pure stock. Isolated populations of unknown numbers occur in Indonesia, especially Borneo, Bali and Java, and in Laos, Myanmar, Thailand and Vietnam.

Threats

This species is threatened by diseases carried by domesticated cattle, from competition for resources by other wild cattle, by small numbers and widely isolated populations, and by the reduction of pure breeding stock caused by inbreeding and by breeding with impure stock. The local human population relentlessly hunts the banteng for meat, and its natural habitat is being destroyed by expanding agriculture.

Conservation and Recovery

Nature preserves have been established on Java, and captive breeding programs are underway at zoos in Europe. The most effective conservation measure could be isolating wild populations from domestic livestock so that the purity of the breeding stocks can be regenerated.

Kouprey
Bos sauveli

Banteng (*Bos javanicus*) close relative   San Diego Zoo

Status	Endangered
Listed	June 2, 1970
Family	Bovidae (Bovine)
Description	Dorsal hump, backward-pointing horns with tips that curve and taper inward to point; coat of the male is dark brown; females are gray with lighter underparts.
Habitat	Open forests, rolling hills, and savannas with patches of forests.
Food	Bamboo grass, ploong grass, leaves, and sedges.
Reproduction	Mating occurs in April, producing one young after gestation of 8-10 months.
Threats	Hunting, transformation of its habitat by farming and logging.
Range	Cambodia, Thailand

Description

The kouprey, *Bos sauveli*, has a dorsal hump, backward-pointing horns with tips that curve and taper inward to a point, and a large dewlap. The coat of the male is dark brown; with lighter underparts; females are gray with lighter underparts and darker chest and forelegs. The lower part of the legs are white with a dark stripe running up the forelegs. There is a chestnut colored patch surrounding each eye and on either side of the muzzle. Males weigh up to 2,000 pounds and stand 6 feet at the shoulder. The horns have the wid-est spread of any of the wild cattle. The male's horns curve inwards; the female's are lyre-shaped.

Behavior

The diet of koupreys includes bamboo grass, ploong grass, leaves, and sedges. They travel sometimes long distances at night in search of suitable vegetation.

During the dry season, males and females mix in herds; other times of the year females herd with their offspring and young males form bachelor herds. Mating occurs in April, producing one young after gestation of 8 to 10 months.

Habitat

Koupreys prefer open forests, rolling hills, and savannas for grazing with patches of forests for protection.

Distribution

The kouprey was not identified as a species until the head of one was seen in the trophy room of a Swiss hunter in 1937. It has always been rare in modern times, perhaps numbering no more than 2,000 individuals, and its numbers rapidly diminished to about 100 during the Vietnam war. It is restricted to the northern plains of Cambodia in two populations separated by the Mekong River; and to eastern Thailand. The total population is no more than 300 animals.

Threats

As one of the world's largest mammals, the kouprey is most threatened by human hunters, especially guerilla militia groups armed with weapons of war. The transformation of its habitat by farming and logging has restricted its range and isolated populations. Inbreeding with domestic cattle may have reduced the viability of breeding stock. The kouprey has a low reproductive rate, possibly as the result of calcium and phosphorus deficiencies in its diet.

Conservation and Recovery

The kouprey is the national animal of Cambodia and receives protection from hunting. Three of its populations are on wildlife reserves, which are secured by the military. The kouprey could be captively bred, and the local people could derive economic benefit from livestock use of the animal, which would help ensure its protection.

Lowland Anoa

Bubalus depressicornis

San Diego Zoo

Status	Endangered
Listed	June 2, 1970
Family	Bovidae (Bovine)
Description	Small Asian buffalo, 3 feet tall; dark brownish, often with white markings on the legs; triangular-shaped horns, pointing straight back from the top of its head.
Habitat	Undisturbed forest on the island of Sulawesi, Indonesia.
Food	Probably grasses near rivers, creeks, or waterholes.
Reproduction	Single calf each year.
Threats	Loss of habitat due to agricultural practices.
Range	Indonesia Island of Sulawesi

Description

The lowland anoa, *Bubalus depressicornis*, is the smallest of the Asian buffalo, standing about 3 feet tall at the shoulders and weighing 330-660 pounds. The adult anoa's color varies from dark brown to black to light tan, often with white markings on its face, throat, chest and forelegs; the thick, woolly hair of the juveniles is usually yellowish-brown; males are darker than females with small white patches. Many mature animals are almost hairless. The animal's horns, triangular-shaped in cross-section, point straight back from the top of its head to a length of approxi- mately 14 inches. This rainforest animal has short legs that give it good footing, and oily, exceptionally tough skin to help it shed water and repel insects.

Other taxons formerly used for *Bubalus depressicornis* are *Anoa depressicornis* and *Bubalus anoa depressicornis*.

Behavior

In the wild, this shy animal is solitary or in pairs with a breeding mate or calf. The female may bear a single calf each year after a gestation period of 275 to 315 days. Newborns can stand within thirty minutes of birth. The calf stays close to its mother in the herd for two years and attains full size within five years.

Little is known about the eating habits of this rare herbaceous ruminant, but its diet includes grasses, leaves, ferns, fruits, saplings, palms and ginger. It prefers to feed near rivers, creeks, or waterholes.

The lowland anoa rests in the shade during the hottest part of the day, and grazes at night or early in the morning.

The lowland anoa can quickly disappear into the heavy vegetation of their habitat, which offers them good protection from predators.

Habitat

The lowland anoa is found only in the swampy undisturbed forest on the island of Sulawesi, Indonesia. Because this rare buffalo stays in the thick underbrush of the island's forests, its habitat requirements are relatively unknown.

Distribution

At the end of the nineteenth century, anoas were abundant throughout their range and were common until the beginning of World War II.

The lowland anoa population is now confined to the lowland areas of the island of Sulawesi, Indonesia. The population probably numbers a few thousand individuals.

Threats

Before World War II, tribesmen armed with primitive weapons were reluctant to provoke this fierce animal, but after modern firearms were introduced after the war, the anoa was widely hunted. The hunting regulations that were strenuously enforced before the war were not enforced afterward, and massive killing was reported.

Destruction of the Indonesian forest because of agricultural practices and population pressures threaten this extremely rare buffalo. The World Bank lists the Indonesian island of Sulawesi as a wildland area of special concern because the forest has been reduced to comparatively small patches and continues to undergo rapid attrition.

The gene pool of the lowland anoa has been seriously depleted so that a continual decline in the health of the remaining population is expected.

Conservation and Recovery

To protect the habitat for the lowland anoa and other species, the Indonesian government and other organizations are setting aside national parks and wildland management areas in Indonesia. Also, the Indonesian government's land management program includes agricultural improvement plans that will relieve the pressure on existing forests.

Small numbers of lowland anoas are living in captivity in Europe and North America and reserves have been established in seven locations in Indonesia.

Tamaraw

Bubalus mindorensis

Philip Jones

Status	Endangered
Listed	December 2, 1970
Family	Bovidae (Bovine)
Description	Dwarf buffalo with short, thick horns and dark gray coat.
Habitat	Forested edge with open grass-lands.
Food	Grasses, bamboo shoots, and aquatic vegetation.
Reproduction	Females bear a single calf each year.
Threats	Alteration of habitat.
Range	Philippines

Description

The Tamaraw, *Bubalus mindorensis*, is a dwarf buffalo and is the largest animal endemic to the Philippines. The tamaraw stands about 39.5 inches high and weighs about 660 pounds. The horns of this species are short and thick and measure 14 to 20 inches long. The coat is dark gray with white markings on the head, nape and legs.

This species is also known under the genera *Anoa* as *Anoa mindorensis*. Tamaraw may also be seen in the literature spelled "Tamarau."

Behavior

The tamaraw feeds on grasses, bamboo shoots and aquatic vegetation near its watering hole. The tamaraw is probably most active during the early morning hours and at dusk. It wallows in mud, often with its whole body immersed.

The female may bear a single calf each year during the rainy season (June to November) after a gestation period of 276 to 315 days. The newborn will stand after about thirty minutes. The youngster stays close to its mother for about two years, but will play with other calves of the herd.

The tamaraw is considered rather fearless and has been compared to a rhinoceros in respect to its ferocity. Males do not like to be around each other. Adult females will group with their young and occasionally with a breeding male.

Habitat

When the tamaraw was plentiful, it preferred extensive grass plains with good water supplies. It now occurs in 12 square miles of forest edged by open grasslands which are easily accessible. The forest provides dense cover and water.

Distribution

This species is known only to have occurred on the Philippine island, Mindoro, where it was widespread in the early 1900s, perhaps numbering 10,000 animals. By 1970 the population has declined to 150 to 200 individuals. Current distribution is fragmented over Mount Calavite, Baco Range and Mount Iglit. In 1987 the population was estimated at 350 animals.

Threats

The tamaraw's habitat has been exploited for agricultural and commercial use, including farms, mines and sawmills. After World War II, guns were readily available in the Philippines and hunting restrictions were difficult, if not impossible, to enforce. Fires set in the summer are used to flush out animals; all animals seen fleeing are immediately shot. The primitive people of Mindoro have historically hunted the tamaraw. It is not believed that these peoples' hunting practices contributed to the current demise of the species. However, domestic cattle spread rinderpest to the tamaraw, which resulted in heavy losses through disease.

Conservation and Recovery

In 1920 an area on Mount Calavite was established as a preserve for the tamaraw. But hunting restrictions are difficult to enforce and the species was afforded little protection by this effort. In 1961 Mount Iglit Game Refuge was established, but the refuge has now been almost completely stripped of its native forests.

In early 1969 the IUCN Survival Service Commission and the World Wildlife Fund evaluated the Philippine situation. The conclusion was that the tamaraw's population had been drastically reduced, but the three remaining populations were most likely viable. This exhibition set the precedent for the establishment of the Philippine Wildlife Conservation Association. This association has made hunting of the tamaraw illegal.

A captive breeding program was begun in the Mt. Iglit Baco National Park, but it has achieved only limited success.

Mountain Anoa

Bubalus quarlesi

Ron Garrison, San Diego Zoo

Status	Endangered
Listed	June 14, 1976
Family	Bovidae (Bovine)
Description	Small buffalo with light-brown coloring.
Habitat	Upland forests on the island of Sulawesi, Indonesia.
Food	Probably on grasses near rivers, creeks, or waterholes.
Reproduction	Single calf each year.
Threats	Loss of habitat.
Range	Indonesia (Sulawesi Island)

Description

The Mountain anoa, *Bubalus quarlesi,* a close relative of the lowland anoa (*B. depressicornis;* see separate entry), is a very small Asian buffalo with uniform dark brown or black coloring. The animal's horns, triangular-shaped in cross-section, point straight back from the top of its head and are very similar to a lowland anoa's horns, except shorter.

The mountain anoa has short, stocky legs and even-toed hooves that enhance its climbing ability. Like the lowland anoa, this species has oily skin to help it shed water.

Until recently, *Bubalus quarlesi* was considered a subspecies of the lowland anoa (*Bubalus depressicornis*). *Anoa depressicornis quarlesi* and *Bubalus anoa quarlesi* are taxons formerly used for *B. quarlesi.*

Behavior

The mountain anoa is most active at night; it grazes or browses on grasses leaves, ferns, fruits, saplings, palms and ginger at night or early in the morning, and rests during the hottest part of the day.

Not much is known about this species in the wild. However, in most species of wild buffalo, the female may bear a single calf each year after a gestation period of 275-315 days. The calf stays close to its mother in the herd for two years and attains full size within five years.

Habitat

The mountain anoa is found only in the

upland forests on the island of Sulawesi, Indonesia. Because this rare buffalo stays in the thick underbrush of the island's wooded mountains, its habitat requirements are relatively unknown.

Distribution

The mountain anoa's population is confined to the upland areas of the island of Sulawesi, Indonesia.

Threats

Destruction of the Indonesian forest because of agricultural practices and population pressures threaten this extremely rare buffalo. The World Wildlife Fund lists the Indonesian island of Sulawesi as a wildland area of special concern because the forest has been reduced to comparatively small patches and continues to undergo rapid attrition. Because this is an island habitat, the anoa cannot retreat to a more hospitable area.

Conservation and Recovery

To protect the habitat for the mountain anoa and other species, the Indonesian government and other organizations are setting aside national parks and wildland management areas in Indonesia. Also, the Indonesian government's land management program includes agricultural improvement plans that will relieve the pressure on existing forests.

Small numbers of mountain anoas exist in captivity with a few being bred, mostly in Germany.

Markhor Goat

Capra falconeri chiltanensis
Capra falconeri falconeri
Capra falconeri heptneri
Capra falconeri jerdoni
Capra falconeri megaceros

Capra falconeri   C. Allan Morgan

Status	Endangered/Vulnerable
Listed	June 14, 1976
Family	Bovidae (Cattle, sheep, goats)
Description	Large, reddish to gray goat; males have a thick beard and a long shaggy mane; legs are white from knees to feet with black stripes; a dorsal stripe runs from the shoulders to the tail; the horns are gray.
Habitat	Steep rocky terrain from 2,300 to 12,000 feet elevation.
Food	Leaves, barks, grasses.
Reproduction	One often two young.
Threats	Hunting.
Range	Afghanistan, Pakistan, Russia

Description

Taxonomically, markhor goats have been treated differently by authorities. Until recently, 5 subspecies of *Capra falconeri* were recognized: *C. f. chiltanensis*, *C. f. falconeri*, *C. f.* *heptneri*, *C. f. jerdoni*, and *C. f. megaceros*. Generally, the subspecies were distinguished by the shape of their horns, and they are commonly referred to as "screw goats" because the horns resembled a screw. More recently, some authorities, including USFWS, classify *C. f.*

chiltanensis as a "wild goat," and have elevated it to a full species, *Capra aegagrus chiltanensis.* Furthermore, other authorities have consolidated the five subspecies into two: one northern species with broadly twisted horns, *Capra falconeri falconeri;* and the southern species with narrowly twisted horns, *C. f megaceros.* USFWS classifies *C. f. megaceros, C. f. jerdoni,* and *Capra aegagrus chiltanensis* as endangered. IUCN considers *C. f. megaceros* as endangered and the other subspecies as vulnerable.

The bucks, which weigh up to 230 pounds and stand 3.5 feet at the shoulders, have twisted horns that spiral and beard on the chin. The northen species have long neck manes. Does have smaller horns that are also twisted and spiraled. The body color changes throughout the year, more reddish in summer and tan to dark brown with black guard hairs in winter; the face may be darker than the body color, with a thick beard starting at the chin, and the mane is white to dirty white. The legs are white from the knees to the feet, with black markings or stripes. A dorsal stripe runs from the shoulders to the tail. The horns, which may grow as long as 4 feet in the males (only 1 foot in the females) are gray. *C. f. megaceros* has larger, straighter horns than the other subspecies, and are much tighter twisted, with as many as two complete spirals.

Behavior

Markhors are adaptable feeders, and prosper in a variety of plant communities. In winter, they may feed primarily on leaves from trees, while in summer they may graze on grass and herbs. Because of their agility, they can stand on their hind legs to reach high branches, or climb the tree altogether. This gives them tremendous advantage in food sources out of reach of earth-bound competitors.

Even among goat species markhors are exceptionally good climbers and leapers. They climb with a deliberate pace, seemingly to assess distance and difficulty of the next step. They can leap wide expanses and stop on a dime. Only the large horns impede the areas they can occupy.

During most of the year the two social groups are comprised of bucks in one group and does and fawns in another. The size of the group is determined by the restraints the terrain places on keeping the group together, but 3 to 12 individuals is common. Males and females form mixed-sex groups of up to 35 individuals for the rut, which occurs in December/January in the north of Pakistan, and October/November in the south. One, often two offspring are born after gestation of 135 to 170 days.

Habitat

The various species of markhor goats inhabit widely varying terrain, from steep slopes in forests to rock gorges. All subspecies retreat to higher elevations in summer.

Distribution

C. f. megaceros, the straight-horned markhor, occurs in Kabul and Sulaiman, Afghanistan, along the Kyber Pass, and in the northwest portion of Pakistan. It is the most endangered of the subspecies; the numbers in the wild are estimated at 2,000, and there are about 30 animals in captivity. *C. f. falconeri,* the flare-horned markhor, occurs in Pir Panjal, Pakistan and in the Laghman Province of Afghanistan. The population estimate is 3,200 to 4,800. *C. f. heptneri* occurs in the Bokharan region of Russia on the border between Afghanistan and Russia, and is the source of lineage for all captive bred markhors in North America. The wild population is estimated at 700 to 1,200.

Threats

Markhors have long been prized as trophy animals as well as their meat; they have also fallen victims to soldiers for food during the war in Afghanistan. Inbreeding with other goats may have reduced the number of pure individuals.

Conservation and Recovery

Markhors breed well in captivity and zoos have healthy populations of *C. f. heptneri* derived from a pair that were exported from Russia in the mid-1900s. All markhors occurring in Russia and Pakistan are protected by law. Pakistan has created 10 wildlife reserves to protect the markhor.

Pyrenean Ibex

Capra pyrenaica pyrenaica

J. A. Fernandez

Status	Endangered
Listed	June 2, 1970
Family	Bovidae (Bovine)
Description	A heavily built, stocky wild goat with a reddish brown coat and enormous horns.
Habitat	Rocky cliffs and Alpine meadows above the timberlines on mountains.
Food	Brush, grass, and herbs.
Reproduction	Rutting season in November and December; gestation is 161 to 168 days, usually resulting in the birth of one young.
Threats	Poaching and loss of habitat.
Range	Spain

Description

The Pyrenean ibex, *Capra pyrenaica pyrenaica*, is a thick-bodied wild goat. Mature males have long horns that curve up and back, swinging outward before curving in and down toward the shoulders, and they can be as long as 30 inches. The bases of the horns are exceptionally thick — thicker than in other wild goats — and cover almost the entire head above the brow. Females have horns, too, but these tend to be smaller than those of males. The faces of Pyrenean ibexes are triangular, wide at the ears and narrowing steadily to the front of the mouth. The animal's eyes are recessed under the bony mass of the brow, and the animal's nose begins between and below the eyes and is flat along its length. Each ear is placed well behind and to the side of each horn. When a Pyrenean ibex sees or hears what may be danger, the ears swivel to face the danger and the head follows so that both eyes and ears are pointed at the source of alarm.

The rest of the body is stocky, perhaps providing the Pyrenean ibex with a low center of gravity, which would help it maintain its balance of the nearly sheer cliff sides that it frequently traverses. Adult males are 51 to 55 inches from tip-of-nose to base-of-tail;

the tail is 4 to 6 inches in length. The adult males are 26 to 28 inches high at the shoulder. They weigh 140 to 180 pounds. Females are smaller than males. Adult females are 40 to 43.5 inches from tip-of-nose to base-of-tail; the tail is 4 to 6 inches in length. They stand 27.5 to 29.5 inches at the shoulder. They weigh 75 to 100 pounds. Their compact mass stands atop four narrow, muscular legs with prominent tendons.

Behavior

Pyrenean ibexes prefer to live in large groups; before their near extermination, these groups could have over one hundred members. For about ten months of the year there would be two kinds of groups: One kind would be composed entirely of adult males; the other would be composed of adult females and their young. During rutting season, November and December, groups would mix together. Grouping is an important defensive strategy for the Pyrenean ibex: Their natural predators — wolves, foxes, and eagles — tend to pick off isolated Pyrenean ibexes or ones at the edge of groups. A large group means many eyes and ears on the alert for predators and a likelihood that all group members will be alerted to their presence before any of the group can be taken. Further, a large group assures that its members can circulate from its edges to its interior, where they can eat and care for their young free from immediate threats from predators. When a threat is perceived, the Pyrenean ibexes whistle, alerting one another. They often flee in single file, each group led by its senior member. They often flee across seemingly sheer rocky cliff sides, where terrestrial predators find it hard to follow them.

Rutting season has two distinct phases. During the first phase, young males court females. This rarely results in unions. During the second phase, senior males, distinguished by their heavier, longer horns, court females and mate with females. Gestation lasts 161 to 168 days, nearly always resulting in a single birth (sometimes, but rarely, twins). Youngsters remain in female-led mixed herds for at least a year; females reach sexual maturity at one-and-a-half years of age; males reach sexual maturity after two years.

Habitat

The Pyrenean ibex spends most of its time above the timberlines on mountains, in rocky areas with sparse vegetation as well as in meadows with brush, grasses, and herbs. Sometimes they venture into the upper reaches of forests to graze. They have shown a willingness to populate areas where forests have been cut down.

Distribution

Pyrenean ibexes occur in the Spanish Pyrenees. Fewer than twenty (one authority suggests fewer than fifteen as of 1994) Pyrenean ibexes remain alive.

Threats

Pyrenean ibexes have long been hunted for their meat and for their body parts. Their horns have long been taken as ornaments for homes in Europe and have locally been used as "horns," instruments to be blown into to make booming cries as signals in the mountains. Their coats are used for clothing. Their horns, organs, stomach stones, and even feces have been used in folk medicine as cures for many ailments, especially poisoning; this pressure has been so high for so long that cousins of theirs have been exterminated from the 1600s to the present throughout central and southern Europe. Only drastic laws, even threatening death, against killing ibexes and vigorous guarding have preserved the few species of ibexes still in Europe (mostly in Italy and Switzerland). The money offered for ibexes has encouraged many poachers to violate the laws against harming them and relentless hunting by outsiders as well as local people has brought the Pyrenean ibex to near extinction. Mature males are the favored prizes, probably because of their large, heavy horns; for the Pyrenean ibex, this means a shortage of fertile males to propagate the subspecies.

Conservation and Recovery

Spain has a good national park system in which many animals are protected. A special problem with the Pyrenean ibex is that its monetary value can make poachers work extra hard to evade the law and to undergo hardships to hunt it down and spirit away the carcass. The Pyrenean ibex has the protection of Ordesa National Park; perhaps the wildlife sanctuary Aiguamolls de L'Empordà in Catalonia, where a wide variety of wild animals and plants survive in their natural state, would be another good place for protecting and breeding the animals.

Walia Ibex

Capra walie

Helmut Diller, WWF

Status	Endangered
Listed	June 2, 1970
Family	Bovidae (Bovine)
Description	Wild goat weighing from 176 to 275 pounds with thick, ridged horns, brown colored on its lateral and dorsal sides, and white underneath.
Habitat	Montane areas at elevations of 8,000 to 14,000 feet along a line of habitual snow.
Food	Grasses, leaves, shoots, and twigs.
Threats	Extensive hunting, drought, disease.
Range	Ethiopia: Simien and Gojjam Mountains

Description

The walia ibex, *Capra walie,* is a wild goat. The male weighs 175 to 275 pounds and stands 35.5 to 43 inches tall; females are smaller. Both sexes have horns, although those of the male are much larger than the female's. The horns are thick and ridged. The walia ibex is reddish-brown on its lateral and dorsal sides, and white underneath. It has a black stripe on the front on each leg. The male develops a black beard that grows throughout his lifetime. The fully mature male has a black chest and black markings on his back. Mature females are more gray.

Behavior

The walia ibex is opportunistic and feeds on grasses, leaves, shoots, and twigs. This species is primarily diurnal and is most active in the early parts of the day. Seasonally (in dry seasons) the walia ibex migrates to valleys to browse. After rains it will migrate back up to its original higher elevated habitat.

Females move and feed together in groups of up to 35 individuals. Males are solitary except during rutting season when they may join the female herds. Breeding can occur year round but peaks between March and May. One young is born at the beginning of the rainy season after a gestation period of 150 to 165 days.

The diet of the walia ibex includes grasses, shoots, twigs, and roots, but it is an opportunistic feeder and adapts to whatever vegetation is available.

Habitat

This species inhabits steep, rocky cliffs at elevations of 9,000 to 14,750 feet. The terrain has been described as "a high undulating plateau deeply intersected by a number of rocky valleys. To the north and east the plateau drops away in immense vertical precipices 2,000 to 5,000 feet in height, and are guarded by pinnacles rising like immense Gothic cathedrals from the broken country beneath the cliffs almost to the height of the plateau itself." It spends the dry season at lower elevations and climbs as the rainy season develops.

Distribution

The walia ibex was considered common until the 1930s. It is now restricted to the Simien and Gojjam Mountains of Ethiopia. This species also occurs in the Simien Mountains National Park, with four small populations outside the park. The population is estimated at 400 individuals in 1989, but some authorities believe that fewer than 100 individuals remain in the wild.

Threats

The walia ibex has probably been rare for quite some time. Extensive hunting has been the primary factor contributing to the demise of this species. It has also been adversely affected by disease and prolonged periods of drought, by the conversion of habitat to agricultural use, by competition for food from other species, by diseases carried by domestic animals, and by civil strife.

Conservation and Recovery

In 1969 the Ethiopian government established the Semien Mountains National Park, but civil war has prevented authorities from maintaining or protecting the reserve.

Although there have been few attempts to captively breed this ibex, there is reason to believe it would do well in captivity and that wild populations could be enhanced by reintroduction programs. However, until the habitat can be protected, there is not much hope of stabilizing the wild population.

Serow

Capricornis sumatraensis

Barry Driscoll

Status	Endangered
Listed	June 14, 1976
Family	Bovidae (Bovine)
Description	Long muzzle; long, floppy ears; black with whitish face; short horns curved backwards.
Habitat	Moist, densely wooded gorges and grassy slopes.
Food	Leaves, grasses, and shoots.
Reproduction	One, sometimes two young.
Threats	Loss of habitat; hunting.
Range	Sumatra

Description

The Sumatran serow, *Capricornis sumatraensis*, stands 36 to 42 inches at the shoulders and weighs up to 300 pounds. While its cousin, the goral, looks like a goat, the Sumatran serow more resembles a cow, with a long muzzle, eyes set far back and in the side of the head, and long, somewhat floppy ears. They are black with some white hairs interspersed within the coat, and a whitish face. The front knees are also white. The rump is rounded. The horns are short and curved backwards.

Behavior

Serows mark territory with acidic-smelling excretion from preorbital glands located in front of the eyes and in the hooves. Competing males fight with their sharp horns, which inflict serious or fatal injury to opponents. Males also kick opponents with their forelegs, as well as force females into submission by kicking. Serows are solitary, shy animals that are occasionally seen in pairs or small groups. They become vocal only when threatened, at which time they emit honking snorts.

The rut occurs in October and November, producing one, sometimes two young after gestation of 210 to 225 days. Life expectancy is

15 years.

Serows are herbivorous, feeding on leaves, grasses, and shoots of bushes and small trees.

Habitat

Serows inhabit moist, densely wooded gorges and grassy slopes associated with rhododendron thickets and oak forests.

Distribution

Serows are widely distributed throughout Southeast Asia, but the endangered *C. sumatraensis* is restricted to the island of Sumatra. The numbers in Sumatra are unknown. In Japan, serows were declared a national treasure and the population increased to 20,000 animals. In Formosa, *C. s. swinho* is experiencing severe population decreases, and the East Chinese serow (*C. s. argyrochaetes*) may be extinct.

Threats

The population explosion on Sumatra, with its attendant increase in agriculture and development, has greatly reduced wildlife habitat. Serows are commonly hunted for their meat and fur, and because they greatly damage their forest habitat. Their natural predators are leopards and tigers, but the reduced population of big cats has relieved natural predation.

Conservation and Recovery

Indonesia does not protect the serow and captive breeding programs are generally unsuccessful because serows do not adapt well to captivity.

Jentink's Duiker

Cephalophus jentinki

Gladys Porter Zoo

Status	Endangered
Listed	March 30, 1972
Family	Bovidae (Bovine)
Description	Short horns rise backward from the head; a vertical white stripe encircles the body, separating the almost black neck from the misty gray back and rump.
Habitat	Equatorial forests.
Food	Fruits, grasses, leaves and birds.
Reproduction	Gestation period of about 120 days.
Threats	Loss of habitat due to agricultural conversion; hunting.
Range	Liberia and Ivory Coast

Description

The extremely rare Jentink's Duiker, *Cephalophus jentinki*, weighs up to 155 pounds and stands 32 inches tall at the shoulders. The head and body measures 53 inches. Both males and females are similar in size. The horns are rather short, measuring about 7 inches and rise backward from the head following the line of the muzzle.

A vertical white stripe encircles the body, separating the almost black neck from the misty gray back and rump. The individual hairs on the back and rump are not gray but striped black and white, and the relatively thin coat allows the gray skin to show through. The legs are white. The neck fur of Jentink's duiker is smooth and short.

The common name for the genus, *Duiker*, means "diver" in Afrikaans and was given to these animals because they literally dive into the undergrowth when alarmed.

C. jentinki is placed in the subgenus *Cephalophus*, one of 4 subgenera in the genus *Cephalophus*. At one time, *C. jentinki* was considered a darker version of *Cephalophus sylvicultor*, but after careful observation was placed in a separate species.

Behavior

Although little is known about the behavior of the species *C. jentinki*, other members of the genus *Cephalophus* are sturdy, active animals with acute vision and hearing. The horns are used for defense and for intraspecific combat. In captivity, the species is characterized as high-strung and can crash head-on into a wall when startled. Based on comparisons with other species of *Cephalophus*, *C. jentinki* probably has a gestation period of about 120 days.

The specific food habits of Jentink's duiker in the wild are not known. However, *Cephalophus* in general mainly eat fruits, grasses, and leaves. Interestingly, *Cephalophus* are one of the few ruminants to eat meat, killing and eating small animals, especially birds. One Jentink's duiker in captivity was fed a diet of grains, grass, vegetables, and dog food. In general, members of the genus *Cephalophus* are nocturnal.

Habitat

Jentink's duikers live in equatorial forests in western Africa from Sierre Leone to the Ivory Coast. Although they prefer the thickest forests, they sometimes move into more open areas. Jentink's duikers reportedly favor marshes and lowlands.

Distribution

Jentink's duiker was at first believed to only exist in Liberia. Evidence for its existence was later found in the Gola forest on the eastern side of Sierra Leone and in the Ivory Coast along the Liberian border. In Liberia, Jentink's duiker has been sighted mainly on Mount Numba and along the Ivory Coast border.

Recent evidence from local hunters suggests that Jentink's duiker may still be found in Liberia. Unfortunately, no sightings have been made in Sierre Leone for many years.

Threats

Habitat destruction is probably the main reason that Jentink's duiker is in danger of extinction. In the past 40 years much of its forest home has been destroyed by humans, principally to use the wood but also to make room for agriculture. Illegal hunting by native people further contributes to its decline.

Conservation and Recovery

Although there are enough individuals in zoos to initiate a captive breeding program, none have been successfully bred in captivity.

Bontebok

Damaliscus dorcas dorcas

Robert Cabello, Dallas Zoo

Status	Endangered
Listed	June 14, 1976
Family	Bovidae (Bovine)
Description	Small two-horned bontebok measuring 55 to 63 inches in length with tail measuring 11.8 to 17.7 inches, with rich dark brown coat with a purple-colored sheen and a white patch on the hindquarters, lyre-shaped horns.
Habitat	Open grasslands with arid scrub vegetation.
Food	Herbivorous, feeding on grasses.
Reproduction	Single calf per season after gestation of 8 months.
Threats	Human encroachment, hunting, lack of food.
Range	South Africa: Cape Province

Description

The bontebok, *Damaliscus dorcas dorcas*, is a small, two-horned *artiodactylan* with a average body length of 55 to 63 inches. Its tail is 11.8 to 17.7 inches long and its weight varies from 132.3 to 176.4 pounds. The name "Bontebok" means "many colored" and its coat contains many shades of brown with a rich purple-colored sheen and a white patch on the hindquarters. White hair is on the underside, below the knees and on the face. The horns of the bontebok are lyre-shaped and grow from 16 to 20 inches.

The bontebok has often been mistaken for the closely related Blesbok, *D. d. phillipsi*. This is prominent throughout early literature.

Behavior

Bonteboks are extremely territorial. Males begin defending territories at age 3 or 4, and females form groups with a dominant social hierarchy.

Bonteboks live in female and bachelor herds or in mixed groups. The mating season is from January to March. During the mating season, it is ritual that the bull will run up to the female, stretching his neck and head forward while simultaneously lowering himself, raising his tail above the horizontal. Gestation lasts about 8 months, after which a single calf is born. The calf of the bontebok weighs about 15 pounds, and is colored a yellow-ocher with brown-black on the bridge of the nose. After four months the youngster is weaned. At 2.5 years sexual maturity is reached.

The bontebok is herbivorous and feeds on grasses. This animal also drinks daily to replenish itself. *Artiodactylan* members are most active in the earliest and latest parts of the daylight hours. The bontebok probably rests during the hottest parts of the day.

Habitat

The bontebok inhabits open grasslands where there are few bushes and trees. This area is characterized by arid scrub vegetation, dominated by plants with a *sclerophyllous* habit (small leathery leaves, well adapted to drought). In the Mediterranean basin the bontebok inhabits, the most common vegetation is garrigue and maquis. This area is susceptible to periodic droughts. An end result to these droughts are fires due to dry vegetation with a high oil content.

Distribution

Prior to the European invasion of South Africa, the bontebok was plentiful along the southwest corner of Cape Province. Fossil records indicate that bontebok has inhabited the same area since the Pleistocene era. This species remains in small numbers on Cape Province, as well as on the Bontebok National Park, wildlife reserves and in zoos.

Threats

When Europeans reached South Africa, the bontebok was already restricted to the southwestern area of Cape Province. With human encroachment and diminishing habitat, hunting nearly brought the bontebok to extinction by 1837. It was forced onto unsuitable habitat where it was vulnerable due to lack of food, deficiency of vital trace elements and parasitic diseases.

Conservation and Recovery

In an effort to preserve the bontebok, preserves where established. One, the National Bontebok Park, was susceptible to flooding and brought parasitic infections to the bontebok.

In 1837 the bontebok was in such dire straits that the Van der Byl family established a reserve near Bredasdorp. Some accounts testify that Van der Byl did not initiate this action until 1864. In 1931 the Bontebok National Park was created and by 1969 the bontebok's population was stable again, although nowhere near recovery. Captive breeding programs have been somewhat successful. The Government has also played a hand in bontebok recovery efforts, reflected in a penalty imposed for any unauthorized killing of the bontebok.

Cuvier's Gazelle

Gazella cuvieri

Status	Endangered
Listed	June 2, 1970
Family	Bovidae (Bovine)
Description	Buff colored gazelle with white markings on the face with S-shaped horns growing up to 15 inches in length.
Habitat	Sandy, stony plains; mountains and hills.
Food	Grasses, herbs, leaves, fruits, and vegetables.
Reproduction	One kid after gestation of six months.
Threats	Hunting, habitat loss, spraying of insecticides.
Range	Morocco, Algeria, and Tunisia.

F. D.. Schmidt, San Diego Zoo

Description

Cuvier's gazelle, *Gazella cuvieri*, has coarse dullish red to gray hair, with white under-parts and a wide dark-brown band dividing the dark and light parts. There is a dark spot in the middle of the muzzle; black stripes run from the bottom of the eyes to just above the corners of the mouth. The tail, which is 6 to 8 inches long, is black and there are two black stripes on the rump. Cuvier's gazelle has a body length of 35 to 41 inches and stands 23.6 to 31.5 inches tall; it weighs about 33.1 to 77.2 pounds. Both sexes have wide horns that curve backward with tips that bend forward. The horns may grow to 15 inches.

G. cuvieri is also treated as subspecies *G. gazella cuvieri*. It is also commonly known as the edmi and the mountain gazelle.

G. cuvieri and another race of gazelle, *G. bennetti*, are considered one subspecies by some authorities.

Behavior

Cuvier's gazelle browses on grasses, herbs, leaves, fruits, and vegetables. This species seems to have a greater demand for water than other gazelles.

After a gestation period of about 6 months females give birth to 1 kid (rarely 2). The kid weighs 4.4 to 6.6 pounds at birth. After 2 to 3 months the young are weaned, and by 6 to 9 months the males are sexually mature; females reach sexual maturity after about 18 months.

Cuvier's gazelle forms mixed herds of up to 100 individuals, although their reduced numbers often limit the herd size to 4 or 5 animals. As bucks become older they become territorial, marking their range with preorbital glands.

Habitat

Cuvier's gazelle, the only mountain-dwelling gazelle, inhabits sandy, stony plains; mountains and hills; and steppes with brush in areas ranging from open oak forests to stony deserts. The preferred food is Alep pine which grows only in high mountain areas.

Distribution

The range of Cuvier's gazelle once included most of Northern Africa. It is now extinct over much of its former range and occurs only in scattered populations in the mountains of Morocco, northern Algeria, and western Tunisia. The largest populations are in the Atlas Mountains, the Oulmes massif, and on the plateau between Djebel chambi and Semana. The total wild population is estimated at under 1,000 animals (400 in Morocco and 200 to 300 in Algeria). There are about 100 individuals in zoos scattered throughout North America.

Threats

Hunting and habitat loss are the primary threats. Because Cuvier's gazelle is prized for both its beautiful fur and tasty meat, it has always been hunted. Habitat loss has occurred as sheep, goat raising and agriculture have converted natural areas to farms. Human pollution and the spraying of insecticides have also adversely affected its population. In some portions of their range, military maneuvers disturb the habitat and subject them to poaching.

Conservation and Recovery

Cuvier's gazelle has received some sort of protection since 1939, although hunting was permitted until 1956. Tunisia enforces strict preservation of this gazelle.

One captive population occurs in a reserve in Spain, and another population occurs in a reserve in the Atlas Mountains in Morocco.

Mhorr Gazelle

Gazella dama mhorr

Rio de Oro Dama Gazelle

Gazella dama lozanoi

G. d. mhorr   Brian Porco, Philadelphia Zoo

Status	Endangered
Listed	June 2, 1970
Family	Gazella (Gazelles)
Description	Reddish coat on the upperparts and on the outside of the legs, and white on the underparts, rump, and a spot on the throat; the tail is white with a black tip.
Habitat	Desert.
Food	Tips of acacia.
Threats	Hunting for medicinal use; competition for food.
Range	Morocco south through Western Sahara

Description

The Mhorr gazelle, *Gazella dama mhorr*, has a reddish coat on the upperparts and on the outside of the legs, and is white on the underparts, rump, and a spot on the throat. The tail is white with a black tip. A broad white band extends from around the nose and mouth to the horns; a black line extends from the eye to the mouth. The horns are black, ringed with ridges; the horns extend upward and back, with the pointed tips extending forward.

The Rio de Oro dama gazelle, *Gazella dama lozanoi*, is similar in appearance. The upper body, tail, and hind legs are reddish; the front legs and underparts are white. There are dark spots on the legs near the hooves.

Behavior

These gazelles' diet consists almost exclusively of the tips of acacia. When there were larger numbers of Mhorr gazelles, they would herd during the migration season and form small groups during other times of the year, but today they are solitary or form groups of 2 to 3 individuals.

Habitat

The Mhorr gazelle inhabits the southeastern desert of Morocco, which is characterized by sparse vegetation. The Rio de Oro dama gazelle occurs further south in similiar terrain.

Distribution

Historically, the Mhorr gazelle may have occurred in Senegal and along the White Nile. Today, a few dozen individuals are scattered throughout southeastern Morocco. Rare in the mid-1800s, the numbers in the mid-1900s were a few dozen.

The Rio de Oro dama gazelle was not known until 1934 when hides were discovered in Western Sahara, south of Morocco. The population is estimated at a few dozen.

Threats

Rare for a long time, these gazelles were especially vulnerable to hunting. Not only was the Mhorr gazelle a good trophy animal, the concentrations in its stomach, called "bezoars," were believed to be an antidote to poison. These and other gazelles also compete with grazing cattle for the limited food resources.

Conservation and Recovery

In 1969 the African Convention prohibited the hunting or capture of these gazelles, but poaching persists.

G. dama lozanoi   Roland Wirth

Moroccan (=Dorcas) Gazelle

Gazella dorcas massaesyla

Lynda Richardson

Status	Endangered
Listed	June 2, 1970
Family	Bovidae (Bovine)
Description	Pale red to yellow fawn coloring with lighter sides, throat and legs, which may be white; the pale muzzle is circled by a brownish stripe around and above the nostril.
Habitat	Savannas, semi-deserts and deserts, preferring open and flat terrain.
Food	Grasses, herbs, leaves, buds and shoots.
Reproduction	1 or 2 young after gestation of 5 to 6 months.
Threats	Overhunting and habitat degradation by domestic livestock.
Range	Morocco, Algeria, and Tunisia

Description

The Moroccan gazelle, *Gazella dorcas massaesyla*, has pale red to yellow fawn coloring with lighter sides, throat and legs, which may be white. The pale muzzle is circled by a brownish stripe around and above the nostril. Unlike most gazelle species, there is no dark spot over the nostrils. Both sexes possess strongly ringed horns; the female's are smaller and more slender. Unlike most other gazelle's, the Moroccan gazelle's horns are straight and diverge at the tips. A whitish stripe flanked by two reddish brown stripes runs from between the ears, past the upper eye to the nostrils. Males stand 22 inches at the shoulders and weigh up to 33 pounds.

This species was formally described *G. d. massaesyla* by Cabrera in 1928 from one specimen found in the Rif Mountains. In 1929 Jeleaud described this same species as *G. d. cabrerai*.

Behavior

Gazelles feed on grasses, herbs, leaves, buds and shoots. Subspecies of *G. dorcas* are active primarily in the early morning, early evening and at night. This gazelle spends the warmest part of the day resting in shallow depressions, although it is capable of withstanding extreme sun. It often feeds while resting on its knees, and has developed thick hair around the knees to protect it.

Moroccan gazelles usually herd in mixed groups of 10 to 15 individuals. The female usually gives birth to a single young each year after a gestation period of 164 days.

The Moroccan gazelle is extremely fast and can attain speeds up to 43 miles per hour.

Habitat

The Moroccan gazelle occurs in the high, dry plateaus of Tunisia and Morocco. It also has been found in the central and lower reaches of the Moulouya River Valley in Morocco. In general, gazelles prefer open and flat terrain. Subspecies of *G. dorcas* excavate resting depressions by scraping the ground with their hooves.

Distribution

The Moroccan gazelle is known from Morocco, Algeria, and Tunisia along the high plateau north of the Saharan Atlas Mountains and in the central and lower reaches of the Mouloya River Valley. The numbers for this species are very small, and it is in danger of extinction in the wild. Between 1953 and 1958 most of the gazelles were exterminated to reduce competition for cattle ranching.

Threats

Overgrazing by livestock has destroyed much of the Moroccan gazelle's former range. Overgrazing can lead to desertification, especially in the fragile soils of Northern Africa. Introduced livestock also carry contagious diseases which infect and kill the Moroccan gazelle.

The Moroccan gazelle also has been ruthlessly hunted, often with vehicles which pursue the animal across open plains until it is exhausted. Because Moroccan gazelles occur on the plains with other, non-threatened species, hunters usually do not differentiate between the endangered and non-threatened animals.

Conservation and Recovery

The Moroccan gazelle has been protected by the African Convention since 1969, and is listed by both the U.S. Fish and Wildlife Service and IUCN. However, Morocco, Algeria and Tunisia do not have laws protecting gazelles.

The Washington (D.C.) National Zoological Park has maintained a herd of Moroccan gazelles since 1960. This first pair were given to the zoo after it had been presented to President Eisenhower as a gift from the president of Tunisia.

Pelzeln's Gazelle

Gazella dorcas pelzelni

Khushal Habibi

Status	Endangered
Listed	June 25, 1979
Family	Bovidae (Bovine)
Description	Both sexes possess horns; pale fawn coloring and no contrasting markings.
Habitat	Savannas, semi-deserts and deserts; preferring open and flat terrain.
Food	Grasses, herbs, leaves, buds and shoots, feeding primarily on Acacia trees and succulents.
Reproduction	1 or 2 young after a gestation of 5 to 6 months.
Threats	Overhunting and habitat degradation from overgrazing.
Range	Somalia

Description

Pelzeln's gazelle, *Gazella dorcas pelzelni*, stands 21.7 to 25.6 inches tall, has a body length of 34 to 43 inches, a tail length of about 5.9 inches, and weighs about 40 pounds. The medium length horns diverge evenly from the base with a slight backwards curve and a more marked forward bend at the tips. Both sexes possess horns, although the female's are thinner and bend more sharply backward. Overall, the Pelzeln's gazelle has brownish fawn coloring with a reddish tinge and white underparts. The forehead and median face stripe are darker. The lateral face stripes are short and slightly indistinct. There are no nose spots. On the flank is a brownish red band that is slightly deeper in tone than the back. The muzzle has a dark middle stripe that runs from the nostrils to between the horns. Two white stripes paralleled by two darker stripes run from the upper side of the eyes to the corners of the mouth

G. dorcas was classified as a distinct species by Linneaus in 1758. The subspecies *G. d. pelzelni* was originally classified by Koln in 1886. Formerly it was considered a full species with the taxon *G. pelzelni*.

Behavior

This subspecies feeds on grasses, herbs, leaves, buds and shoots. Pelzeln's gazelle has been observed feeding primarily on *Acacia* trees and succulents with a high water content. In some areas of occurrence, *Acacia* makes up both the food and water content for the diet.

Pelzeln's gazelles are active primarily in the early morning, early evening and at night. This species spends the warmest part of the day resting in shallow depressions.

In general, gazelles will give birth to 1 or 2 young after a gestation period of 5 to 6 months. For a period of several days to a few weeks, the young gazelle will lie hidden in the grass, as its mother feeds nearby. She returns to the hiding place several times a day to nurse.

Habitat

Pelzeln's gazelle inhabits the hot arid lowlands of the Gutan country of Somalia and prefers open, flat, rocky terrain covered with scrub vegetation.

Distribution

Historically, Pelzeln's gazelle was found in the Gutan country of Somalia, with the base population occurring on the north side of the Golis mountains. It was rarely seen beyond Laferug just a few miles away. Currently, it is known only from the northern Somalia coast and inland for 12 to 20 miles. It is not known whether the species is extinct or if a small population survives.

Threats

Threats include hunting and habitat degradation from overgrazing by domestic livestock. Overgrazing facilitates desertification.

Conservation and Recovery

As a result of Pelzeln's gazelle limited range and endangered status, IUCN has recommended captive propagation programs and reintroduction to suitable habitats. It is also protected in the Reserve for Speke's Gazelles which adjoins the Borana Controlled Area.

Saudi Arabian Gazelle

Gazella dorcas saudiya

Khushal Habibi

Status	Endangered (Possibly extinct)
Listed	June 25, 1979
Family	Bovidae (Bovine)
Description	Brown gazelle with white interspersed over its coat; face is a darker tinge of brown over the cheeks, snout, and ears; both sexes possess horns.
Habitat	Savannas, semi deserts and deserts.
Food	Grasses, herbs, leaves, buds and shoots.
Reproduction	1 or 2 young after gestation of 5 to 6 months.
Threats	Loss of habitat due to uncontrolled cutting of trees and shrubs.
Range	Israel, Saudi Arabia, Jordan, Syria

Description

The Saudi Arabian gazelle, *Gazella dorcas saudiya*, is a dainty (only 23 inches tall at the withers), graceful animal designed for running in open country. Both sexes possess strongly ringed horns, with the female's being smaller and more slender. The male's horns may reach 12 inches in length. The necks are short and lack folds. The short upper hair is tan to ochre and the belly is white. The long muzzle has dark stripes running from the eyes to the corners of the mouth.

G. d. saudiya was originally described by Carruthers and Schwarz in 1935. Some authorities consider this gazelle to be a distinct species, *G. saudiya*.

Behavior

Gazelles in general feed on grasses, herbs, leaves, buds and shoots, are active primarily in the early morning, early evening and at night. This gazelle spends the warmest part of the day resting in shallow depressions.

Habitat

The Saudi Arabian gazelle roams over the great gravel plains east of the Hejaz Mountains and the wastelands of Saudi Arabia, Kuwait, Yemen, Israel, Syria, and Jordan.

Distribution

The Saudi Arabian gazelle was once distributed throughout Israel, Iraq, Jordan, Syria, and the Arabian Peninsula. It may be extinct in the wild; 50 captive animals survive.

Threats

The Saudi Arabian gazelle is primarily threatened by overhunting.

Conservation and Recovery

Hunting bans are the only reported conservation measures taken for this subspecies. No parks or reserves have been created in any of its host countries, although gazelles are legally protected in Israel.

Arabian [=Mountain] Gazelle

Gazella gazella

Status	Endangered
Listed	June 25, 1979
Family	Bovidae (Bovine)
Description	Soft, medium-length hair on the back is reddish-brown, the sides and outside of the legs are tan, and the underparts are white.
Habitat	Semiarid deserts and mountainous deserts associated with acacia trees.
Food	Grasses and other available vegetation.
Reproduction	Single young is produced after gestation of 6 to 6.5 months.
Threats	Sport hunting
Range	Arabian Peninsula

Chester Zoo

Description

The Arabian or mountain gazelle, *Gazella gazella*, has a body length of 37 to 41 inches. Its tail is measured at about 3.9 inches. This species weighs 44 to 77 pounds. Both sexes possess short ringed horns that are slightly lyre-shaped. Horns in the males grow to 10 inches; female horns grow to 6 inches.

The soft, medium-length hair on the back is reddish-brown, the sides and outside of the legs are tan, and the underparts are white. A broad dark brown stripe runs from the top of the foreleg to the top of the hind leg, and around the white rump patch. The long muzzle is the reddish color of the back and has three whitish stripes: two of those run from the nostrils to around and above the eyes, and the third stripe runs from the center of the nostril to between the eyes.

This gazelle is also known as the mountain gazelle and as the idmi.

Behavior

The Arabian gazelle eats grasses and other available vegetation from which it acquires most of its water.

Social behavior is variable. Territorial

males, all-male herds and female herds are observed. Territorial males will mate with females from female herds that wander through their territories. The all-male herds circulate around the established territories of the nomadic males.

Parturition occurs after a gestation period of 165 days and a single young is produced. It is hidden in vegetation, suckling the mother until it is large enough to join the herd. Sexual maturity occurs at about 1.5 to 2 years of age.

Habitat

The Arabian gazelle inhabits semiarid deserts and mountainous deserts associated with acacia trees.

Distribution

This gazelle is known from the Arabian Peninsula, although the current distribution is fragmented in comparison to a once thriving population. It is presently known only in Saudi Arabia, Oman, Yeman, and Israel. It also occurs on the Farsan Islands in the Red Sea. A small population of a few dozen mountain gazelles survives in the Negev Desert in Israel, but the species has not been observed in Oman and Jordan in two decades.

Threats

Like other animals in the Arabian Peninsula, this species' decline can be attributed to the introduction of modern firearms and motorized vehicles. Sport and subsistence hunting have long been a favorite activity over this species' range. With the introduction of better equipment more animals can be shot at longer distances. With the discovery of oil in the gazelle's ranges, many foreigners with sophisticated weapons inhabited the host countries, and the population of the mountain gazelle rapidly declined in just 25 years.

Conservation and Recovery

Israel protects the largest population of some 10,000 animals, and there is an effort by the other host countries to reduce the hunting of the species. The populations that live on the Farsan Islands in the Red Sea appear to be stable. There is no captive population that can sustain significant captive breeding.

Slender-horned (=Rhim) Gazelle

Gazella leptoceros

Montgomery Zoo

Status	Endangered
Listed	June 2, 1970
Family	Bovidae (Bovine)
Description	Reddish to pale yellow with white underparts with a dark lateral stripe; a white stripe runs from the corners of the mouth, past the upper eye to the ears.
Habitat	Deserts.
Food	Grasses, herbs, leaves, buds and shoots.
Reproduction	1 or 2 young after gestation of 5 to 6 months.
Threats	Overhunting and habitat degradation by domestic livestock.
Range	Sudan, Egypt, Algeria, Tunisia, Chad, Niger, and Libya

Description

The slender-horned gazelle, *Gazella leptoceros*, stands 25 to 38 inches tall, has a head-body length of 39 to 43 inches, and a tail length of 5.9 to 7.9 inches. This gazelle weighs 44 to 66 pounds. Both sexes possess straight, ringed parallel horns that bow out at the center; the male's are slightly larger than the females. The slender-horned gazelle has long hooves with a wide base, which gives it more support and makes this species somewhat better adapted to desert life than other gazelles.

The overall body color is reddish to pale yellow with white underparts and a dark stripe running laterally between the dark and light parts. A white stripe runs from the corners of the mouth, past the upper eye to the ears, which are straight and unusually long.

This species is also commonly known as the sand gazelle, Rhim gazelle, and Loder's gazelle. *G. leptoceros* was originally classified a distinct species by F. Cuvier in 1842. There are two described subspecies, *G. l. leptoceros* and *G. l. loderi* that are currently not accepted as subspecies.

Behavior

Feeding on grasses, herbs, leaves, buds and shoots, the slender-horned gazelle utilizes the dew on vegetation for its water intake and it can survive without water for a long time. In times of drought it migrates to more humid areas where plant life can absorb moisture from the air.

Breeding can occur year round but peaks during the wet season. Females produce one, seldom two, offspring after a gestation period of 160 to 220 days. The young mature rapidly and can run with the adults after one week. They form groups consisting of one male and many females and their young. Typical group size is 5 to 30; groups will herd together numbering in the thousands. In captivity they live for up to 12 years.

Habitat

The slender-horned gazelle inhabits sandy dunes and mountainous areas of the Sahara Desert where enough vegetation exists to support the gazelle.

Distribution

Historically, the slender-horned gazelle occurred in the deserts of northern Africa from southern Algeria to the western side of the Nile river near Faiyum, including the central Sahara as far as northwestern Sudan extending into Tunisia and the Atlas Mountains. Currently, it is restricted to the greater part of the northern half of the Sahara Desert from Algeria to Egypt and northwestern Sudan to the mountains in the extreme northwest of Chad. These countries include in Sudan, Egypt, Algeria, Tunisia, Chad, Niger,

and Libya. The large population near Wadi El Raiyan (Egypt) has been reduced to a few dozen individuals. The large population near the Bahariya was hunted to extinction and there are no longer any animals along the Nile Valley. It is estimated that there are fewer than 2,500 animals remaining in the wild. The largest population is in the Air and Tenere National Nature Reserve in Niger. It may also occur in Mali and Mauritania, but these locations have not been confirmed.

Threats

Once a plentiful species throughout its range, the slender-horned gazelle is endangered because of overhunting and habitat degradation from overgrazing by domestic livestock. Soldiers, using jeeps and armed with automatic weapons, ruthlessly hunted this species to extinction in many parts of its range. This gazelle has been forced into terrain inaccessible to jeeps, and this habitat is given to extreme conditions and is not well suited to sustaining gazelles.

Conservation and Recovery

Although generally protected by the 1969 African Convention, only Libya has passed laws protecting this and other endangered gazelles.

Captive breeding programs are underway in zoos in Tunis, Tunisia, Hanover, Germany; San Diego, Palm Springs, and San Pasqual, California; and Tampa, Florida.

Sand Gazelle

Gazella subgutturosa marica

San Antonio Zoo

Status	Endangered
Listed	June 25, 1979
Family	Bovidae (Bovine)
Description	Light yellowish brown gazelle with white interspersed over its coat; distinctive swelling around the throat, males possess horns which are thin and curve inward.
Habitat	Grassy plains.
Food	Grasses, herbs, leaves, buds and shoots.
Reproduction	1-2 young after gestation of 5-6 months.
Threats	Loss of habitat due to soil erosion.
Range	Jordan, Abu Dhabi

Description

The sand gazelle, *Gazella subgutturosa marica*, has a distinctive swelling around the throat, displayed in both sexes. The male's horns are long, 8.2 to 12.2 inches, and diverge widely at their tips to form a strongly lyre-like shape. As an extreme example, one specimen from Kuwait had tips so strongly curved inwards that they overlapped one another. Unlike a female of the subspecies *G. s. subgutturosa*, a female sand gazelle generally has well developed horns; although their horns are smaller and more slender than the males.

More so than *G. s. subgutturosa*, the sand gazelle has a white face with indistinct markings on the face and forehead. The lower part of the throat, neck, abdomen, inner part of the legs, and glutei are white. The tail is black. The hooves are fringed with black. It derives its name from an enlarged Adams apple that looks like a goiter.

G. s. marica is smaller than the other subspecies of *G. subgutturosa*, with the skull measuring 6.7 to 7 inches compared to 7 to 7.9 inches.

G. s. subgutturosa was originally described in 1897 by Thomas. Formerly, it was considered a full species with the designation *Gazella marica*. This subspecies is also commonly known as the goitered gazelle and rhim.

Behavior

The sand gazelle browses primarily on dwarf shrubs. Following the winter rains, it supplements its diet with herbaceous plants. Habits of periodicity are unknown for this subspecies. Other gazelles are most active in the early morning and early evening hours but are most active at twilight.

Congregating in flocks of 50 to 100 individuals, the whole herd can move as a closely packed unit at deceptively fast speeds. *G. s. subgutturosa* does not leap or bound like other Arabian gazelles.

Usually twins are born during March and April. This gazelle reaches sexual maturity in its first year.

Habitat

The sand gazelle prefers sand deserts, limestone plateaus, and gravel plains with occasional shrubs. It also inhabits the rocky headlands among the salt flats on the mainland.

Distribution

The sand gazelle was once found from the eastern deserts of Jordan southwards throughout the entire Arabian peninsula with some samples collected from northern and central Saudi Arabia, Kuwait, Bahrain Island, Afalil, and Rub-al-Khali. It seems to have been exterminated from much of its former range.

It reportedly has been found on many of the islands to the west of Abu Dhabi, as well as on the mainland and in Jordan.

Threats

Along with hunting, habitat degradation because of overgrazing threatens the sand gazelle. Its natural predator is the Arabian wolf, but the wolf's numbers have been greatly reduced as well and does not pose a serious threat to the gazelle's survival.

Conservation and Recovery

Although the hunting of the sand gazelle is banned throughout most of its range, the banning may have come too late in Saudi Arabia and other nations outside of Jordan. Jordan appears to be making a good effort to protect the sand gazelles within its borders, although poaching remains a problem. The sand gazelle requires a large desert range in order to maintain a healthy population and whether Jordan's reserves are large enough remains to be seen.

Arabian Tahr

Hemitragus jayakari

Himalayan Tahr (*H. jemlahicus*) close relative   Helen B. Meissner

Status	Endangered
Listed	June 25, 1979
Family	Bovidae (Bovine)
Description	Shaggy, coarse hair that is light brown in summer and much darker in winter; the belly is white; a broad, brown muzzle stripe runs around the nose almost to the base of the horns.
Habitat	Steep, rocky cliffs.
Food	Fruits and leaves.
Reproduction	After gestation of about 180 days, 1 or 2 young are born, usually in January or February.
Threats	Insufficient food supplies; trophy hunting.
Range	United Arab Emirates, Oman

Description

The Arabian tahr, *Hemitragus jayakari*, has shaggy, coarse hair that is light brown in summer and much darker in winter. The belly is white; a broad, brown muzzle stripe runs around the nose almost to the base of the horns. A less pronounced stripe runs from below the eyes to the corners of the mouth. The horns of the male are thick at the base and curved almost in a half circle. The female's horns are the same length (about 10 inches) but are not curved. The Arabian tahr is the smallest of the tahr species, standing 24 to 36 inches at the shoulders and weighing up to 50 pounds.

Behavior

Mating occurs during the monsoon season in July and August when the males leave their group to join a group of 3 to 4 females. After gestation of about 180 days, 1 or 2 young are born, usually in January or February. If the infant dies, the doe may mate within two weeks and give birth to a second young.

The Arabian tahr is a herbivore and its diet is limited to the fruits and leaves of a few plant species that grow in its barren habitat. The *Ziziphus spinachristi,* once an important plant source for the tahr, is now in decline.

Habitat

The Arabian tahr occurs in steep, rocky cliffs above 3,000 feet and may climb as high as 6,500 feet. The land is arid with little vegetation, and the Arabian tahr must search for deep water pools that it requires for drinking.

Distribution

A small population of a few dozen Arabian tahrs survive in the Jebel Hafit mountains in the United Arab Emirates, and another 2,000 occur in the Jebel Akhdar mastif in Oman.

Threats

Because of expanding agriculture and deforestation, the Arabian tahr was forced into habitat less suitable to sustain it. The quality and abundance of food in its barren, rocky home is less than required for the species to be healthy, and its range is much smaller than this deer needs to establish territories. The Arabian tahr was also prized as a trophy animal and was hunted with modern firearms until 1976. Once a remote area, the Jebel Hafit plateau is now accessible by a cable car, and this will certainly lead to more pressure on the animals.

Conservation and Recovery

The Arabian tahr is legally protected in Oman, although poaching is a continuing problem. International conservationists have identified several areas of Jebel Akhdar that could be made into reserves to better protect the animals. A few Arabian tahrs exist in captivity and the possibility of captive breeding is being explored.

Giant Sable Antelope

Hippotragus niger variani

H. Douglas Pratt

Status	Endangered
Listed	June 14, 1976
Family	Bovidae (Bovine)
Description	Dark brown to nearly black with almost white fur underneath and a black muzzle; females are light brown with a lighter muzzle; two white stripes run from the chin nearly to the eyes.
Habitat	Forests with small clearings that have suitable pasture in Angola.
Food	Grass and tree leaves.
Reproduction	One calf after a gestation of 261 to 281 days.
Threats	Destruction of wooded areas for agricultural purposes; hunting
Range	Angola

Description

The giant sable antelope, *Hippotragus niger variani*, is a subspecies of the sable antelope, *Hippotragus niger*. The males weigh 330 to 440 pounds and measure 43 to 51 inches high at the shoulders. The shoulder height is approximate because the back slopes gradually down from the head to the rear without any distinct high point. The females are smaller.

The striking horns of the male rise almost straight up from the top of the head and then make a long downward curve toward the animal's back. These very long horns measure up to 63 inches long and have distinct rings encircling the horns. The female's horns are smaller and do not have as sharp a curve.

As with size and horn shape, coat color differs between males and females. The general color of the male is dark brown to nearly black with almost white fur underneath and a black muzzle. The female is generally light brown with a lighter muzzle. Both sexes have two thin white stripes above the eyes and two white stripes from the chin nearly to the eyes.

The giant sable antelope has thick, tough skin and long pointed ears. A short mane covers the back of the neck. The medium-length tail is black on top and white underneath with a tufted tip. Some authorities consider *H. n. variani* to be a separate species, *Hippotragus variani*, instead of a subspecies of *Hippotragus niger*. *H. n. variani* has two fewer stripes on its muzzle and longer horns than *Hippotragus niger*.

Behavior

During the wet season, the giant sable antelope primarily feeds on grass. However, during the dry season, when the moisture content of grass is low, the giant sable antelope may supplement its diet with tree leaves. As they need to drink every few days, giant sable antelopes always live within 1 to 2.5 miles of drinking water.

Giant sable antelopes are very aggressive animals when cornered, charging and using their horns with surprising skill and agility. They have even been known to scare off lions. If an escape route is available, they can run up to 35 miles per hour for short distances.

The females give birth to one calf after a gestation period of 261 to 281 days. The calf's fur is tawny colored and the white stripes on the muzzle are less distinct than on an adult's muzzle. The newborn calf remains hidden for about ten days. The young begin to grow horns at about a month and a half of age and reach sexual maturity at about two years.

The size and composition of the herd change with the season. Large groups congregate during the dry season. When the rain starts, these break up into smaller herds consisting of 10 to 20 females and their young, usually lead by one adult male. Bachelor males, up to 6 years of age, live together in groups of up to 10 individuals. At the end of the rainy season, the calves are born, and the herds divide up into even smaller groups. After the calves leave concealment and can move around, the animals again congregate into larger groups.

Habitat

Giant sable antelopes live in wooded areas in central Angola. The animals prefer forests with small clearings that have suitable pasture. They do not like large open spaces.

Distribution

Presently, the giant sable antelope can only be found in small areas in central Angola, from the town of Malanje and the Bie plateau and in the area between the Cuanza and Locando rivers. Historically, they ranged further to the southeast and southwest.

Threats

At the turn of the century, the newly arrived Boers decimated the populations of the giant sable antelope for their valuable horns. However, even though hunting of these animals is currently banned, destruction of wooded areas for agricultural purposes continues to threaten their survival.

Conservation and Recovery

The giant sable antelope is fully protected in Angola and hunting is forbidden. Angola has set aside several reserves for the giant sable antelope, including the Integral Reserve of Luanda, established in 1938, and the Cangandala National Park. However, especially in the Luanda reserve, large populations of humans live within the protected areas. As the settlers are allowed to clear forests for farms, the giant sable antelope is being forced out of its favored habitat and must try to survive in less suitable terrain.

Lechwe

Kobus leche

Art Wolfe

Status	Endangered
Listed	June 2, 1970
Family	Bovidae (Bovine)
Description	Nearly white ventral parts, clearly separated from the brown or black body color; legs are dark in front with an almost black vertical stripe.
Habitat	Damp, marshy areas.
Food	Prefers newly grown tender grass.
Reproduction	Mating season runs from November to the first half of January.
Threats	Excessive hunting; exploitation of habitat.
Range	Republic of Congo; Southwest Angola; Namibia; and Zambia.

Description

The lechwe, *Kobus leche*, is a species of antelope. There are three subspecies: *K. l. leche*, the red lechwe; *K. l. smithemani*, the black lechwe; and *K. l. kafuensis*, the Kafue lechwe.

The body of *K. l. leche* is a chestnut-brown color tending to tawny, whereas the body of *K. l. smithemani* is darker, tending to black on the sides and back. *K. l. kafuensis* is similar in color *to K. l. leche*, but has two darker spots at the shoulder level.

All three subspecies have very pale ventral parts, nearly white, that are clearly separated from the color of the body. The legs are dark in front with an almost black vertical stripe and a white spot just over the hooves.

There is no particular spot on the muzzle, but there is a lighter, blurred area above the eyes.

The long and narrow hooves are an adaptation for the marshy habitat in which the species occurs, allowing them to bound through the swamps with amazing speed.

The horns are present only in the males, and are 28 to 35 inches long. They have the shape of a lyre, and are rather thin; they start almost vertically from the forehead, growing apart soon and bending backward considerably, then rising again in an almost vertical direction.

Behavior

Lechwes are highly gregarious, living in large herds of both sexes during the breeding season though separating at other times of the year. During the mating season, which runs from November to the first half of January, the males will establish and defend a small territory, although they will do this without fighting one another. This kind of territorialism is a behavior found only in two species of mammal: the lechwe, and the Uganda kob (*Kobus kob thomasi*).

When females go into heat, they will enter these small territories spontaneously, thus forming small harems.

The mortality of the young is said to be very high, perhaps because by the end of the first year of life, the young animals are particularly afflicted by warble flies.

K. leche is an herbivore whose preferred food is the tender grass newly grown in the areas that intense evaporations have just drained. Unfortunately, in times of heavy rain, the marshy areas do not dry, sometimes causing the death of many animals due to the shortage of food.

Habitat

The lechwe typically live in damp, marshy areas in central-southern Africa. They spend much of their day in the shallow water. They are strong swimmers and will take refuge in the water if necessary. When the seasonal floods come, lechwes will move to the peripheral grasslands, but return to the richer lowlands as soon as the waters recede.

K. l. leche live in southwest Angola (the Cubango and Cuando areas); in central Angola (the Luando area in Botswana) in the Okavango marsh, and in the Chobe National

Park in western Angola; in Nambia (former Southwest Africa) at the border with Botswana; in Zambia, in the northern part of the Kafue National Park; and in the Republic of Congo (formerly Zaire), near the Lualaba River and the Kundelunga National Park.

K. l. smithemani occurs only in Zambia, in the Bangweulu marsh.

K. l. kafuensis is found only in the Kafue area (Zambia), after which it is named.

Distribution

The black lechwe, *K. l. smithemani*, occur only in Zambia, in the Bangweulu marsh, where the population is estimated at 40,000. They appear to have been extirpated in Lake Mweru and the Chambeshi area.

The kafue lechwe, *K. l. kafuensis*, was highly diffused at the beginning of this century, but is now found only in the Kafue area (Zambia), after which it is named. Its numbers are thought to be 25,000 animals.

The red lechwe, *Kobus leche leche,* occurs in several populations and the number is estimated at 35,000.

Threats

The reasons for the decline of the lechwe are twofold: excessive hunting, and exploitation of the land where they live. It has been zealously hunted, both for the delicious meat and for the trophy trade.

During the 1950s, trophy hunting reached its peak. Trophy hunting parties were organized in Zambia, often with over 100 participants. These hunters, taking advantage of the lechwe's marshy habitat, were able to surround and kill hundreds of animals. For example, in 1951, over 3,000 specimens were killed in three days.

Another reason for the lechwe's is the exploitation of its habitat. The marshy areas where these wild Bovidae occur have undergone fast and profound changes; land reclamations, dikes, and river dams have radically changed the natural features of many areas populated by the species.

Conservation and Recovery

The countries in the lechwe's range contain many natural preserves and national parks which now protect this species from extinction. In Zambia, the Kafue National Park, created in 1950, contains a large group of *K. l. leche* in its northern part.

In 1974, the president of Zaire (now the Republic of Congo) signed a project for the reintroduction of *K. l. smithemani* into the Nashinga marsh by taking some animals out of the Bangweulu area. Captive breeding programs for the red lechwe have been successful but the instability of the political situation in its range has prevented reintroduction.

Goral

Nemorhaedus goral

Lisbon Zoo

Status	Endangered
Listed	June 14, 1976
Family	Bovidae (Bovine)
Description	Undercoat is short and woolly; the outer coat has long, coarse hairs; males have a short mane.
Habitat	Rugged, wooded terrain.
Food	Opportunistic vegetation.
Reproduction	One or two offspring are produced after gestation of 6-8 months.
Threats	Hunting.
Range	Tibet (China) to Siberia (Russia)

Description

Gorals, *Nemorhaedus goral*, are small goats resembling domestic goats but with a longer tail. The undercoat is short and woolly; the outer coat has long, coarse hairs; males have a short mane. The coat color varies from gray, to dark brown, to red; the underparts are lighter than the upper parts. A white spot occurs on the throat, and a dark stripe runs down the middle of the back, which is curved from mid-back to the tail. The conical horns curve backward.

Behavior

Gorals are most active in the early morning and evenings when they forage for twigs, shrubs, grass, and nuts. They spend the day sunning on open rocks. They are often found in groups of 15 to 30 individuals except for old males, who are solitary. Two or three males share a territory which they mark with secretions from glands behind the horns and with feces. During the rut, they excrete a yellow, waxy substance which they use to mark females. Only bucks with females living in their territory mate, and he mates with all the females under his jurisdiction. Pregnant females withdraw to give birth in a cave or sheltered place, preferably near water and food resources. One or two offspring are produced after gestation of 6 to 8 months. Sexual maturity is reached at age three.

Habitat

Gorals occur in rugged, wooded terrain at

elevations between 3,300 and 13,000 feet.

Distribution

The goral occurs in the Himalayas from Tibet (China) to Siberia (Russia).

Threats

Humans have hunted the goral for its fur, meat, and stomach content (bezoars), which are believed to have medicinal value. The horns, kidneys, heart, blood, and embryos are used by Chinese and Korean apothecaries for folk remedies. Gorals are extremely agile and can escape most of their predators (leopards, lynx, tigers, and martens) except people. Population numbers are unknown except for the far east area of the former Soviet Union, where approximately 550 goats survive.

Conservation and Recovery

Much of the habitat where gorals live is unsuitable for human occupation, and gorals are not threatened by natural predators, so controlling human hunting will relieve pressure on the species. In Russia, gorals were given protection in 1924, but they are not protected throughout their range.

Zanzibar Suni

Neotragus moschatus moschatus

Alan Shoemaker

Status	Endangered
Listed	June 25, 1979
Family	Bovidae (Bovine)
Description	Grayish coat that is more red on the back; the belly and throat are whitish; males have short, thick, straight, backward-growing horns.
Habitat	Dry areas with shrub vegetation.
Food	Sprouts of shrubs.
Reproduction	Young are born in November and December.
Threats	Habitat degradation leading to decline in food resources.
Range	Tanzania: Zanzibar Island

Description

The Zanzibar suni, *Neotragus moschatus moschatus*, is a small antelope standing up to 18 inches at the withers and weighing up to 15 pounds. The coat is grayish but more red on the back; the belly and throat are whitish. The males have short, thick, straight, backward-growing horns. Below the eyes are scent glands that emit a strong, musky odor.

There are five subspecies of *N. moschatus*: *N. m. moschatus*, *N. m. akeley* (Kenya), *N. m. kirchenpaueri* (border of Tanzania and Kenya), *N. m. livingstonianus* (Tanzania, Mozambique, Malawi), and *N. m. zuluensis*, Mozambique, South Africa). These antelopes are also known as the musk dwarf antelope.

Behavior

The suni is diurnal, grazing on the sprouts of shrubs in the early morning and evening.

It is presumed that the young are born in November to December, but mating and gestation have not been recorded.

Habitat

The suni lives in dry areas with shrub vegetation. Like some other antelopes, it can go for very long periods without water.

Distribution

The Zanzibar suni occurs on the island of Zanzibar and the Tanzanian islets of Chapani and Bawane. It is presumed that this species is near extinction; the last sighting was in Zanzibar in 1972.

Threats

Habitat degradation, more than hunting, seems to have reduced the already scarce population of the suni. Because of the harsh conditions within its habitat, weather and competition for scarce food resources may have contributed to its decline.

Conservation and Recovery

The Tanzanian government has not passed protective laws although the suni is generally protected by the African Convention. There are some individuals in U.S. zoos, which seem to breed easily in captivity.

Scimitar-horned Oryx

Oryx dammah [=Oryx tao]

Rich Block

Status	Endangered
Listed	IUCN Red List
Family	Bovidae (Bovine)
Description	Large, heavy antelope with a white coat on its back and sides, dark brown on its neck and chest, and mostly white, with brown patches on its legs. It is named for its long, back-curving, pointed horns.
Habitat	Semi-arid grasslands.
Food	Grass.
Reproduction	Gestation may last 8 months, resulting in a single birth.
Threats	Loss of habitat and sport hunting.
Range	Chad

Description

The adult Scimitar-horned oryx, *oryx dammah*, stands 4 feet high at the shoulder and weighs about 450 pounds. It has a heavy, muscular build. Both males and females have horns that are curved like scimitars and can be as long as 50 inches. Its coat is smooth and white or pale brown, with a chest of dark brown or dark red-brown.

Behavior

The Scimitar-horned oryx forms tightly knit herds of about 20 animals; each herd is a mixture of adult males, females, and young. Even though these animals once would gather in the hundreds or even thousands at water holes recently replenished by rain, they would retain their small herd identifications within the larger group. A herd is dominated by a bull, the only male in the herd allowed to mate. The herd's hierarchy is linear, with the second-in-dominance being either a bull or a cow, and so on down to the animal that is at the bottom of the hierarchy. Usually bulls will dominate cows, but sometimes cows will work their way up the hierarchy and dominate even bulls, especially young ones.

An unusual behavior for antelopes and herding animals in general is exhibited by scimitar-horned oryxes. When bulls attempt to leave the herd, the dominant male will try to force them to remain. Perhaps by keeping other bulls in the herd, the dominant bull provides added protection for its progeny. With their long, sharp horns, the scimitar-horned oryxes make forbidding opponents for predators, as well as other oryxes.

The horns are used mostly to keep away other members of the herd as an individual animal feeds. The scimitar-horned oryx is adapted to life in a semi-arid region with sparse foliage. Staking out an area for feeding is important to the survival of each member of a herd. In spite of the potential for much conflict between oryxes competing to share the limited resources of their environment, conflicts rarely come to blows. Instead, the species has developed a ritualized tournament which helps them determine movement up and down in their hierarchy. Several animals in a herd will run around in circles, varying their pacing and including jumps and sprints; occasionally they will clash horns in a manner that threatens no harm. As the circling continues, punctuated by brief clattering of horns, animals settle down, with the horn clashes seeming to settle who dominates whom. The horns could do great damage to an oryx, which in its inhospitable climate could easily be life threatening; the ritual seems to be an adaptation that allows a herd to remain intact and its members strong.

Habitat

The scimitar-horned oryx's traditional habitat is that which surrounds the Sahara Desert, especially an area called the Sahel, a semi-arid grassland bordering on the south of the Sahara.

Distribution

In ancient times, the scimitar-horned oryx was domesticated by the Egyptians. Even until modern times, it roamed most of North Africa except for the desert. Its decline came with human expansion, loss of habitat to desertification, and hunting. It first disappeared north of the Sahara Desert, then west of the desert, and finally south of the desert, with Chad perhaps being its last refuge. In its last years in its native habitat, the animal was hunted ruthlessly into extinction. There is only very faint hope of individual oryxes surviving in Chad. It presently is found on a ranch in the United States.

Threats

The scimitar-horned oryx was doomed in its native habitat by the activities of humans. Their first mass extinction was in the regions north of the Sahara, where they were pushed out of their range by agriculture, and where they were excessively hunted. In the last years of its existence south and southwest of the Sahara Desert, their grasslands were being turned into desert at the rate of 250,000 acres per year because of the overgrazing by livestock, especially cattle. However, hunters were the ones who exterminated them. Large caravans of all-terrain vehicles would carry hunters to the herds, and for sport, the hunters would use automatic weapons to slaughter the animals.

Conservation and Recovery

Chad set aside a reserve for its oryxes, but years of civil war, invasion by Libya, occupation, and more war made it difficult for the nation to protect its natural resources. Poachers killed the animals simply for the fun of it. It is very unlikely that any individual scimitar-horned oryxes exist in the wilds of Africa.

There is probably only one herd of scimitar-horned oryxes in existence; it is in Texas, on a ranch owned by an elderly philanthropist. There is concern among naturalists that when the rancher passes on the oryxes will be left without a home.

The scimitar-horned oryx is listed in CITES, Appendix I: Trade Prohibited, and it is listed as endangered in the *IUCN Red List*. In 1992, it was proposed for inclusion in the endangered species list of the U.S. Fish and Wildlife Service, which would give it legal protection in the United States, but it has not been placed on the list.

Arabian Oryx

Oryx leucoryx

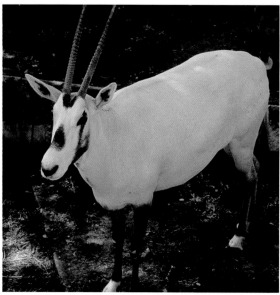

San Antonio Zoo

Status	Endangered
Listed	June 2, 1970
Family	Bovidae (Bovine)
Description	Smallest of *Oryx* species; white with black stockings; black face markings and black cheek strips; two long slender horns.
Habitat	Flat plains of gravel and stone fringing the sand desert.
Food	Grasses, herbs, roots, fruits, melons, leaves.
Reproduction	One calf per season after a gestation period of 9 months.
Threats	Introduction of sheep and goats, agricultural development, and sport hunting.
Range	Arabia, Israel, Jordan, Oman.

Description

The Arabian oryx, *Oryx leucoryx*, is the smallest of all *Oryx* species. It is white over its entire body with black below the knees and black markings on the face. The fur around the eye is black; cheek stripes are black. These cheek stripes widen to the jaw angle. Oryx are about 63 inches long with an 17.8 to 23.6 inch long tail. The Arabian oryx stands at about 43.3 to 49.3 inches at the shoulders and weighs from 121 to 150 pounds. Both sexes possess two long, back curving slender horns that grow to 29 inches long.

Some taxonomists regard all species of the genera *Oryx* as subspecies of *Oryx gazella*. This classification is not considered valid. *O. leucoryx* is commonly known as the white oryx.

Behavior

The Arabian oryx feeds on grasses, herbs, roots, fruits, melons, leaves, and other available vegetation. Oryx drink water whenever it is available, however, if necessary, this species can go several days without water. During the hottest parts of the day, the Arabian oryx may scrape out a shallow depression under a bush or shaded area to rest.

The Arabian oryx is probably found in herds of 2 to 20 individuals. Oryx are considered gregarious. Dominant, older males remain solitary. Pairs can be observed during mating season.

The dominant male will mark his territory by defecating after pawing the ground. Another ritualistic behavior is displayed by the female. If the female is not ready to mate, she will run away from the male and circle in the reverse parallel position.

Fighting patterns of oryx are the typical antelope fencing, an exchange of diagonally downward blows. The oryx will frequently go down to its knees during these confrontations. Gestation last about 9 months, after which one white, 20 to 33 pound calf is born. The calf is weaned after 3.5 months. Sexual maturity is reached at 2.5 to 3 years.

Habitat

The Arabian oryx inhabits rocky deserts, dunes and other arid habitats including barren steppes, semideserts and deserts. Oryx habitat has been described as a flat plain of gravel and stone that fringes the sand desert of the Arabian peninsula. This area is known as the "jol."

Distribution

The Arabian oryx was once wide-ranging throughout Levant, Arabia and Iraq but by 1972 the last specimen had been taken from the wild. Captive bred individuals have been reintroduced into reserves in Jordan, Oman and Israel. The Arabian oryx is also held in several zoos in Arabia and the United States.

Threats

Threats include agricultural development and introduced sheep and goats that compete with the Arabian oryx for food.

This fleet-footed animal was a great match for camel-mounted Bedouin hunters, even if they were armed with guns. The Arabian oryx was extremely pressured by motorized hunting, however. Fleets of vehicles could be observed carrying hunters and supplies; these hunters would shoot anything in sight. It is believed that the last wild specimen (prior to reintroduction) was killed in 1972.

Conservation and Recovery

Captive breeding programs initiated in the 1960s brought this wild oryx from the very brink of extinction to a population viable enough to be successfully reintroduced.

Argali
Ovis ammon

(*Ovis ammon ammon*)   Jim Dolan, San Diego Zoo

Status	Endangered
Listed	June 14, 1976
Family	Bovidae (Bovine)
Description	Large wild sheep with massive spiral horns, light brown in color with large white rump patch.
Habitat	Broad valleys, high pastures, or cold deserts of Central Asia, southern Siberia, Tibet.
Food	Grasses, herbs, leaves, shoots, and twigs.
Threats	Loss of habitat, competition with domestic animals, and hunting.
Range	Afghanistan, China, India (Kashmir), Pakistan, Tibet, Kazakhstan

Description

The argali, *Ovis ammon*, is an Asian relative of the North American bighorn sheep (*O. canadensis*), but averages somewhat larger in size, and, indeed, is the largest species of wild sheep. In adult males, length is about 70 to 80 inches, its height is 43 to 49 inches, and it weighs 210 to 310 pounds. The massive spiral horns are up to 75 inches long and 20 inches in circumference. The general coloration is light brown to grayish brown, with pale underparts, a large white rump patch and white legs. There is considerable disagreement regarding the subspecific division of *O. ammon*. Nadler *et al.* listed 17 subspecies

that had been named by various authorities. In a 1991 revision, Geist recognized only 7, including *O. a. hodgsoni*, which he considered to occupy the Himalayas, the Tibetan Plateau, and adjacent areas from northern India and Nepal to Gansu Province of north-central China. Much controversy centers on the distribution of *O. a. hodgsoni*. Some authorities, including Pfeffer and Valdez, give basically, though not always precisely, the same range accepted by Geist. Others, such as Ellerman and Morrison-Scott and Sopin, restrict its range to the Himalayan region and Tibet. They recognize another subspecies, *O. a. dalailamae*, in the Kun Lun Shan Mountains and other parts of the northern Tibetan Plateau. According to these writers, farther north in parts of Gansu Province and areas north and east, the subspecies present would be *O. a. jubatat* and/or *O. a darwini*. Still other authorities, including Clark, consider the range of *O. a. hodgsoni* to extend all the way from the Himalayas to the Gobi, but also recognize the presence of *O. a. dalailamae* in a limited area to the west.

There is also disagreement with respect to the subspecies *O. a. severtzovi*, which formerly occurred in much of Uzbekistan and which now is restricted largely to the Nuratau Mountains in that country. It is considered *O. ammon* by some authorities and a urial (*O. vignei*) by others, though Geist indicated that further studies are needed to determine its affinities.

The argali is commonly known as Marco Polo's sheep.

Behavior

The argali forms herds of up to 100 individuals that include females, young and immature males. Adult males form their own herds and join females only during mating season, which occurs in autumn and early winter. Males fight for females and for social status. One or two young are born after a gestation period of 150 to 180 days. The young are weaned after 3 to 4 months.

This species is known to migrate to lower elevations in the winter to find better feeding grounds. Little is known of the argali's food habits, but it is known to forage in broad valleys, high pastures, or cold deserts. Bovids utilize grasses, herbs, leaves, shoots and twigs as part of their herbivorous habit.

Habitat

The argali generally forages in broad valleys, high pastures, or cold deserts. It may seek refuge in adjacent mountains. The argali's range falls within the Palaearctic region. This region contains some of the world's highest mountain ranges including the Himalayas. Food is scarce in these mountainous areas. Additionally, the terrain is inconsistent and the climate consists of high winds, low humidity and sometimes, very low temperatures.

In the Himalayas, the argali may withstand an elevation of 20,000 feet and occurs between 4,000 and 20,000 feet. It prefers open grasslands in dry climates.

Distribution

O. ammon was historically known from Kazakhstan, Kyrgyzstan, Tajikistan, Uzbekistan, southern Siberia, Mongolia, north-central and western China, including Tibet, Nepal, and the Himalayan portions of Afghanistan, Pakistan, and India.

The argali has disappeared from or become rare in much of the periphery of its historical range. It has disappeared from much of northeastern China north and west of Beijing. It has been extirpated south and east of Lake Baikal in Siberia. It has also disappeared from northeastern Mongolia in the early 20th century. The population of northeastern China, east of Gansu Province, is possibly extinct. In the former Soviet Union, the species had disappeared from much of its former range. The argali can still be found in eastern Kazakhstan and the northern Tian Shan Mountains, in the Kara Tau Mountains in southern Kazakhstan, in the Tian Shan

Mountains of Kyrgyzstan, in the Kikshaaltau Mountains of Eastern Kyrgyzstan, in Xinjiang in northwestern China, Afghanistan, Pakistan, in the Himalayas in Jammu and Kashmir in India, and in Tibet.

The total population for the argali may be as high as 60,000 individuals, but they are widely scattered and probably exceed no more than 500 animals in any single location.

Threats

The argali has been on the decline since the 1920s. Loss of habitat, competition with domestic animals, and hunting pressures are the major causes of its decline.

In northeastern China the species has nearly disappeared due to agricultural expanses in its habitat and excessive hunting by Western sportsmen. The species is rare or vulnerable in Russia due to the disappearance of its former range. One of the main reasons for its decline is competition with livestock. The great majority of habitats presently or previously used by the argali are now occupied by domestic sheep or other livestock. Construction of a highway in northern Pakistan has disrupted the species' habitat and made it more accessible to hunters. Excessive hunting was a major factor in the historical disappearance of the species from Siberia and China, as well as other areas. Throughout all areas of the argali's range, loss of habitat, competition, and hunting threaten its existence.

Conservation and Recovery

The argali is protected by law throughout its range. Because it is so prized as a trophy animal, there is incentive to develop sustainable harvesting, but such a management program requires better population data.

Protection of the remaining habitat of the argali is needed to establish its recovery. Much of its habitat has been lost to agriculture or human encroachment. Reduced competition with domestic animals is important to the survival of this species, especially in wintering areas where food is more scarce and competition higher. Restricted zones for domestic sheep and cattle are needed to protect the argali. Stricter guidelines on hunting, and possibly the elimination of trophy hunting, should be considered to protect the remaining individuals. Stiffer penalties enforced on illegal hunting may also deter the taking of this animal. Finally, captive breeding programs should be considered to maintain genetic diversity and reintroduce the species in appropriate habitat.

Cyprian Mouflon

Ovis gmelini ophion

Eleftherios Hadjisterkotis

Status	Endangered
Listed	June 14, 1976
Family	Bovidae (Bovine)
Description	Narrow snout, small ears, and long, thick, sharply decurved horns in the males; reddish on its back with a white belly.
Habitat	Steep mountainous terrain.
Food	Mainly grasses; bushes during the winter and twigs and shoots during the summer.
Reproduction	One young, occasionally two.
Threats	Restricted range; competition for food resources; diseases spread by domestic sheep.
Range	Cyprus (Paphos Forest)

Description

Three populations of mouflon occur on islands in the Mediterranean Sea. The European mouflon, *Ovis gmelini musimon*, exists on the islands of Corsica and Sardinia, and the Cyprus mouflon, *Ovis gmelini ophion*, on Cyprus. USFWS lists the taxon as *Ovis orientalis [=musimon] ophion*, and only lists the Cyprus population as endangered. The 1996 *Red Data Book* lists the Cyprus mouflon as endangered and the other two island populations as vulnerable. The Cyprian mouflon until recently was known as *Ovis orientalis*

ophion and this is the name which was used in the *Status Survey and Conservation Action Plan for Caprinae* of the IUCN/SSC Caprinae Specialist Group. Recently, the taxonomy of wild sheep and goats was reviewed by the Caprini Working Group of CIC, which recognizes the taxonomy of the Cyprian mouflon as *Ovis gmelini ophion*.

Mouflon have a narrow snout, small ears, and long (up to 27 inches), sharply decurved (sickle shaped) horns in the males; females of the European mouflon may or may not have small horns, whereas all female Cyprus mouflon are hornless. The males' horns are thick at the base and taper to a point as they curl around, above the neck. The horns of the European mouflon might be supracervical, similar in shape as the Cyprus mouflon; however, the European mouflon also has spiral horns.

The Cyprian mouflon's winter coat is dull brown with a light whitish-gray saddle across its withers. During the breeding season, October to November, the saddle patch is predominantly white. The summer coat is reddish on its back with a white belly. It has a dark tail and white rump patch. The belly is white year round, and in winter the adult males have dark, longish hair along the lower side of the neck.

Behavior

Mouflon are adaptable feeders, eating bushes during the winter and twigs and shoots during the summer. In spring a large quantity of tree leaves are eaten, particularly in April when they are sprouting. In fall they eat fruits as well. Generally, they prefer large amounts of grasses and forbs when available.

Cyprian mouflon usually bear one young between the end of March and the beginning of May. Occasionally, a small percentage of females give birth to twins. They migrate from the feeding grounds to lambing grounds, which are areas with steep cliffs.

Habitat

The Paphos forest, which the mouflon inhabit, is a mountainous area of 620 square km, located in the northwestern part of Troodos massif. The central point of Paphos Forest is the most elevated rising to 1407 meters above sea level, with valleys radiating

from the center. During the summer the mouflon ascend to the higher ranges, and spend the winter in the valleys where the temperature is warmer. The vegetation comprises evergreen dwarf oaks, cedars, pine, turbentine trees and sumach.

Distribution

During the Middle Ages the mouflon was distributed throughout much of the island, but by the time the British occupied Cyprus in 1878, it was restricted to the southern range of Troodos mountains and Paphos Forest. By 1937 the mouflon population was extirpated at Troodos due to persistent poaching. The population in the Paphos Forest was reduced to 15 animals by 1937. In 1988 the population was estimated at 2,000 but a 1992 aerial survey indicated a decline, and the current population is estimated at 1,200 mouflon.

Threats

The mouflon is the only wild living large mammal on Cyprus, and is unique to this island. Since Paphos Forest is surrounded by villages and agricultural land, the mouflon's range is restricted, putting pressure on its food supply. Mouflon are susceptible to diseases and parasites transmitted by domestic sheep and goats. The mouflon's range at the periphery of the Paphos Forest overlaps the area grazed by domestic animals so it is possible that livestock diseases will continue to affect wild sheep. Mouflon sometimes are attracted to agricultural crops growing just outside the Paphos Forest. Wheat and barley have been planted at certain areas along the boundary to try and discourage such movements, but these efforts have not been totally successful in eliminating the mouflon's use of agricultural areas.

The greatest mortality results from predators, road kills, poaching, and accidental death from falling from cliffs. Towards the end of the summer and early autumn, mouflon may suffer from dietary deficiencies, and the highest mortality results from starvation, parasites, and stress from cold during October, November and December.

In 1974 during the Turkish invasion, one third of Paphos Forest was burned by the Turkish air force. The Turkish occupation of part of the island up to the edge of the forest continues, so new hostilities could lead to the loss of the forest and the mouflon.

Conservation and Recovery

After the populations at Troodos and Paphos were reduced to near extinction by 1937, the Society for the Preservation of the Fauna of the Empire, a British conservation organization, brought pressure to declare the Paphos forest a game reserve. The ordinance prohibited guns and domestic goats in the 148,500 acre park; banning the goats reduced the poaching by shepherds who routinely hunted the mouflon. The quality of the forest improved as a result of banning livestock, and forest fires started by people were reduced. For the next 20 years the mouflon population had increased considerably.

The mouflon's unique status has economic, cultural and recreational significance for the Republic of Cyprus, not the least because it is the island's national emblem. Tourism makes a major economic contribution to the island, and mouflon are one of its attractions.

The Game and Fauna Service of the Ministry of the Interior is gradually expanding and passing new laws making its operations more efficient. A 1974 law governing wildlife management including mouflon prohibits shooting, killing, capturing or chasing mouflon without a special permit. The penalty for infringement is up to 3 years in jail and/or a fine of $1,000. Anyone found in possession of the meat or parts of mouflon faces up to 2 years jail and/or a fine of $600. The law seems to be well enforced. A 1990 law gives more powers to game wardens.

In 1995 the Game and Fauna Service, which is also presently known as Game Fund, assigned a team of game wardens to work for the conservation and management of mouflon. The team, which is under the direction of Dr. Eleftherios Hadjisterkotis, is involved with law enforcement, ecology research, constructing monitoring stations and radiotelemetry, cultivating food patches, and building bridges to facilitate females which are crossing from the lambing grounds to the feeding grounds during torrential spring rains.

A small captive group comprised of 1 male and 2 females was established in 1950 at Stavros tis Psokas Forest Station. By 1988, a total of 64 animals had been reintroduced from this group to the wild. In 1987, the captive group numbered 30 animals, but by April 1992 only 8 remained, mainly because several had escaped during the previous 2 years. Two mouflon were transferred in 1955 from the group to the Limassol Zoological Garden for public viewing and for another captive breeding program from which 16 animals have been reintroduced into the wild. At present, only 1 female and 3 males remain in the zoo, and apparently due to intensive inbreeding which took place over 37 years, this has led to high lamb mortality and low fecundity during the last 12 years. At Stavros tis Psokas Forest Station there are 3 females and 6 males.

Shapo

Ovis vignei vignei

Status	Endangered
Listed	June 14, 1976
Family	Bovidae (Bovine)
Description	Large horns that curve behind the head and then up toward the chin; in general the coats are brown on the head, upper body, and sides, and white on the muzzle and underbody.
Habitat	Rocky, somewhat dry, highlands.
Food	Grass
Reproduction	Gestation is 150 t6 160 days, resulting in a single birth.
Threats	Human predation.
Range	India: Kashmir

Description

The shapo, *Ovis vignei vignei*, is a little known wild sheep that has long been considered endangered. Male shapos are better known than females, perhaps because hunters prefer to take males, which would make male carcasses more readily available for study than those of females. The adult male shapo stands between 2 feet 11 inches and 3 feet 4 inches high at the shoulder. The tail is unusually long and thin for a wild sheep. The adult male's head-and-body length is 3 feet 7 inches to 4 feet 9 inches. An adult male weighs 79 to 191 pounds, with the average being 132 pounds. Males tend to be larger than females.

Like other wild sheep, the shapo features spectacular horns. On males, these horns curve over the back of the head, down toward the forefeet and then up toward the jaw. Females have smaller horns that do not curve nearly as much as male ones do. Both genders share similar coloration: brown along the top of the head, the back, and the sides. The upper outer legs tend to be brown, as well, with the inner and lower legs being white; the underbody and tail are also white. The male has a small beard and a fuzzy fringe under his jaw; these are usually white. Individual shapos will vary in the proportion of brown to white. Their hair is short and coarse.

Other common names include steppe sheep and urial.

Behavior

The shapos are most active during the day but sometimes move about at night. They spend most of the active time searching for food and eating; during the hottest time of the day, they tend to rest. They gather in herds, apparently a mixture of males and females. There is a strong male hierarchy in which only the most dominant males mate with females. Dominance is demonstrated by a dominant male mounting a subordinate male as if to mate.

Late fall is the shapo's rutting season. The exact mating habits of the shapo seem to be unrecorded, but if it is like other wild sheep, males rarely actually fight over mating rights; rather the hierarchy dictates who gets to mate and who does not. Gestation lasts 150 to 160 days and results in a single birth.

Shapos are strong animals with powerful legs. When disturbed, they leap high and far, and then will run away.

Habitat

The shapo lives in a dry but temperate zone with hot summers and cold winters. It seems to prefer high ground. The primary vegetation of the habitat are grasses and brush.

Distribution

The shapo may once have ranged far into India to the south and east and into Pakistan in the north. It is now restricted to Kashmir.

Threats

The shapo has been a source of meat for local people for centuries. It is now being hunted into extinction.

Conservation and Recovery

The shapo has the misfortune of living in a very dangerous part of the world; its range is disputed territory between India and Pakistan. It needs a preserve where hunting is excluded. For the long term, it may need a permanent presence of park rangers to protect it.

Chamois

Rupicapra rupicapra ornata

Zoological Society of Philadelphia

Status	Endangered
Listed	June 14, 1976
Family	Bovidae (Cattle and oxen)
Description	Winter coats are long and shaggy, and are darker than their summer coats which are light brown; males have two stout horns that taper to narrow, sharply curved, backward pointing tips.
Habitat	Steep, rocky terrain at or above the tree line, characterized by sparse vegetation.
Food	Grasses and low vegetation.
Reproduction	1 to 2 young after gestation of 160 to 170 days.
Threats	Hunting, competition for food.
Range	Italy

Description

The USFWS lists only the Abruzzo (Italian) chamois, *Rupicapra rupicapra ornata,* as endangered, although the Chartreuse (French) chamois, which is not listed, has even lower numbers. These goat antelopes are separate populations of the same species. Their winter coats are long and shaggy, and are darker than their summer coats which are light brown. The winter coats have light markings around the chin, neck and abdomen, and a white rump patch while the lighter summer coat has dark marks on the face. Males have two stout horns that taper to narrow, sharply curved, backward pointing tips. Males weigh up to 110 pounds and stand up to 36 inches high at the shoulder.

Behavior

In summer, the chamois stay high in the Alps, above the tree line. In winter they move to lower elevations and are forced into smaller groups by the trees and scarcity of food resources. Females remain with their parent group their entire lives and the herd enlarges as offspring increases. Males leave the herd when they are sexually mature at 2 to 3 years.

Herds are led by a dominant male and may change leadership as one male displaces another. Males wage fierce battles for dominance, using their sharp-pointed horns as the primary weapon of attack; females also fight for dominance among themselves.

Breeding occurs in December and January, with the birth of 1 to 2 young about 6 months later.

The diet of the chamois includes grasses and low vegetation.

Habitat

These endangered chamois occur in steep, rocky terrain at or above the tree line, characterized by sparse vegetation.

Distribution

The chamois is not endangered in many parts of the world, including South America, North America, and New Zealand, and the European population alone numbers hundreds of thousands. The Chartreuse population, however, may have as few as 100 individuals, and the Abruzzo population, fewer than 500.

Threats

The chamois is a prized game animal and has been hunted extensively. It also competes with domesticated sheep for scarce food resources, especially in winter. Even though laws were enacted to protected the endangered populations, poaching remains a problem.

Conservation and Recovery

Both populations are under strict protection and surveillance in their limited habitat.

Mongolian Saiga

Saiga tatarica mongolica

Warsaw Zoo

Status	Endangered
Listed	June 14, 1976
Family	Bovidae (Bovine)
Description	Heavy, wool-like coat with a mane of long hair from the chin to the chest; fur color is yellowish-red in summer with a lighter shade on the sides and white underneath, and a white tail; an unusual large and flexible snout that hangs over the mouth.
Habitat	Grassy arid steppes and semi-deserts.
Food	Grasses, forbs, and shrubs.
Reproduction	Females usually give birth to twins, although about one-third of the births produce one calf.
Threats	Hunted for its horns, the muttonlike meat, hides, and fat.
Range	Western Mongolia

Description

The Mongolian saiga, *Saiga tatarica mongolica*, is a subspecies of the saiga (*S. tatarica*). The animal has a heavy, wool-like coat with a mane of long hair from the chin to the chest. In summer, the general fur color is yellowish-red with a lighter shade on the sides and white underneath. A broad, dark band runs from the top of the head to the back of the neck. The tail is white. In winter, the fur is longer and of a more uniform pale, dull color. The semi-transparent horns, found only on the males, are lyre-shaped with heavy ridges.

S. t. mongolica, like the other subspecies of *S. tatarica*, has an unusual large and flexible snout that hangs over the mouth. The down-pointed nostrils are lined with hairs, glands, and mucous tracts. The nose bones are large and greatly convoluted. Unlike any other mammals, except whales, each nostril has a sac lined with mucous membranes. The purpose of this unique organ is not exactly known. Some authorities believe the nose and connected structures warm and moisten the dry, winter air. Keeping dust away from the delicate respiratory tract could also be a purpose for the extensive nasal passages. One authority suggests that the expanded nose may help cool off the animal by diverting blood through the large membrane sacs.

S. t. mongolica is one of two subspecies of *S. tatarica*. The other subspecies, *S. t. tatarica* was originally placed in a separate genus, *Capra*, by Linnaeus.

Behavior

The major food sources for Mongolian saigas are grasses, forbs, and shrubs. The time of year determines how much of each type of vegetation is eaten. Mongolian saigas get some of their water requirements from the plants they eat. During the summer, when the moisture content of plants is low, the animals use waterholes. Under good conditions, they drink at waterholes twice in a day, in the morning and evening. Normally, they go belly-deep in the water and drink for 3 to 5 minutes. Mongolian saigas always keep their nose wrinkled and above the water with nostrils dilated.

During most of the year, Mongolian saigas are active throughout the day. In the summer, the animals graze in the morning and evenings and rest during the midday heat.

The Mongolian saiga can run up to 50 miles per hour. When escaping predators, they run and make jumps to see their pursuers. Unlike some populations of *S. tatarica*, seasonal migrations of Mongolian saigas were not observed in Mongolia. During most of the year, the animal has no fixed home range, generally wandering several dozen kilometers per day. However, during mating season, adult males form territories in order to gather together a harem of approximately 5 to 15 females. The male constantly challenges other males encroaching on its territory and fierce fights, sometimes resulting in death, fre-

quently break out. By the end of the rut, many of the exhausted males perish.

After a gestation period of 139 to 152 days, females usually give birth to twins, although about one-third of the births produce one calf. Approximately one female is born for each male. Newborns weigh about 8 pounds and mature rapidly, running faster than a human by the second day of life. Small horns appear on the males by about one month and achieve adult size by one year. Females reach sexual maturity at 7 or 8 months of age and the males mature later, at approximately 2 years of age.

Habitat

Mongolian saigas inhabit grassy arid steppes and semi-deserts. In general, they live on open plains, avoiding broken country and dense vegetation. However, during winter storms they may move onto the hilly steppes and sand ridges.

Distribution

In historic times, Mongolian saigas lived in a wider area of western Mongolia and its population may have overlapped the range of *P. t. tatarica*. The present distribution of this subspecies has shrunk to a smaller portion of western Mongolia and is now separated from *P. t. tatarica*.

Threats

Centuries of hunting decimated both of the *S. tatarica* subspecies. During the early 19th century, hundreds of thousands of head were taken annually. While the rest of the subspecies has made a remarkable recovery, the Mongolian saiga has not.

Conservation and Recovery

Commercial hunting bans have been established for different populations of *S. tatarica* at various times. The bans have been lifted for some of the more numerous populations of the species *S. tatarica*.

Western Giant Eland
Taurotragus derbianus derbianus

Alan Shoemaker

Status	Endangered
Listed	March 30, 1972
Family	Bovidae (Bovine)
Description	Largest African antelope, with a shoulder hump, a dewlap between the throat and chest, and rounded hooves; dark red coat marked by 14 or 15 vertical white stripes on the side; a thin black stripe runs along the back.
Habitat	African savanna, covered with grasses and other herbaceous vegetation, with occasional shrubs and trees.
Food	Mainly tree leaves and herbaceous plants.
Reproduction	Usually one calf is born after a 9 month gestation period.
Threats	Hunted for its high-quality, tender meat; trophy hunting.
Range	Senegal, Mali

Description

The western giant eland, *Taurotragus derbianus derbianus*, is the largest African antelope, with the adult male weighing up to 2,000 pounds and standing about 70 inches tall. In general, females are smaller than the males. Both sexes of this massive animal have a hump on their shoulders, a dewlap between the throat and chest, and rounded hooves.

This beautiful animal has a dark red coat marked by 14 or 15 vertical white stripes on the side. A thin black stripe runs along the back from the head to the tail. On the neck, The western giant eland has a brown mane tipped with white. The end of the tail is darker than the rest of the body. The male has a dark brown spot on his forehead. The long, wide ears have slightly rounded tips and are lighter inside than the rest of the body.

The massive twisted horns of the male measure from 35 inches to a record length of 47 inches long. The females have thinner horns.

T. d. derbianus is one of 2 subspecies of the species *Taurotragus derbianus*. The other subspecies, *Taurotragus derbianus gigas*, is also very large, but only has 12 vertical stripes on its sides, instead of 14 or 15 stripes. The species *Taurotragus derbianus* is closely related to the common eland, *Taurotragus oryx*, and is often considered to be the same species.

The genus *Taurotragus* is considered separate by Meester *et al.* However, other authorities, such as Corbet and Hill, Honacki, Kinman, and Koepl, and Van Gelde place *Taurotragus* within the genus *Tragelaphus.* Another common name for the western giant eland is Lord Derby's eland.

Behavior

During the heat of the day, the western giant eland prefers to lie in sheltered areas. The animal feeds during the night.

These strong, agile animals have been known to jump 6 foot fences and smash down barriers when the migration urge arises. The western giant eland can run up to 43 miles per hour.

Western giant elands live in herds of up to 60 members. Unlike many other antelope, *Taurotragus* in general do not spread out across the plains during the wet season. Instead, they continue to maintain their large herds. Usually, one calf is born after a 9 month gestation period. The females reach sexual maturity in 2 years, and the males in 3 years.

Habitat

Western giant elands typically live in the African savanna, from Senegal to the Ivory Coast. The savanna is covered with grasses and other herbaceous vegetation, with occasional shrubs and trees. Western giant elands will also live in rocky areas. The animal prefers to live near water courses.

Distribution

Historically, western giant elands widely roamed many west African countries; along the Falem River in Senegal, along the Gambian River in Gambia, mainly in the Fouta Djallon mountain area of Guinea, in Guinea-Bissau, and in the Ivory Coast. Now, however, the western giant eland is extinct in the Ivory Coast and probably Gambia and Guinea-Bissau. The animal is currently found in scattered pockets in Mali such as the Kengebaoul protected forest, the Mandinque Mountains and in the Fina Reserve. The population in Senegal seems to be stabilizing.

Threats

The western giant eland has been hunted for centuries by both local tribesmen and foreign hunters for the animal's tender meat and beautiful hide. Also, the western giant eland is susceptible to the usually fatal disease rinderpest, or bovine plague, caught from domestic cattle. Environmental degradation caused by the expansion of human settlements is another reason for its decline.

Conservation and Recovery

Many reserves have been set aside to protect the western giant eland. In Senegal, the Niokolo-Koba National Park has been established near the Gambia river specifically to protect this species. Encouragingly, the population has tripled in 5 years. The park is successful because hunting is strictly banned and local human populations were encouraged to move away. However, the situation in Mali is not so hopeful. Although many parks and reserves have been set aside, the western giant eland can only be found in the protected areas of Kengebaoul, Mandique Mountains, and the Fina reserve. Unfortunately, the eland can be hunted outside of the protected areas in Mali through the payment of a tax.

A few animals are being bred in captivity. Attempts have been made to domesticate these docile animals for milk production and for the veal-like meat. As the western giant eland is immune to sleeping sickness which kills domestic cattle, experiments in domestication have been encouraged in areas heavily infested with the tse-tse fly. However, the animal's ability to leap 6 foot high fences and susceptibility to rinderpest, may prove to be drawbacks to domestication attempts.

Wild Pigs
Family: Suidae

Giant Forest Hog (*Hylochoerus meinertzhageni*)

H. Douglas Pratt

General Characteristics of the *Suidae*

The *Suidae* are adaptable survivors able to inhabit forests, thickets, woodlands and grasslands. Their well-developed, upturned canines provide good defense combined with their powerful, agile bodies and keen sense of hearing. They are social animals, usually feeding in family parties and constantly vocalizing their attitude through grunts and squeaks. They have a simple stomach and can feed on a wide variety of fungi, ferns, grasses, leaves, insect larvae, small vertebrates, and fruits.

Sexual maturity in most wild pig species is reached at 18 months, although mating may not occur in males until they reach physical maturity at 3 to 4 years. The litter size is influenced by habitat conditions and by the number of the mother's teats; each piglet has its own teat. The young are born in grass nests constructed by the mother. They are weaned at three months but may remain with the mother until she farrows again. Several generations of the same family may band together. Other social units are solitary boars and bachelor groups. Wild pigs are probably non-territorial and will share feeding grounds, water holes, wallows and sleeping dens. They mark their home ranges with secretions from lip glands or foot glands.

Although domestic pigs have provided a source for meat since neolithic times, and some societies have formed pig cultures, feral pigs cause much destruction to habitats, and many species, particularly plant species, have become extinct or endangered because of habitat degradation caused by wild pigs. They also carry diseases or are hosts to disease-carrying insects, such as the blood sucking tsetse fly that causes sleeping sickness in people and ngana in domestic livestock.

Babirusa

Babyrousa babyrussa

Rich Block

Status	Endangered
Listed	June 14, 1976
Family	Suidae (Wild pigs)
Description	Lower canine teeth grow out of the sides of the mouth and curl back toward the animal's back in a long arch; skin is either rough and brownish-gray, or smooth and sparsely covered with short whitish-gray to yellowish hairs.
Habitat	Prefers moist forests, canebrakes, and the shores of rivers and lakes.
Food	Omnivorous.
Reproduction	One or two young after gestation of 160 days.
Threats	Habitat loss; excessive hunting.
Range	Indonesia

Description

The male babirusa, *Babyrousa babyrussa*, has lower canine teeth that grow out of the sides of the mouth and curl back toward the animal's back in a long arch. The upper canines grow out of the top of the animal's snout instead of growing in a downward direction. They grow up and back in the same fashion as the lower canines. These teeth grow throughout the animal's life, and an older babirusa male has four great tusks.

The head and body length is usually 34 to 40 inches, tail length is 10.5 to 12.5 inches, and its weight is up to 220 pounds. The skin is either rough and brownish-gray, or smooth and sparsely covered with short whitish-gray to yellowish hairs. The underside and inner sides of the legs are sometimes lighter than the rest of the body. Often, this whitish color extends along the sides of the upper lip.

Behavior

The babirusa is a shy animal that travels in small parties of up to eight individuals and reveals its presence with low, grunting moans. Offspring are born in the early months of the year and are not striped like the young of most pigs. One or two young are born after a gestation period of approximately 160 days. The offspring are precocious and take some solid food after just 10 days of life.

Captive babirusas have lived up to 24 years. It is an excellent swimmer and will sometimes swim in the sea.

Natives say that the tusks of the babirusa are like the antlers of a deer; thus the name babirusa, which means "pig deer."

Like other Suidae, the babirusa tends to be omnivorous, feeding on leaves, roots, fruits, nuts and small mammals. Babirusa are diurnal, with activity concentrated in the morning.

Habitat

The babirusa occurs in moist forests, canebrakes, and the shores of rivers and lakes in a relatively small area on the islands of Sulawesi, Togian, Buru, and Sula in Indonesia. This animal is a swift runner and often swims in the sea to reach small islands.

Distribution

The babirusa occurs on Sulawesi, the nearby Togian and Sula islands, and Buru Island in the Moluccas. Its presence on Buru and possibly Sula is evidently the result of human introduction.

Threats

The babirusa is threatened mainly by habitat loss and excessive hunting. The babirusa is often captured young and tamed by native people. Natives also regularly hunt the animal for food.

Conservation and Recovery

Babirusas have been bred in captivity since the 1800s but they do not reproduce well. If the female does not have complete isolation, she may kill her babies or totally ignore them. Inbreeding has also weakened the gene pool.

Babirusas are held in wildlife reserves and national parks in Sulawesi.

Pygmy Hog

Sus salvanius

J. Bacon, San Diego Zoo

Status	Endangered
Listed	June 2, 1970
Family	Suidae (Old World Pig)
Description	Smallest of the wild pigs, with a squat-shaped back and sharp snout; dark brown fur, and; the bristles on its back form a small mane; has short, hairless ears and a stub tail.
Habitat	Elephant grass jungle.
Food	Roots, bulbs, insects, earthworms and some soil.
Reproduction	3 to 6 young after gestation of 4 to 5 months.
Threats	Poaching for its meat; loss of habitat.
Range	India: Nepal

Description

The pygmy hog, *Sus salvanius*, is the smallest of all pig species. It weighs approximately 22 pounds and stands only 10 to 12 inches tall. The color of its fur is dark brown to rusty red. It has a squat body, sharp ears, and a bristly, short mane. It is the only pig species with a stub tail.

S. salvanius is one of the Old World pigs, which are characterized by having upper canines that turn upward as tusks; a lower pair of tusks that are often curved; four toes on each foot (although only the front two are functional); a two-compartmented stomach; and sparse, bristly hair on the thick skin. Unlike other *sus* species, females have only three mammary glands.

Behavior

Pygmy hogs herd in groups of 15 to 20, and except during mating season the individuals are inseparable. Males aggressively defend the herd by throwing themselves against the intruders at high speeds and spearing with their tusks.

Gestation lasts for approximately 4 to 5 months, after which 3 to 6 young are born.

The young are striped with yellow-brown bands.

The pygmy hog spends six to ten hours per day foraging, rooting up the ground with their snouts on elephant trails or in small clearings to feed on roots, bulbs, insects, earthworms and even some soil. They have been observed to kill and eat mice in zoos. Since their food contains a high water content, they rarely drink water. *S. salvanius* is active from sunrise until two hours after sunset, spending only the period of midday heat in their nest.

Habitat

The pygmy hog lives in the impenetrable elephant grass jungle, which stands as high as an adult human, but through which the hog slips easily, aided by its small size.

The pygmy hog uses self-built nests throughout the year. Nests are constructed of dirt that is formed into a trough on top of which the species bends the surrounding grasses. More grass is torn up or broken and transported to the nest site. The animals then creep inside and hollow out the interior with body movements until a cave is formed in which the temperature is easily raised with body heat.

Distribution

The range of the pygmy hog originally encompassed the entire elephant grass belt on the southern slopes of the Himalayas, from southwestern Nepal to north central Assam. After 1950, it was presumed that the species was extinct, as none had been observed for some time. However, during a brush fire in the Barnadi forest reserve in 1971, the pygmy

hog were among the animals observed leaving this inaccessible habitat.

In 1984, only one verified wild population remained, in the Manas National Park.

Threats

Populations of the pygmy hog have declined for several reasons. First, its habitat is becoming more and more restricted due to land development. Additionally, the native human population uses the elephant grass that the hog needs for cover to roof their huts. During the dry season in January and February, the grass is burned to eliminate the bushes growing within it, so that the grass can be better cut after its growth phase. Thus, the pygmy hog loses its cover twice yearly, and food becomes scarce at this time as well.

Finally, the hogs' tender meat is popular, and they are often poached.

Conservation and Recovery

Attempts to breed the pygmy hog in captivity have been unsuccessful. Restricted to the Manas Tiger Reserve in Assam, India, it is protected by law, but poachers are easily able to hunt wildlife there because political instability prohibits government troops from patrolling the reserve.

Cats
Family: Felidae

Cheetah (*Acinonyx jubatus*)   Rich Block

General Characteristics of the *Felidae*

There is remarkably little variation in body form among the many species of *Felidae,* the family of cats. Their bodies tend to be long, with flexible spines and deep chests, and they usually have long tails that they can wrap around themselves when they rest, to help conserve body heat. Their heads have somewhat flat faces and domed skulls; their ears can swivel to and fro, their eyes are close together and point forward, and they have whiskers sprouting from around their noses, with no two cats having the exact same pattern of whiskers. Their hearing may be their most acute sense; even when the cat is asleep, its ears swivel toward various sounds, ever listening for the sound of danger or food that will awaken the cat. It is possible that their hearing gives cats a three dimensional picture of their surroundings. Although folklore sometimes holds that cats have weak eyesight, in fact most species of cat see as well as humans do in the light, and about six times better than humans do in the dark. It is not true that cats can see where there is no light; if the darkness is absolute, cats see no better than anyone else, although their hearing will give them an advantage over most other animals as they move through a dark area. The retina of a cat has a thin reflective tissue over it; when light comes into the eye, some of it bounces off the retina, but the reflective tissue bounces the light back into the retina, acting as a light gatherer that intensifies the amount of light a cat sees. It is this reflective tissue that enables cats to see well in dim lights, and it is this tissue that people see when light reflects off the eyes, making them seem to shine.

The cat's sense of smell is much maligned in popular literature, with some reason. The cat's skull features small, sometimes compressed nasal cavities; these small cavities are the result of having the eyes pointing forward and being low on the head. Even so, a cat can smell well enough to detect nearby food, identify individual animals by their scent, tell whether a creature is male or female, and detect scents left to mark territorial boundaries. For most cats, the sense of smell is very important for their social lives; they even have scent glands on their cheeks for marking objects and thus letting other cats know of their whereabouts.

Many an adventurer has mentioned the fright that comes when a campfire glows off the eyes of a big cat such as a lion, and they have good reason to be frightened. Cats are probably the most evolved and sophisticated of the world's carnivores. Their feet have long, sharp, curved claws that can rip through flesh. Many species of cat can wound an animal with its foreclaws, while the hind legs come forward and rapidly stroke, tearing open the belly of the prey. A cat's lower jaw can drop far down, almost perpendicular to the upper jaw, and it has highly developed muscles that allow the jaw to exert enormous force; even a domesticated cat can bite hard enough to sever a human's finger. The dentition of cats has evolved entirely for eating meat; the teeth are either pointed like daggers or sabers, sometimes with serrations along the inside of the teeth, or are razorlike, for sheering through meat. The pointed teeth not only can pierce arteries, they can pierce the muscles of a neck, enabling the cat's jaw to hold onto its prey while it clamps down hard enough to prevent the creature from breathing. When cats eat meat, they turn their heads to one side or another; this is to allow chunks of meat to fall into the slicing teeth, which sheer though the chunks to make them small enough to swallow. Their tongues feature rough papillae that enable them to tear off small bits of meat from bones.

The origins of the family *Felidae* are probably in the Eocene epoch, when small cats evolved. Since those early times numerous variations on the basic cat structure have evolved and then passed away; some features such as long sabre teeth have evolved, disappeared and then re-evolved. Indeed, ours is an unusual time for cats because no sabre-toothed felines exist today. However, our human ancestors would likely have known most of the ancient cat species well, and coexisted with some frightful creatures. The evolutionary line for modern cats probably dates back to the very late Eocene or very early Oligocene epoch, when it broke away from two major lines of cats (the *Nimravinae* and the *Hoplophoneinae*) that evolved into many species, including ones with sabrelike teeth, all of which were extinct by the end of the Pliocene. In the Miocene, the line that led to modern cats broke into two branches, the *Machairodontinae* and the *Felinae*. The *Machairodontinae* featured the famous "sabre-toothed tigers" or "sabre-toothed lions" that cohabited the earth with humans. One of these, *Smilodon*, grew to be as big as an African lion and had very long sabre teeth. These ancient teeth have much in common with the fangs of modern cats: The teeth were built of layers, some thin and some compressed, an evolutionary compromise that made the teeth to be long and still strong enough to pierce muscles, but not strong enough to bear the stresses that would be caused by biting into bone; the insides of the sabre teeth were serrated, to help the teeth slice into muscle. Modern cats also run the risk of breaking their fangs on bone; their ability to drop their lower jaws wide enables them to bite over or around neck bones when they bite their prey, so that the pointed teeth meet flesh below the bone. Nature has experimented considerably with the basic cat form, and the *Machairodontinae* even featured a cat that walked plantigrade on their hind feet — that is they place the full heel to toe of the foot on the ground when walking, the way humans and bears do. This feature may have evolved to give the cat *Homotherium* secure footing on the ground while it reared up to bite, in typical cat fashion, the necks of large prey.

It is the cat group *Felinae* that evolved into the cats of the present age. Some of *Felinae's* species have evolved, flourished, and become extinct, but the modern age still has numerous species of cat; exactly how many is not known because some species have not been studied well enough to be identified and because human destruction of cat habitats have driven rare species into remote areas. For example, the Andean cat may not be just one species; it could actually be four, but naturalists have not been able to outrace the destruction of the Andean cat's habitat and conduct the studies necessary to identify the cat's speciating characteristics. During the Miocene, the evolutionary line that leads to the lynx parted from the other evolutionary line of *Felinae*; these other lines went extinct during the Pliocene epoch. Also during the Pliocene epoch, the lynx line divided into the modern species of cat. Today, scientists divide the modern species of *Felidae* into two groups: the big cats and the small cats.

The Big Cats

The big cats are typically divided into three genera with seven species, although there are occasional disagreements about which species goes where. The genus *Panthera* has five species: the tiger, the lion, the leopard, the snow leopard, and the jaguar (*Panthera tigris, Panthera leo, Panthera pardus, Panthera uncia,* and *Panthera onca*). The genus *Neofelis* has one species, the clouded leopard (*Neofelis nebulosa*), and the genus *Acinonyx* also has only one species, the cheetah (*Acinonyx jubatus*). The big cats are differentiated primarily from small cats by size, but they also differ in other ways. For instance, the bone below the palate in the back of the throat is soft in the large cats, but not the small ones. It is this loose bone that creates the open-throated roar typical of all the big cats. The social habits of big cat species are complex and sometimes strange to humans. The lion is the most social of all cats, featuring prides with intricate relationships between males and females; degrees of kinship often dictate a lion's place in a pride, and naturalists are still trying to completely sort out how lions determine who goes where and does what. Even how the pride spreads out to rest involves complex interrelationships that place certain lion in certain places when they all settle down. Other big cats are more solitary, and their social lives depend upon scent markings, roars, and changes in the season. It is mistaken to assume that cats such as the tiger have little or no social lives because they are territorial and tend to stay away from each other. To the tiger, the scents, cries, and occasional meetings all tell it where it is in a social group that can be spread over hundreds of square miles.

Among the big cats, mating is an adventure for males. First, the male often has to fight for the privilege of mating with a receptive female. Then, it needs to have the approval of the female, who may refuse the male. Sometimes, as with tigers, the female needs to initiate mating. Once the cats have mated, the male moves quickly away from the female, because she usually turns and swipes with one of her forepaws or even bites at the male. Mature male big cats often bear many facial scars; some of these come from serious combat with other males, but some come from a female's swipe when the male was too slow in getting away. In spite of this impediment, a male and female will usually mate several times in a day; lions may mate fifty times in a day.

The care of young varies greatly among the big cat species. In lion prides, the chore of raising young is shared. Females will tend to the basic needs of cubs, and males will tolerantly endure to the play of cubs that either they or a close kin have sired. Among other big cats, males may have nothing to do with raising the cubs, who are cared for by their mothers until they are old enough to survive when forced out of her territory into relatively solitary lives of their own. Adult males who are unrelated to cubs are generally threats to those cubs; when male lions take over a pride, often by killing or driving away the resident males, they will often kill the cubs as well, making the females available to them for breeding. Among other big cats, females sometimes must fight off an intruding male that may kill her young.

The Small Cats

The small cats are more numerous than the big ones; different references will cite different numbers of small cat species because not all have been identified with certainty, as yet, but there are at least twenty-eight different species of small cat, including the oldest evolutionary lineage, the lynx (*Felis lynx*), and domesticated cats (*Felis sylvestrus catus*). All small cats are part of the genus *Felis*. Physically, the small cats are very much alike. Like their big cat cousins, they have deep chests, long bodies, and adaptations for hunting and for eating meat, but whereas big cats will hunt large animals, small cats eat primarily rodents — mostly mice and rats.

Small cat species differ from one another in their behavior in significant ways, although certain similarities persist: Adult males are dangerous to kittens that are not their own progeny, even the most solitary breeds require some sort of social life. They rely primarily on stalking and pouncing to capture their prey, they are enormously patient when it comes to waiting out prey, and they are good tree climbers. The domestic cat reveals much of this common behavior in its own life, including such actions as rubbing its forehead against another cat (or a person; the cats seem to regard people as large domestic cats) to indicate affection, bringing home dead animals as their contributions to their family units (birds, squirrels, mice, or other small game left on the doorstep), and purring. It seems that all small cats purr. They even have in common the trait of landing on their feet when falling a great distance; their inner ears are sophisticated in their sense of balance and coordinate well with eyes in maintaining a cat's orientation, and when a cat falls, its inner ear maintains its orientation with the ground so the cat's head turns upright, twisting the neck, and then the body follows around, adjusting to the neck's upward orientation. Small cats have in common with the big cats strong, very thick and muscular necks. Such muscularity is important when the cat bites and tries to hold struggling prey with its mouth.

On the other hand, domestic cats vary from other small cats in important ways. They are desert animals — their ancestry is North African and they retain adaptations to desert life such as retaining fluids, with their urine thick and pungent with wastes, and lacking warmth. A few of its wild cousins are also desert animals (for example, the Pakistan sand cat, *Felis margarita scheffeli*), but the majority are forest dwellers and fond of trees and water. According to many authorities, domestic cats also may have had a genetic mutation in North Africa several thousand years ago that makes it retain kittenlike behavior even when adults; this accounts for its rubbing its side against people when it wants food — this is typical behavior for kittens. Although a few other species of small cat can be to some degree domesticated, none has the warm friendliness of the domestic cat. In fact, most dislike the company of humans altogether.

In other matters, small cats vary widely in how they live. Some mate for life (for instance, the tiger cat, *Felis tigrinus*), forming small, cohesive family units with their young, while others mate only for a season, and while still others tend to avoid one another's company except for mating or the raising of young. Nearly all are territorial, with their territories varying in size according to the availability of food. Most avoid confrontations with one another, except for mothers protecting their young from marauding males (even adult males of the domestic cat will kill unrelated young), but when they fight they tend to swipe at one another's noses. Nearly all have mating calls, high pitched squeaks to deep-throated yowls to very loud roars. They also make cries to let others of their species know their whereabouts, to proclaim a territorial boundary, and to alert others to the presence of predators. For small cats, the purr is a sophisticated form of communication, with intonations that indicate pleasure, a demand for food, and a friendly warning to stay away; the purr is also a comforting sound, used by mothers especially to calm kittens.

Cheetah

Acinonyx jubatus

Rich Block

Status	Endangered
Listed	June 2, 1970
Family	Felidae (Cats)
Description	Long slender body, short rounded ears and large eyes on a relatively small head; long tail is over half the length of the body.
Habitat	Grass savannas, bush savannas.
Food	Birds, small mammals, antelope.
Reproduction	3 to 4 kittens after gestation of approximately 270 days.
Threats	Hunting; use as pets; loss of habitat due to farming.
Range	Kenya, Tanzania, Botswana, Namibia, Zimbabwe, South Africa, Iran, Malawi, Mozambique, Sudan, Ethiopia, Republic of Congo.

Description

The cheetah, *Acinonyx jubatus*, is the fastest carnivore on earth, reaching speeds of up to 60 miles per hour for short sprints. Using its long legs and extremely flexible spine, the cheetah can achieve great strides when running. The long tail is over half the length of the body and can be used as counterbalance when turning. With its wide nostrils, the cheetah can cool off after a fast run by breathing in more oxygen.

As another adaptation for running, the cheetah uses its extended claws like running spikes to grip the ground. More similar to those of dogs than those of other cats, the claws are only weakly retractable and do not have a protective sheath of skin. The cheetah has a sharp dew claw that does not touch the ground and is used to help drag down prey.

This animal has a long slender body, measuring 55 to 59 inches long. At the shoulders, this cat can reach a height of 35 inches. The cheetah can weigh from 99 to 132 pounds. The canine teeth have characteristics more similar to dogs than to the other cats.

The animal has short rounded ears and large eyes on its relatively small head. The yellowish-brown fur is covered with small, round dark spots. On its small head, the cheetah has a distinctive black stripe from the inner corner of each eye to the upper lip. The hair on the neck forms a short crest.

Although up to six subspecies of cheetahs have been described, most of them are probably not distinct races. One subspecies, the king cheetah (*Acinonyx rex*) with an unusual coat color, turned out to be a single gene mutation that can occur in any litter). Formerly, the cheetah was classified under the genus *Cynailurus*, which means "dog-cat," because of its many caninelike characteristics.

Members of this species have been found to be almost genetically identical to each other, with only a 2% difference in captive populations and a 4% difference in some wild populations. This genetic similarity is believed to be caused by a severe population bottleneck about 10,000 years ago at the end of the last ice age. A similar bottleneck occurred in the South African population during the nineteenth century, possibly due to human persecution. Because of this lack of genetic diversity, cheetahs are notoriously difficult to breed in captivity.

Behavior

The cheetah normally lives alone and is not usually territorial, although males occasionally form groups of two or three in small territories. Females give birth to three or four kittens after a gestation period of approximately 270 days. The cubs are covered in a long grayish-green mane for the first three months of life.

The cheetah feeds on birds, small mammals, small antelope up to the size of the impala, and occasionally the young of larger antelopes. The cheetah is mainly diurnal since it needs light to see its prey. However, it has been known to hunt at night by moonlight. It hunts its prey by selecting an animal, making a lightning dash, and then knocking the prey to the ground. It has to be careful not to select an animal too far away because it can only run at top speeds for about 300 yards. Even so, the cheetah has a very high rate of hunting success. Because it is so successful, it does not normally scavenge dead animals as other cats do. After it has killed its prey, the cheetah usually drags the kill off to a shady spot to eat. Unlike most big cats, the cheetah normally does not return to a kill after a first meal.

Habitat

The cheetah lives in the grass savannas, bush savannas, and thin open woodland savannas of Africa, the Middle East, and formerly India. This fast cat is absent from well-developed forests because it needs level open space to see and chase down its prey.

Distribution

Historically, the cheetah was very widely distributed throughout the grasslands of India, the Middle East, and Africa. Now, however, it is extinct in India and much of Asia. Only tiny populations still survive in Baluchistan and Iran. The African cheetah population is declining rapidly with relatively large numbers found only in East and South Africa.

The total number of individuals remaining in Africa has been estimated at 10,000 to 15,000 with the main populations in Kenya, Tanzania, Botswana, Namibia, Zimbabwe, and South Africa. Smaller populations of between 50 and 200 individuals can be found in Malawi, Mozambique, Sudan, Ethiopia, and Republic of Congo. In Iran, a well protected, fairly stable population of over 250 individuals exists.

Threats

The cheetah has long been hunted for its beautiful spotted fur and poaching still occurs. Hunting of both the cheetah and its prey has helped to devastate cheetah populations. These animals face a severe loss of habitat because their grassland homes have been broken up for farms and ranches. Also, the removal of live cheetahs from the wild to be used as pets has contributed to its decline.

Conservation and Recovery

In the past, captive breeding programs have not met with success, partly because of the cheetah's lack of genetic diversity. However, recently some zoos have had success breeding cheetahs by carefully selecting animals from different populations and also by carefully managing the animals' behavior.

The cheetah was listed in CITES, Appendix I: Trade Prohibited on July 1, 1975. In the *IUCN Red Data Book* as of 1972, the cheetah is listed as vulnerable, and the subspecies *Acinonyx jubatus venaticus* is listed as endangered.

Leopard Cat

Felis [=Prionailurus] bengalensis bengalensis

Bruce Bunting

Status	Endangered
Listed	June 14, 1976
Family	Felidae (Cats)
Description	Small, domestic cat-sized animal; small head with a short muzzle and moderately long, rounded ears; fur is yellowish above and white underneath with dark spots on the body and tail.
Habitat	Forested areas.
Food	Wide variety of prey including hares, rodents, young deer, birds, reptiles, and fish.
Reproduction	1 to 4 cubs after gestation of 65 to 72 days.
Threats	Hunting for its fur and probably to protect domestic livestock.
Range	India, China, and Thailand.

Description

Felis bengalensis bengalensis is a subspecies of the leopard cat, *Felis bengalensis*. This small, domestic cat-sized animal weighs 7 to 15 pounds. The body length measures 17 to 42 inches, and the tail length is 9 to 17 inches. The head is small with a short muzzle and moderately long, rounded ears. They are excellent swimmers.

This subspecies of the leopard cat has yellowish fur above and white underneath with dark spots on the body and tail. Four black bands run from the forehead to behind the neck and then break up into short bands on the back. Indistinct dark bands ring the tail toward the tip. White streaks are found on the cat's cheeks and from the eyes to the top of its head.

Other common names include Bengal cat and monkey cat.

Behavior

Females give birth to one to four cubs after a gestation period between 65 to 72 days. In India, births are reported to occur in May.

In Southeast Asia, however, births can occur throughout the year. Newborn cubs open their eyes after 10 days. They reach sexual maturity at about 18 months. The fathers may help with the raising of the cubs. If the cubs die, the female may mate soon after and produce another litter within 4 to 5 months.

Although the dietary habits of the subspecies *bengalensis* are not described in scientific literature, the species leopard cat, in general, has been known to eat a wide variety of prey such as hares, rodents, young deer, birds, reptiles, and fish. Reportedly, these cats may also kill and eat poultry from nearby villages.

Mainly nocturnal, *bengalensis* also has been frequently spotted moving about during the day.

Habitat

The *bengalensis* subspecies typically lives in forested areas of southern and eastern Asia. They can be found at both low and high elevations. Fairly tolerant of human activity, the animals are often found near villages. They may occupy dens in hollow trees, small caves, or under tree roots.

Distribution

The *bengalensis* subspecies of the leopard cat can be found in peninsular India, China, and Thailand. Bengalensis numbers are dwindling throughout its range.

Threats

Hunting for its fur and probably killing cats to protect domestic livestock has diminished the populations of the leopard cat. General destruction of the rain forest diminishes the natural habitat of this cat, too, forcing the animal to live close to humans.

With the banning of trade in larger cat's furs, there has been a trend towards trade in the furs of the smaller cats such as the leopard cat. It takes 15 pelts of leopard cats to make one garment.

Conservation and Recovery

F. b. bengalensis, except for the Chinese population, is listed in CITES, Appendix I: Trade Prohibited as of July 1, 1975. The Chinese population is listed in Appendix II, which allows regulated trade, as of July 1, 1975. According to one souce, China may have killed and exported more than 2 million *bengalensis* skins since 1989. This would represent virtually China's entire population of this animal. Since the non-Chinese population of *bengalensis* is listed in Appendix I of CITES, the cat's fur from outside of China is banned from legal trading. However, if the cat is to have any hope for survival, it must be given refuge in wildlife preserves, and people must stop buying products made with its coat.

Costa Rican [=Central American] Puma

Felis [=Profelis] concolor costaricensis

Felis concolor

C. Allan Morgan

Status	Endangered
Listed	June 14, 1976
Family	Felidae (Cats)
Description	Rich cinnamon-red coat that is redder overall and darker on its back than for other puma.
Habitat	Tropical forests.
Food	Small animals such as rodents and large ones such as deer.
Reproduction	Gestation is 92 to 96 days, and litters are 2 to 6 cubs in size.
Threats	Loss of habitat; hunting for its skin.
Range	Costa Rica

Description

The Costa Rican Puma, *Felis concolor costaricensis*, is distinguished from other puma subspecies by its coat, which is redder than most and darker on the back. It also may be distinguished by its skull, which has wider, flatter nasal passages and longer postorbital processes (almost 3 inches) than those of other subspecies.

Adults are smaller than most of the other subspecies. Adults are about 3.5 to 5 feet long, not counting the tail, with the tail adding about 26 inches. It weighs 80 to 150 pounds. Its coat is cinnamon-red to dark red, growing paler as it progresses down the legs to the feet. Its undersides, from chin to tail, are white. The Costa Rican puma's ears are black, but edged in gray. One to three inches of the tail at its tip are black. Sometimes a Costa Rican puma is "melanistic," meaning all black. Overall, the coat has shorter, more bristly hairs than found on other pumas. As with other pumas, it has a powerful build, with its hind legs slightly longer than its forelegs. And as with other pumas, its head is rounded, although somewhat flatter in back than with other subspecies of puma.

Behavior

Costa Rican puma cubs are weaned by 6 months of age; they reach maturity between

2 and 2.5 years of age, although their mother will have driven them off at between 1 and 1.5 years old. The pumas are somewhat opportunistic eaters, with their prey including small mammals and birds, as well as larger creatures such as deer. Farmers and ranchers may kill the Costa Rican puma because it may prey on poultry or other livestock. They hunt in evening twilight and at night, rarely by day. They shun humans if at all possible and will avoid daytime movement if human beings live nearby.

They are stalkers who carefully use ground cover to hide their movements. It is possible that like some South American pumas, they can leap from tree branch to tree branch in pursuit of arboreal prey. The quarry is usually dispatched by a powerful leap onto its back by the puma, often breaking the spine. If the prey survives the first ferocious attack, the puma may kill it with a bite to the neck. Should the initial attack fail, the puma will usually give up and look for other prey. The pumas have tremendously powerful jaw and neck muscles and will drag even large prey as much as a quarter mile to a secluded spot where they can feed unmolested. After feeding, the puma will cover what is left of its meal with leaves and debris. If it needs to, it may return to feed on the remaining carcass as much as a week later.

The Costa Rican pumas are solitary creatures, and very territorial. A single adult may have a territory as large as 20 square miles. Given how compressed the Costa Rican puma's habitat has become, the average territories are probably much smaller now. Pumas avoid one another almost as much as they avoid human beings, and physical conflicts among them are rare. The territories of males and females may overlap, but by leaving scent markings from glands or with urine or dung, the animals let each other know not only whose territory they are in, but whether they are nearby. The scent markings may also let males know when nearby females are in estrus.

Habitat

The Costa Rican puma lives in tropical rain forests and prefers areas with abundant ground cover. Although it is now found mostly in highlands, at one time it could be found in lowland areas. These lowlands are now heavily populated by humans.

Distribution

The past distribution of the Costa Rican puma is open to speculation. Early researchers thought it might range throughout Costa Rica, Nicaragua, and Panama, but they were not sure. Even as late as the mid-1940s, researchers had only eight examples of the subspecies to study, three of which were only skulls, and none of which came from Nicaragua. It is probable that the subspecies now only exists in eastern Costa Rica.

Threats

Loss of habitat is the Costa Rican puma's foremost threat, although like other pumas it is hunted as a pest, as a threat to human safety, and for sport. It now exists in small numbers in eastern Costa Rica because its habitat in western Costa Rica has been lost to agriculture. It rarely ranged into Nicaragua, and its habitat there has been lost to logging, agriculture, and warfare. Its habitat in Panama has been lost to logging, human settlements, and agriculture.

Conservation and Recovery

Costa Rica has outlawed the exportation of puma skins, and the animal is listed in CITES, Appendix I: Trade Prohibited, which discourages the trade in puma skins. The Costa Rican law has had a beneficial effect because it has discouraged the hunting of the Costa Rican puma for commercial gain, and the subspecies is evidently increasing in numbers in the eastern part of the country. It has been reported on occasion in the western part, but its best habitat is in the eastern rain forests that are protected reserves.

Iriomote Cat

Felis [=Prionailurus] iriomotensis

USFWS

Status	Endangered
Listed	March 30, 1972
Family	Felidae (Cat)
Description	Long body, short tail and short legs; dusky brown fur has spots arranged in longitudinal rows that coalesce into bands.
Habitat	Lowland, subtropical rain forest of the Japanese island of Iriomote.
Food	Wide variety of mammals, birds, reptiles, amphibians, fish, and insects.
Reproduction	1 to 4 kittens born in April or May.
Threats	Destruction of habitat for agricultural development.
Range	Japan: Iriomote in the Yaeyama Islands at the southern end of the Ryukyu Islands.

Description

The Iriomote cat, *Felis [=Prionailurus] iriomotensis*, is similar in size to the domestic cat, weighing 7 to 9 pounds. The cat has a long body, measuring 23 inches, with a short tail of 8 inches, as well as short legs. The dusky brown fur has spots arranged in longitudinal rows that coalesce into bands. Five to seven dark lines run from the back of the neck to the shoulders. The rounded ears are dark with a white spot on the back; the eyes have distinct white markings below each eye and on the inside of the eye next to the nose. The

pattern on the animal's fur effectively camouflages the animal in the shadows of its forest home.

Behavior

These extremely rare cats have small home ranges, not exceeding 1.2 square miles, with the male's range being larger than the female's. Individuals' home ranges may overlap.

The Iriomote cat hunts during the night. These small cats eat a wide variety of mammals, birds, reptiles, amphibians, fish, and insects. Their mammal prey includes fruit bats, black rats, and wild pigs. They hunt many different species of bird including night heron, quail, rail, pigeon, dove, scops owl, kingfisher, robin, thrush, and crow. According to one study, they regularly consume 39 species of beetle. The Iriomote cat also eats crabs and mud skippers. In the summer, the cats eat fewer mammals and more birds and reptiles than in the winter.

Irimote cats are loners. They spend the day resting in a rock or tree cavity. They are agile climbers and hunt in trees as well as on the ground. They are excellent swimmers and may also hunt in water. They are more nocturnal during the summer, becoming diurnal during the winter. They probably mate in winter when they form pairs. One to four kitten are born at the end of April or May. The young mature rapidly and can hunt by three months.

Habitat

The Iriomote cats live only in the deep subtropical rain forest on the 181 square mile Japanese island of Iriomote, which is located 1,300 miles south of Tokoyo and 125 miles off the coast of Taiwan at the end of the Ryukyu chain. Because of its isolation, many species have evolved distinctive characteristics on this island.

Distribution

The Iriomote cat can only be found on the island of Iriomote in the Yaeyama Islands at the southern end of the Ryukyu islands south of Japan and east of Taiwan. Since the species was only discovered in 1967, it is not known if it had a broader historical range, or if Iriomote island has always been its only home. It is believed that 50 to 100 individuals survive.

Threats

The main cause of the decline of the Iriomote cat population is the destruction of its subtropical forest habitat for agricultural development. Cats are also killed in boar snares.

Conservation and Recovery

Two-thirds of Irimote Island has been established as a nature reserve.

The Iriomote cat is listed in Appendix II: Trade Restricted of CITES as of February 4, 1977 along with all other *Felis* species except those listed in Appendix I and house cats. In the *IUCN Red Data Book*, *F. iriomotensis* is listed as endangered as of 1978. This species is completely protected under Japanese law.

Andean Cat

Felis jacobita

Gunter Ziesler/Peter Arnold

Status	Endangered
Listed	June 14, 1976
Family	Felidae (Cats)
Description	Coloring varies from pale gray belly, dark gray ears, dark gray spots on legs and underparts, brown and yellow spots on back, to an overall golden brown undercoat, tinged with gray, and turning to gray and almost white on its head.
Habitat	Cold, windy, semi-arid, treeless, rocky, often snowbound terrain above 10,000 feet.
Food	Small mammals, mostly chinchillas, visachas, and other rodents.
Threats	Hunting; degradation of habitat.
Range	Northern Argentina, Bolivia, northeastern Chile, and southern Peru.

Description

The Andean cat, *Felis jacobita*, is a beautifully sleek animal. Its hair is short to medium-length and laid front-to-back flat along its body, about 2 inches long on its body and 1 inch long on its tail, and its fur is soft. Its head looks disproportionately small compared to its body, and its neck appears long and especially thick. Its tail is notable for being uniform in diameter until it reaches its tip. From nose to tail, the adult Andean cat is 27 to 30 inches long. Its tail is about 20 inches in length. It weighs 8 to 15.5 pounds.

Descriptions of its coloration vary considerably. This is likely due to a natural variation in coats among members of the species; as a point of speculation, it could be due to age differences, with younger Andean cats having grayer coats with spots — valuable as camouflage in their rocky environment, and older cats having the more golden fur that poachers covet; the difference could be due to poor observations — the cat is extremely rare and elusive, making observing it very difficult. It is typically brown-gray or silvery gray with a pale gray or white belly and spots and stripes of brown, orange, or yellow on its legs and body, with dark rings on its tail.

There has been some suggestion that the Andean cat is actually the pampas cat or a subspecies of the pampas cat, but this is unlikely because of its double-chambered bullae in its skull, which is different enough from others cats' skulls that the Andean cat is sometimes given its own genus and called *Oreailurus jacobita*.

Behavior

The Andean cat's prey are small mammals, primarily rodents. Notable prey are chinchillas and visachas.

It has only been recorded live once in the wild, and its behavior is undocumented. What little is known of it comes mostly from the skulls that have been gathered in museum collections and the one-time only observation. Zoos have more than once thought that they had acquired a specimen only to discover it was a similarly colored pampas cat.

Habitat

The Andean cat lives in an area in which its coloring would provide very good camouflage. The region has little rainfall and its terrain consists of rock and snow. It is not only treeless, but offers few shrubs for camouflage. The area is windy and very cold, and the animal's heavy, soft fur presumably offers it protection from the elements.

Distribution

The Andean cat inhabits the northern Andean mountains, primarily in southern Peru, although its range includes northern Argentina, Bolivia, and northeastern Chile. Some naturalists would extend this range farther south, along the highest mountains of the Andes. Given the nature of its habitat, it is unlikely that the Andean cat ever had a large range, although it may have included the highest elevations at which humans now live.

Threats

There is hope that the Andean cat survives, but it is likely to be very rare. It has been hunted primarily for its fur, although it has also been hunted for sport. There is some evidence that air pollution is poisoning the high Andean flora; this would pose an indirect threat to the Andean cat because its prey depends on the flora as a food source.

Conservation and Recovery

The Andean cat's habitat needs to be protected from human exploitation, and the cat needs to be observed in the wild by naturalists so that its food cycle and mating patterns can be recorded. With this information, a feasible conservation plan could be created. The Andean cat has the good fortune to have a habitat that humans do not like to visit and would not care to live in, which enhances its long-term chances for survival. It is protected by international treaty, in CITES, Appendix I: Trade Prohibited.

Pakistan Sand Cat

Felis margarita scheffeli

Ron Austing, Cincinnati Zoo and Botanical Garden

Status	Endangered
Listed	January 23, 1984
Family	Felidae (Cats)
Description	Golden brown, yellowish brown, or grayish brown coat, whitish under the body, with dark brown rings on its black-tipped tail.
Habitat	Flat, sandy arid/semi-arid lands.
Food	Small mammals, birds, lizards, and insects.
Reproduction	Usually 2 to 4 kittens.
Threats	Hunting and trapping for pet trade.
Range	Pakistan, India, Iran.

Description

The Pakistan sand cat, *Felis margarita scheffeli,* has a beautiful coat with soft, thick fur. The undercoat varies from one individual to another from golden brown, to yellowish brown, to grayish brown, with pronounced stripes in kittens that fade to orange or golden stripes slightly darker than the undercoat in adults. The legs have dark stripes, the tail has dark rings and a black tip, and the cheeks often have a dark reddish stripe angled down from the eye toward the neck. Its beautiful skins have fetched good prices from coat makers, and during the late 1960s and early 1970s, there was such a frenzy of hunting that the Pakistan sand cat was driven to near extinction. Even now, this already uncommon species is very rarely sighted in the wild.

An adult's nose and body length varies between 15.5 and 22.5 inches, with the tail adding another 10 to 14 inches. It is about 10 inches high at the shoulder. It weighs roughly 4.5 to 5.5 pounds.

The animal's head is broad, with a somewhat flat, wide forehead. The ears are spread far apart and are small. This configuration for the head is an excellent adaptation for a small desert animal that must avoid larger predators; the Pakistan sand cat flattens itself on the ground and flattens its ears, and with its flat forehead it can disappear from sight, as if having merged into the ground beneath it. Although its ears are small, the Pakistan sand cat has excellent hearing; its skull has enlarged tympanic bullae to enhance its hearing, compensating for the size of the ears. The sharp hearing this adaptation enables helps it stalk its prey at night. Another adaptation to its environment is the hair it grows between its toes. This hair forms pads eight tenths of an inch thick under the paws. This helps the cat walk across shifty sand and enables it to walk or run across hot desert surfaces without burning its feet.

Some variations in its skull from those of other cats have led some naturalists to argue that the Pakistan sand cat is a species unrelated to the sand cats of North Africa and Arabia, but the great majority of naturalists classify it as a subspecies, *scheffeli*, of the sand cat (also called "sand dune cat" and "Margueritte's cat") species, *Felis margarita*, that once had an uninterrupted range from the Sahara through Arabia and perhaps into southern Russia. When declaring it an endangered species, the U.S. Fish and Wildlife Service classified it as *Felis margarita scheffeli*, indicating its agreement with most scientific opinion that its skeleton and anatomy make it part of the sand cat species. Yet another significant adaptation is the Pakistan sand cat's urinary system, which is exceptionally efficient. The cats get their water primarily from the bodies of their prey, and go for long periods — perhaps years — without drinking fresh water. This helps them survive in waterless environments that would be deadly to most predators.

Those researching the Pakistan sand cat for the first time should beware that sometimes people mislabel it as a Pallas's cat (*Felis manul*), which lives in a neighboring range in Iran and Russia and has a superficial resemblance to the Pakistan sand cat. Put the animals side-by-side and they look very different; they also have notable skeletal differences, making them different species. Also, a researcher should beware that in old accounts of the cat it may be called *Eremaelurus thinobia*. This name was given to the sand cats of the northern Middle East in 1927 by a Soviet naturalist, S. I. Ognev, who did not see how the sand cat could exist in the Sahara and also in southern Russia with a vast area of land in between. He suggested that the cats looked similar because of parallel evolution: They lived in similar environments and had evolved similar adaptations to those environments, he thought. Later, sand cat populations were found in Arabia and elsewhere in the Middle East, revealing an unbroken territory throughout the sand cat's range, and naturalists in general agreed that *Eremaelurus thinobia* was actually a subspecies of sand cat.

Behavior

These are nocturnal animals who hunt at night and rest in burrows during the day — they move in the day to avoid their predators by running away or perhaps because food is especially scarce and their must hunt by day. They eat almost any small animal in their environment: small mammals such as rodents, birds, reptiles, and insects such as locusts.

At birth, kittens tend to weigh about 1.5 ounces, but then gain about a quarter ounce daily for over twenty days. Their eyes open after about fourteen days, and they emerge from their burrow after about forty days. Their play includes digging. As adults they will be industrious diggers. Litters and their mothers tend to stay together (it apparently has not yet been definitively shown that males do not stay with them, too) until the kittens are nearly full sized, when they part company.

The Pakistan sand cats communicate with mews and cries similar to those of domesticated cats, although the male has a loud bark when it is calling a mate.

Habitat

The Pakistan sand cat lives in the most dry regions of its range. It is typically found in areas with almost no water, perhaps because these are areas that humans — even poachers — will avoid. It would appear that it would prefer areas without rocky surfaces so that it may dig its burrows, but this is not a certainty.

Distribution

The Pakistan sand cat has been found in Pakistan, northwestern India, and southeastern Iran. It may also have ranged (and possibly still ranges) in southern Russian territories north and northeast of Pakistan. Where it occurs now is uncertain. The last reported sighting seems to have been in India's northwestern desert.

Threats

The Pakistan sand cat is near extinction. It was hunted and killed for its coat, and it was trapped to feed an international desire for exotic pets. It makes for a poor pet and reportedly does not live long in captivity.

The Pakistan sand cat is desperately in need of protection. It needs a reserve where it will not be hunted, and international trade in its skins and of living cats needs to be regulated, perhaps prohibited. Sightings in the wild are now so rare, perhaps years apart, that some naturalists suspect that the cat is extinct in the wild.

Conservation and Recovery

There is hope that in some particularly unpleasant places for people to live, especially in sparsely populated areas of northwestern India, the cat still survives and is simply not often seen because it takes care to stay away from humans and humans do not care to venture into the lands the cat favors.

Whether or not there is a sufficiently large breeding population in zoos in uncertain, particularly since much of its breeding practices is unknown. Because they were nearly wiped out in such a breathtakingly short period, naturalists had little opportunity to observe these cats in the wild, and many questions remain about their socialization, hunting techniques, and their role in the natural history of their environment.

Marbled Cat

Felis [=Pardofelis] marmorata

Phan Viet Lam, Saigon Zoo

Status	Endangered
Listed	June 14, 1976
Family	Felidae (Cats)
Description	Long, brown fur with interweaving stripes and spots.
Habitat	Rain forest.
Food	Rodents and other small mammals, birds, lizards, snakes, frogs, and insects.
Reproduction	Gestation lasts a little more than 11 weeks.
Threats	Loss of habitat to logging and human hunters.
Range	Indonesia, Nepal, and southeast Asia.

Description

The marbled cat, *Felis marmorata*, is a spectacularly beautiful animal. Its coat is an interweaving of golds, reds, yellows, tans, and dark browns of varying shades, in stripes and spots framed in grey or black, and its fur is long and soft. Adults are between 15.5 and 24 inches long from tip of nose to tail, with long tails between 17.5 and 21.5 inches long that are covered with long, fluffy hair. They weigh about 12 pounds and stand between 12 and 16 inches at the shoulder.

Behavior

If one were to imagine a fantasy jungle populated by enigmatic, mysterious creatures, the marbled cat would fit in well. An enigmatic animal, it is seldom observed in the wild, partly because it is rare, partly because it moves through its environment with graceful ease, and partly because it is primarily nocturnal and arboreal. It moves among the branches of the trees in its rain forest habitat, and tends to avoid the ground, although the marbled cat has been seen in clearings and once-forested terrain that has been clear-cut by loggers. The marbled cat is an excellent climber of trees, and moves about in tree branches with great speed. The cat is also notable for its great ferocity, which is one of the factors that make it difficult to keep in captivity.

Because it has been seldom observed in the wild by scientists, little has been recorded of its behavior. It has been seen stalking prey; it creeps along branches on long, powerful legs, its coloration helping to hide its movements in the night, and it seems to spring upon its prey when within range. It eats a wide variety of small animals: rodents and other small mammals, birds, lizards, snakes, frogs, and insects, with birds being its primary prey.

Very little is known about its mating practices, making it difficult to breed in captivity. Its social practices are also mysterious; individual cats may have their own territories, but having been observed together in clearings, the cats may be social animals.

Habitat

The marbled cat has been found in the rain forests of Nepal and India, through southeast Asia, to Borneo and Sumatra. It seems most comfortable in dense forest, but also inhabits lightly forested areas. Oddly, it will continue to inhabit areas that have been stripped of trees, a behavior that may indicate strong territoriality, adaptability, or a desperate effort to survive after its habitat has been lost. The marbled cat has been observed in clearings, venturing from the forest to hunt. It seems to be comfortable both on mountains and lowlands.

Distribution

The marbled cat ranges over a large area from Nepal, through northeastern India, through most of southeast Asia, and well into the islands of Indonesia, most notably Sumatra.

Threats

No one knows how many marbled cats may still survive in the wild. It is extremely rare, even in habitat that has yet to be disrupted by humans. Its population has surely declined because of logging. Its rain forests are being clear-cut, denuding the landscape, and depriving the marbled cat of the trees that would normally shelter it. Unfortunately for the marbled cat, the people likeliest to see it are hunters, who shoot it for its coat.

Conservation and Recovery

In Indonesia, the marbled cat's habitat is nearly gone. It is protected by law in India. Thailand, too, protects it, as well the native tiger, but it needs international cooperation to put an end to trade in the animal and its coat. The cat has been sighted in recent years in Nepal, and if Nepal protects its range, there is hope for its long-term survival there. Captive breeding of the animal has some urgency, because it could become extinct in the wild at any time, but so far only the Los Angeles zoo has had success in mating marbled cats. More needs to be known of its natural behavior for captive breeding efforts to have good hope for success.

Black-footed Cat
Felis nigripes

Roland Wirth

Status	Endangered
Listed	June 14, 1976
Family	Felidae (Cats)
Description	Black pads on its feet; coat is light brown; legs have black stripes or bars; its body has dark brown spots; typically weighs 2 to 4 pounds.
Habitat	Savanna
Food	Rodents, birds, lizards, insects, and grass.
Reproduction	Gestation lasts between 63 and 68 days. Litters usually consist of two or three kittens that weigh 2 to 3 ounces each.
Threats	Loss of habitat, human hunters, and large natural predators.
Range	Botswana, Namibia, and South Africa, Zimbabwe

Description

The black-footed cat, *Felis nigripes*, is probably the smallest of the wild cats. Its adult weight is usually about 4 pounds, although it can weigh about 2 pounds. Male and female adults differ in size, with males usually measuring about 18 inches not counting the tail, the tail adds about 7 inches; females usually measure about 14 inches not counting the tail, with a tail length of about 6 inches. Males stand about 10 inches at the shoulder.

The base color of its coat is usually pale brown, although it can be darker, especially for the black-footed cats that live in Karroo, the subspecies *Felis nigripes thomasi*, which can have a very dark coat. The legs have stripes or bars of dark brown, and the rest of the body features spots that vary from dark brown to black. There are dark streaks on each side of the face, and the back of the ears are light brown.

The black-footed cat is also known as Sebulabulakwana, Karroo cat, and the anthill tiger.

Behavior

Adult black-footed cats are small and fluffy and look very much like kittens of domesticated cats, but they should be treated as wild animals. They have ferocious dispositions and will attack, and according to accounts of encounters with them, they can do great damage to the people they attack. They are legendary animals in their part of Africa, and local people tell outrageous stories of the black-footed cats (called "Sebulabulakwana" locally) attacking giraffes and bringing the huge animals down by biting into their jugular veins. Somewhat more seriously, the cats are said to fell sheep by biting their necks, and this reputation — whether true or not — means that local herders may kill the black-footed cats as threats to their sheep.

The cats are described as having very loud roars, comparable in volume to those of tigers, but higher pitched. This unnerving roar seems to serve to inform individual cats of prospective mates; the adults tend to be very solitary, except when there are mothers with young. The females' estrus lasts no more than 10 hours, which restricts their opportunity to breed. Gestation lasts about 65 days, resulting in the birth of 2 or 3 kittens. Black-footed cats prefer underground lairs, often taking over a burrow of another species such as hares or setting up residence inside a hollow termite mound, and they are skilled and energetic diggers. It is in an underground chamber that newborns are usually kept, although naturalists have observed kittens hidden under bushes. Even kittens have the fierceness of their parents, and will hiss, spit, and make threatening faces at intruders. They will, if able, scatter and run to escape persistent intruders; this differs from the behavior of the young of most cats, who run for their lairs when frightened. The mother cat signals that all is well with a sharp staccato cry that may be unique to the species and by a flattening of its ears. Perhaps also reassuring is the black-footed cat's purring; they are able to purr from the moment they are born. At about 8 days of age, the kittens' eyes open. Initially pink, the pads on their feet turn black after 40 days of life. The kittens venture out into the open after 28 days of life.

At about 34 days old, the kittens begin eating solid food, and at about 40 days, they begin catching their own food. The black-footed cat prefers small game, mostly rodents but includes birds, lizards, and insects for its prey. The mother teaches its young to hunt by carrying live prey such as mice to them; it releases the prey and keeps it from getting away while the kittens learn their hunting skills. Grass is very important to the black-footed cat's diet, and it may stop eating without it. Perhaps the grass plays a significant role in the animal's digestive processes. At about 21 months of age, the black-footed cat reaches maturity. It lives about 10 years.

Habitat

Sandy plains and savannahs such as those of the Kalahari region make up the black-footed cat's favorite habitat. The region has reddish soils and dry grasses, making the cat's coloration effective camouflage. The black-footed cat's solitary nature may be an adaptation to its semi-arid environment, in which the cats probably have to range far away from each other in order to find enough prey for each to survive.

Distribution

The black-footed cat has long ranged throughout southwestern and south central Africa, notably in the Kalahari, Karroo, and Namib deserts. Today, it can still be found through much of Botswana, in natural reserves in Namibia, in northwestern and central South Africa, and southwestern Zimbabwe. It has become rare through most of its range and has its greatest population density in Namibia's reserves.

Threats

The black-footed cat is threatened by the loss of its habitat to human communities. It is usually killed by humans by accident, in traps set for other animals such as jackals.

Conservation and Recovery

There is much reason to hope for the black-footed cat's future prosperity. In South Africa's Kruger National Park, the black-footed cat seems well protected, with enough range to provide a good breeding population. Namibia has also taken steps to protect the black-footed cat, and the animal seems to be flourishing there.

The black-footed cat is protected by international treaty and is listed in CITES, Appendix I: Trade Prohibited.

Ocelot

Felis [=Leopardus] pardalis

C. Allan Morgan

Status	Endangered
Listed	March 30, 1972
Family	Felidae (Cats)
Description	Brownish yellow to orangish yellow to almost gray, with numerous black stripes and spots; the tail is wrapped by stripes; the underbody is white.
Habitat	Brushlands, grasslands, and forests, from humid to semi-arid.
Food	Agoutis, birds, coatis, mice, monkeys, pacas, rats, and reptiles.
Reproduction	Gestation lasts 70 days and results in litters of 2 to 4 kittens.
Threats	Hunting; loss of habitat.
Range	Mexico, Central America, Argentina, Brazil

Description

The head-and-body length of adult ocelots, *Felis pardalis*, varies from 25.5 to 38 inches. Their tail adds another 10.5 to 16 inches. They stand between 16 and 20 inches at the shoulder. They weigh between 24 and 35.5 pounds. The base color of their coats seems to vary with the habitat in which they live. In open areas such as grasslands the base color is gray or grayish yellow, but in forested areas the base color is pale orangish yellow to a rich, dark orangish yellow. The base coat is overlaid with numerous black stripes and spots, with the tail having several stripes ringing around it. There is a white spot on the back of each ear; the ears are outlined in black. The undersides of ocelots, including the insides of the legs, are pale, often white. A notable trait is the forward laying hair on the upper neck. There is a wide variety in sizes and builds among ocelots, including individual animals of the same subspecies. In general, they are stocky, but some may be tall and sleek, with their tails barely touching the ground.

Behavior

Ocelots are territorial, with a male and female sharing a domain, but they hunt and live separately. They stay in touch with each other with their mewing calls and by depositing their stool in the same place. It seems likely that they mate for life. Their prey consists of small-to-medium-sized animals, including rodents, rabbits, small deer, wild pigs, monkeys, birds, snakes, and lizards.

Ocelots shun human settlements and in the wild they stay as far away from people as they can manage. Even so, their temperament is mild, and some have been domesticated as pets. They are good swimmers and are known to inhabit very wet areas such as marshes and swamps. They climb trees primarily to rest in the crook of a tree branch or to escape humans (they seem to have no other predators). Authorities disagree over the ocelots' climbing skills, asserting that ocelots are such good tree climbers that they hunt in trees, to asserting that the ocelots are effective tree climbers when necessary, to asserting that they stay out trees except when sleeping. In any case, they hunt primarily on the ground, using ground cover to hide them as they stalk their prey, and they prefer to hunt at night, although they have been seen moving about by day. Their elaborately spotted coats may be an adaptation for camouflaging them in dimly lighted underbrush, making it hard for their prey to see them. Rather than leaping on prey from ambush, when close enough they charge and chase down their quarry.

Depositing their droppings in the same place not only helps pairs of ocelots communicate with each other, with a change in the scent of the droppings, it alerts the male to when the female is in estrus. Mating probably occurs year round, but it may be seasonal for some subspecies, with South American ocelots mating in November and bearing young in February and northern ocelots mating in summer and bearing young in the fall. Mating involves yowling similar to that made by mating domestic cats, and it occurs primarily at night. The kittens are born 70 to 77 days after mating; the mother hides them in a den, which may be a hollow in a tree or a small cave or a similar shelter that will hide the kittens from sight. Litters have between two and four kittens (one authority suggests one to three). An important feature of the ocelots' breeding behavior is that the male participates in the care and feeding of the young, guarding the den and bringing back food for them when they are able to eat prey. The kittens are weaned after about seven weeks and have been observed traveling at night on hunts with their mothers. They will not reach maturity until after two years of age. Whether they are forced out of their parents' territory or simply wander off at some time is not yet established. It appears that they voluntarily leave their parents' territory and travel many miles (as many as 45) to find a territory of their own. It has not been established whether ocelots establish a territory before they mate, or if they mate first and establish a territory together.

Habitat

The ocelot's principal requirements for its habitat are ground cover and prey. With these requirements met, it lives in tropical rain forests, temperate deciduous forests, and semi-arid brushlands, and in lowlands and highlands.

Distribution

The ocelot once ranged from Arkansas through southern Texas, into Arizona and

New Mexico, south through central Mexico and eastern Mexico, through all of Central America, through northern South America, branching to the west through Bolivia but not into Chile, and east all along the eastern slopes of the Andes into northern Argentina, spreading east though all of the Amazon basis and all of Brazil. It now is very rare throughout its range, which presently includes Texas, some of Mexico, Central America, northern South America and Brazil. Definitive data on its presence in some areas is sketchy, and it very likely has been wiped out all together in much of Central America and South America. The ocelot was suspected to have been exterminated in the United States, but scientists have discovered a breeding population in Texas. Exactly where they live is kept secret for fear that publication of the location will attract poachers.

The following is a list of subspecies of ocelots by their range, roughly north to south. Please keep in mind that naturalists are still unsure of exactly what subspecies there are and this information will likely undergo revision. Further, one should note that some of these subspecies are likely extinct or soon to become extinct:

Texas into central Mexico: *Felis pardalis albescens* (or *Leopardus pardalis albescens*); Arizona into western Mexico: *Felis pardalis sonoriensis* (or *Leopardus pardalis sonoriensis*); eastern and southern Mexico: *Felis pardalis nelsoni* (or *Leopardus pardalis nelsoni*); southern Mexico into Honduras: *Felis pardalis pardalis* (or *Leopardus pardalis pardalis*); Costa Rica to Peru: *Felis pardalis aequatorialis* (or *Leopardus pardalis aequatorialis*); Nicaragua to Panama: *Felis pardalis mearnsi* (or *Leopardus pardalis mearnsi*); Colombia and Venezuela: *Felis pardalis pseudopardalis* (or *Leopardus pardalis pseudopardalis*); Ecuador: *Felis pardalis pusea*

(or *Leopardus pardalis pusea*); Bolivia: *Felis pardalis steinbachi* (or *Leopardus pardalis steinbachi*); Amazon basin: *Felis pardalis maripensis* (or *Leopardus pardalis maripensis*); central Brazil into Argentina: *Felis pardalis mitis* (or *Leopardus pardalis mitis*).

Threats

The ocelot's hide is much prized by fashion designers for fur coats, as well as by the fur-buying public. As a consequence, this once numerous animal has been hunted to near extinction throughout its range and has become very rare.

For the exceptionally adaptable ocelot, loss of habitat is not quite as significant a problem as it is for animals that must have one specific kind of climate or environment. Thus, even though loss of habitat is an important problem for the ocelot, it pales in comparison to the ruthless hunting of it for its fur. Laws against killing ocelots do not seem to have had an effect on the hunting, which means that its best hope for preservation is for consumers around the world to stop buying coats and other products made of ocelot skins.

During the 1970s, the lack of evidence of ocelots in the United States suggested to some that the species had been exterminated on United States soil. Dogged research by wildlife biologists uncovered a small number of ocelots in Texas and Arizona, with the largest population being in Texas near the border with Mexico. Researchers have placed radio collars on some of the ocelots and are now making discoveries about the animal's behavior. In spite of all the killing of the ocelot, little was learned about its habits until the late 1980s. In the United States, the biggest threat to the ocelot is accidental killing. The cats are run over by cars or caught in traps meant for other animals. The encroachment of humans onto their traditional ranges has resulted in the ocelots trying to live in perilously close proximity to human beings.

Elsewhere in the ocelot's vast traditional range, its condition is very bad. It may have been hunted to extinction in Paraguay, which serves as a center for the trade of ocelot skins from animals killed in other South American countries.

Conservation and Recovery

The ocelot is listed in CITES, Appendix I: Trade Prohibited, which means that signatories to CITES promise to halt trade in ocelots, living or dead, as well as in ocelot parts. This seems to have had beneficial effects. Brazil, responded to the CITES listing by legally protecting the ocelot and outlawing trade in ocelot skins, and its legal efforts seem to have so far had a beneficial effect, and poachers can no longer find a ready market for ocelot skins.

Spanish Lynx

Felis pardina

Roland Wirth

Status	Endangered
Listed	June 2, 1970
Family	Felidae (Cats)
Description	Medium-sized cat with large eyes, large well-furred paws; fur is yellowish-red, with round black spots on the body, tail, and limbs.
Habitat	Open forest of juniper, pine, and pistachio scrub on old sand dunes.
Food	Rabbits, birds, rodents, and deer.
Reproduction	Litter sizes range from 2 to 4 cubs.
Threats	Hunting; widespread deforestation.
Range	Spain

Description

The Spanish lynx, *Felis pardina*, is a medium-sized cat with a head and body length of 33 to 43 inches and a short tail 5 to 12 inches long. The animal stands 23 to 27 inches tall at the shoulder. The eyes are large with roundish pupils. The Spanish lynx has a digitigrade posture and stands on five toes on the front feet and four on the back. The paws are large and well-furred, with sharp retractile claws.

The animal's fur is yellowish-red, with round black spots on the body, tail, and limbs. The ears are brown with a central silvery-gray spot and end in long, black ear tufts. White fur covers the eyelids, chin, inside of ears, underparts, and throat. Like all lynxes, the Spanish lynx has a flared facial ruff, short body and long legs.

The bigger, paler male has a larger head, neck, and feet, as well as longer ear-tufts than the female. During mating season in January, the two partners call to each other at night with a loud raucous howl. Litter sizes range from two to four cubs. Newborn cubs have closed eyes, folded ears, no teeth, and poorly developed ear tufts. Their fur is thick, with dark stripes on the back and legs and less dark stripes on the flanks. The cubs open their eyes after ten days and begin to walk at 24 to 30 days. The rapidly maturing young leave the lair around four months of age and become independent of the parents a month or two later.

The Spanish lynx is also known as the Iberian lynx and is sometimes classified as *Lynx pardinus*.

Behavior

The Spanish lynx needs space, and each one has a territory between 2.5 to 6 square miles with a possibly larger area in the winter. It mainly preys on rabbits, but will prey on birds, rodents, and even young deer. One report notes that 25 fawns were killed in an area where a mother and young kittens were found. The red-legged partridge is probably one of the most common birds eaten by the Spanish lynx. Like most cats, the Spanish lynx stalks the animal from the cover of bushes, and then pounces when the prey is within reach.

Habitat

The Spanish lynx lives in open forest of juniper, pine, and pistachio scrub on old sand dunes in the Iberian Peninsula. The habitat of the Spanish lynx is more open than the essentially forest habitat of the other lynxes. The animal dens in a wide variety of places, including hollow trees, burrows, and "nests" made of twigs and grass in dense thorn or briar thickets. Lairs have been found in old storks' nests, one of which was in a pine tree 30 or 40 feet above the ground.

Distribution

The Spanish lynx formerly occupied the greater part of the Iberian Peninsula, possibly as far north as the Pyrenees. Presently, this species is confined to the remote mountainous regions, such as the Sierra Morena, the Sierra de Guadalupe, and Montes de Toledo, as well as the Guadalquivir delta of southern Spain.

The Spanish lynx's total population is estimated at between 1,000 and 1,500. During the 1950s and 1960s, the species declined precipitously because the disease myxomatosis hit the local rabbit population. The population was estimated as low as fifteen pairs in the Guadalquivir delta where the bulk of the species occurs. As the outbreak of disease in the local rabbit population shows, the Spanish lynx's survival is extremely susceptible to outside factors.

Threats

Spanish lynxes have long been considered vermin because of the damage they sometimes inflict on domestic livestock and have been ruthlessly hunted by the local farmers and shepherds. Outside of the Cota Donana reserve, it was still classified (as of 1975) as vermin and can be legally killed on sight. Even when not hunted, widespread deforestation for cereal cultivation and tree plantations has destroyed much of its natural habitat.

Conservation and Recovery

To protect the Spanish lynx and other rare animals, the World Wildlife Fund and the Spanish government have set aside part of the Spanish lynx's territory in the Guadalquivir delta in southwestern Spain as the Cota Donana nature preserve.

The Spanish lynx is listed in CITES: Appendix I: Trade Prohibited as of February 4, 1977. In the *IUCN Red Data Book*, it was listed as endangered as of 1978.

Flat-headed Cat

Felis planiceps

Art Wolfe

Status	Endangered
Listed	June 14, 1976
Family	Felidae (Cats)
Description	Unusually long, narrow, flattened skull; long body with short legs and tail; thick reddish brown to dark brown fur above and white fur spotted with brown underneath.
Habitat	Rivers and other waterways in tropical forests and brushlands.
Food	Mainly frogs and fish; sometimes small mammals, birds, and fruit.
Threats	Destruction of tropical rain forests; limited population.
Range	Indonesia (Borneo, Sumatra), Burma, Thailand, Malaysia.

Description

As both the common and scientific names suggest, the flat-headed cat, *Felis planiceps*, has an unusually long, narrow, and flattened skull. The cat's eyes are close together and toward the front of the face. The paws are long and narrow, with claws that cannot be completely retracted. The odd-shaped skull and other features are probably adaptations for fishing. The long, narrow muzzle and large first top premolar seem effective for catching slippery quarry. The long body with short legs and tail help the cat move efficiently through the water. As observed in captivity, kittens enjoy playing in the water.

The adult flat-headed cat weighs approximately 12 to 17.5 pounds. The head and body are approximately 16 to 20 inches long, and the tail measures 5 to 6 inches long. The animal has thick reddish brown to dark brown fur above and white fur spotted and splashed with brown underneath. The top of the head is reddish brown with light reddish fur on the face below the eyes. The head has white streaks between the eyes and on the cheeks and a yellow line runs from the eye to the ear. The tail is yellowish underneath.

Although *Felis planiceps* is the most generally accepted scientific name for the flat-headed cat, other recent treatments include *Prionailurus planiceps*; *Prionailurus ictailurus planiceps; Ictailurus planiceps; Prionailurus planiceps.*

Behavior

These cats seem to mainly hunt frogs, fish, crustaceans and small animals. Under observation in captivity, a kitten took pieces of fish from the water and captured live frogs, but ignored live birds. Interestingly for a member of the carnivorous cat family, though, flat-headed cats will reportedly also eat fruit. They are primarily active at night.

When raised in captivity from kittens, flat-headed cats make for even-tempered pets. They will not eat many foods prepared for domesticated cats, and as adults must be fed mostly fish.

Habitat

Flat-headed cats live along rivers and other waterways in the tropical forests and brushlands of parts of southeastern Asia. They can be found at altitudes of up to 2,300 feet.

Distribution

The flat-headed cat occurs in the Malaya Peninsular (Burma, Thailand, Malaysia) and in Indonesia on the islands of Borneo and Sumatra.

Threats

The destruction of the tropical rain forest has severely limited this rare cat's habitat.

Because of the small size of flat-headed cat populations, this rare animal is susceptible to extinction from disease or natural catastrophes.

Conservation and Recovery

So little is known about this cat's natural history that it is hard to determine what needs to be done to protect it. From what is known about its habits, it clearly needs access to fresh water streams and to fresh water fish. Without fish, the species probably cannot survive. Fortunately, there are still some unpolluted streams in its range in Malaya, Borneo, and Sumatra, although the increasing pollution of water in Borneo poses a significant problem for the cat's future survival there. Malaysia has established wildlife reserves that may contain flat-headed cats in northern Malaya and on Borneo, although the Borneo populations are severely threatened by logging and agriculture. There is some reason to hope that the watery reserves that protect tigers and other species on Sumatra may also protect flat-headed cats, but this needs to be confirmed by scientific observation.

Bobcat

Felis rufus escuinapae [=Lynx rufus]

Zoological Society of Philadelphia

Status	Endangered
Listed	June 14, 1976
Family	Felidae (Cats)
Description	Red-brown to yellow-brown, profusely covered by dark-brown spots and stripes.
Habitat	Usually open grasslands and brushlands, usually dry but sometimes wet.
Food	Mostly small rodents, but also fish, frogs, lizards, and birds.
Reproduction	Gestation lasts 60 to 70 days, resulting in 1 to 6 young (rarely more than 4).
Threats	Loss of habitat, hunting for its coat, and extermination as vermin.
Range	Mexico

Description

There is sharp disagreement among authorities on cats about the taxonomy of the central Mexican bobcat, *Felis rufus escuinapae*, and bobcats in general. A minority of present-day authorities hold that the bobcat belongs in the genus *Lynx* and give it the scientific name of *Lynx rufus*. Other authorities cite evidence that the bobcat (and the central Mexican subspecies, in particular) had spread through North America millions of years before the ancestors of lynxes migrated to North America from northern Asia. Further,

bobcats, while similar in shape to lynxes, are dissimilar in coloration, length of hair, size of paws, configuration of teeth, and in habits. Hence, the bobcat is most commonly assigned to the genus *Felis*, with which its ancestors are associated in the fossil record.

The bobcat of central Mexico, *Felis rufus escuinapae*, is usually about 2 feet from tip-of-nose to base-of-tale, although if it were not under constant pressure from humans, it might live long enough to grow larger like its cousins to the north — about 3 feet. Its tail has the characteristic bobcat brevity, 5 to 7 inches, and it stands just under 2 feet at the shoulder. It weighs 10 to 40 pounds, with its weight apparently fluctuating with the seasonal variations in the abundance of prey.

The coat of the *escuinapae* subspecies is darker and redder brown than of the other subspecies; the ones in the United States tend to be lighter and grayer. Its pattern of spots and stripes tends to be darker and more dense than in the other subspecies. Like other bobcats, it has prominent ear brushes that are smaller than those found in lynxes.

Behavior

Bobcats are territorial animals, but the size and shape of their territories vary greatly from season to season. When prey, mostly rodents, are abundant in spring and summer, male territories may be only 2 square miles, with female territories being only 1½ square miles; as the populations of prey decline in fall and winter, the territories expand — 20 square miles is common for the *escuinapae* subspecies, and rarely much larger, up to 70 square miles. Male territories overlap those of two or more females and sometimes even overlap some of the territories of other males. The boundaries of territories are marked mostly through urination and piles of feces, although where trees, tall bushes, or large rocks are available, markings from scent glands will be used, too. Males take care to avoid each other; even where territories overlap they rarely meet and confrontations are few. A female's territory may be overlapped by more than one male, but rarely do female territories overlap each other. Females are much more protective of their territories than males are of theirs. This difference in behavior may have evolved because a female with kittens needs to secure as much food as she can for them and herself, and other females with kittens could deprive them of much needed nutrients, especially as the seasons of abundance change to the seasons of scarcity.

Habitat

As is typical of bobcats, the *escuinapae* subspecies prefers open ground to wooded areas, although it seems to like living on the edges of woodlands; it requires ample ground cover for keeping out of sight of prey. It is most often found in dry, even parched areas.

Distribution

This subspecies of bobcat presently ranges through the interior of central Mexico.

Threats

The bobcat is mercilessly hunted for its fur, which supplies some of the international market for fur clothing. In the case of the bobcat of central Mexico, local people regard it as vermin and it bears the additional burden of being killed as a pest. Thus, as human settlements and agriculture expand, they not only eliminate the bobcat's habitat but bring with them the relentless killing of any bobcats that may try to survive near them. Loss of habitat, hunting for their fur, poisoning, and trapping have brought the *escuinapae* subspecies to near extinction.

Conservation and Recovery

The bobcat of central Mexico urgently

needs the protection of a wildlife sanctuary. The sanctuary should have dense brush or grass ground cover and should have large rodent populations, and it would need to be well protected from poachers, as well as those who would kill the bobcat as vermin. What would constitute a viable breeding population for the *escuinapae* subspecies of bobcat is uncertain, but given the size of the territories of individual animals — and the need for the territorial borders to be seasonally flexible — the sanctuary may need to be 100 square miles or more in size, which suggests that a bobcat sanctuary could be used as a sanctuary for other wildlife, as well.

Barbary Serval

Felis [=Leptailurus] serval constantina

Michael Kinsey, Denver Zoological Gardens

Status	Endangered
Listed	June 2, 1970
Family	Felidae (Cats)
Description	Coat is orange to brown to grey, with black spots. It is a slim and long-legged cat.
Habitat	Savanna near water.
Food	Rodents, small deer and antelopes, and birds.
Reproduction	1 to 3 kittens after gestation of about 75 days
Threats	Hunting; loss of habitat; predation by dogs and hyenas.
Range	Algeria

Description

The Barbary serval, *Felis serval constantina*, tends to be somewhat larger than other varieties. The adult serval is 27.5 to 40 inches long from tip of nose to tail, with its tail adding another 13.5 to 16 inches. It weighs 30 to 42 pounds. It is a slim animal with a small head, long neck, and long legs, making it between 18 and 26 inches high at the shoulder. Since the serval prefers moist lands, some scientists see the long legs as an adaptation for marshy or swampy ranges. Its ears are large and tall. These ears are essential to its hunting; the serval prefers to roam in tall grass, and its ears are carried high and swivel around, listening for sounds that will lead the serval to its prey.

Coloration varies among individual servals, with coats being overall orange, reddish brown, grayish brown, or brown, and covered with black spots. The Barbary serval's large spots are typical of servals that live in open lands; those in more densely vegetated habitats tend to have a plethora of small spots. These large spots become rings on the tail, which ends with a black tip. The undercoat, from chin down along the throat across the chest and over the belly, is paler in color, sometimes even white. The ears are black with a pale spot on the back.

Behavior

The Barbary serval is territorial, with solitary animals or pairs having ranges typically between 3 and 4 square miles in size. This is one of the reasons it is threatened: a healthy breeding population needs vast amounts of territory, and this may conflict with climatic changes that reduce the size of the grasslands they favor, or human expansion may crowd them out of previously good ranges. Further, their populations are very sparse, making it easy to endanger an entire serval community with the deaths of only a few. The territories are typically marked by urine.

Litter size typically is 1 to 3 kittens. The kittens live within the territory of their mother until she pushes them out at about one year of age. They are weaned between 4 and 5 months old and reach maturity between 1.5 and 2.5 years. Young adults often migrate for many miles before they find an unoccupied territory. Once they establish a territory, it likely will remain fixed for several years.

Servals may hunt during the day or night, usually at dusk. As with several other species of cat, the serval will become nocturnal if its territory is often disturbed — for instance, by intruding humans, hunters or otherwise. It is a patient hunter, slowly stalking its prey. Although it superficially looks like a cheetah, it does not chase down prey in sudden spurts of speed as the cheetah does. Instead, it hunts like other cats: stalking, waiting, closing in slowly, and then pouncing on its quarry. It then bites the neck of its prey.

The serval purrs when pleased, growls when annoyed, and when threatened, it throws punches with its forepaws. It communicates over large distances with other servals with several high-pitched meows in a row.

Habitat

The Barbary serval is the northern variety of the species *Felis serval*. It lives in a drier climate than do its southern relatives, but like them, it prefers areas with water. Its present habitat is located in part of the fertile area near the coasts of Algeria and Morocco and extends southward through grasslands toward the desert. This habitat typically features flat plains and tall grass, both of which well suit the animal's hunting patterns.

Distribution

Servals were once to be found throughout sub-Saharan Africa except for the far south, as well as throughout much of Morocco and Algeria. The Barbary serval is approaching extinction in the wild. Its current range is very restricted: it extends in a bar several miles wide, westward from Algeria's eastern Mediterranean coast, perhaps a hundred miles south of the northern coast, bending somewhat southwestward toward Morocco. Loss of suitable habitat and excessive hunting creates a break in the bar, which reappears in the middle of Morocco, and then extends southwestward and along Morocco's west coast to its southern border. The Barbary serval has disappeared from most of its traditional range in Algeria and Morocco. Once numerous in the Atlas Mountains area, they disappeared from there in the early 1970s.

Threats

The servals have long been hunted by humans for their fur, which may be used in traditional clothing or ceremonial garb, and which, more recently, may appear in fashionable coats.

The loss of habitat is the Barbary serval's greatest threat. Humans are expanding their communities southward from the coast, while at the same time the climate to the south is becoming more arid and unsuitable to servals. The Barbary servals are trapped between large, perhaps beyond control, forces, and their survival is dependent on human help. Servals in general seem to do well in captivity. Around humans they know, they are usually mild in their behavior. Indeed, their somewhat meek response to human threats may be part of their undoing. Hunters find them easy to kill.

Conservation and Recovery

The U.S. Fish and Wildlife Service has declared the Barbary serval an endangered animal, which affects its importation and the importation of its skins into America. However, the international community has been slower to respond to the Barbary serval's impending demise, although both Algeria and Morocco seem alert to the problem and sale of its skins has been curtailed.

The servals are easy to tame and seem to be able to live comfortably among humans — although their fondness for domestic poultry needs to be taken into account when establishing a range area for them. Although not sociable with one another in the wild except when mating, servals do not seem particularly annoyed by the nearby presence of others, even though their solitary nature is always evident in their aloof demeanor. Zoos may have good success with providing Barbary servals with suitable homes and with breeding them.

Temminck's Cat

Felis [=Profelis] temmincki

Joe Maynard, Exotic Feline Breeding Compound

Status	Endangered
Listed	June 14, 1976
Family	Felidae (Cats)
Description	Fur is golden brown, reddish, or grey-brown; its head features stripes and spots of blue, gray, and white, with the pattern varying from one individual cat to another.
Habitat	Forests and scrublands.
Food	Rodents, deer, and birds.
Reproduction	A litter usually consists of two or three kittens, weighing a little more than a half pound.
Threats	Loss of habitat to deforestation; hunting.
Range	Southern China, Indonesia (Sumatra, Borneo), Nepal, Indochina

Description

Temminck's cat, *Felis temmincki*, is often called the "golden cat" because of its rich golden brown coat that pales to near white on its belly. (The name "golden cat" can be confusing because the African golden cat is frequently called "golden cat," too.) This coat may be tinted brown, gray, or red. Rarely, the coat will be totally black. The Temminck's cat's head is elegantly decorated predominantly with stripes, but with spots too, of blues, grays, and shades of white. An adult stands between 20 and 24 inches at the shoulder. Its body length, from tip of nose to tail, is between 29.5 and 41.5 inches, with its tail being 15.5 to 21.5 inches long. The adult weighs between 13 and 24.25 pounds.

There are at least two subspecies Temmincki's cat, *Felis* (or *Profelis*) *temmincki dominicanorum*, or northern Temmincki's cat, and *Felis* (or *Profelis*) *temmincki temmincki*, or southern Temminck's cat. The northern subspecies lives from northern Burma to Nepal and into China. The southern subspecies lives in Burma south into the islands of Indonesia, especially Sumatra. A possible third subspecies would be *Felis* (or *Profelis*) *temmincki tristis*, or Fontainer's cat, which lives in Burma and Tibet, but this may be the same as *dominicanorum* — scientists seem unwilling to agree on this. Some believe that the Fontainer's cat is not at all a subspecies of the Temminck's cat but is, in fact, a leopard cat (see separate entry); others think it may be its own separate species of cat. The southern Temminck's cat may be distinguished from the northern subspecies by dark spots on its underside and inner legs; the northern subspecies is sometimes spotted on its flanks. The Temminck's cat is so rare that naturalists disagree about what its coat normally looks like, having seen too few to confidently generalize. Therefore, while most descriptions say that the cat's coat is uniformly golden, others say that it actually consists of spots of finely varying shades of golden brown, brown, and grey, and still others say that it is reddish. What is probable is that the species has considerable variation in coloration from one individual cat to another, although all seem to have a golden glint to their coats, whatever the dominant color. It is primarily the northern subspecies that is hunted for its coat.

The Temminck's cat is a slender animal with sleek fur. It resembles a cougar and was therefore once given the genus *Catopuma*. Very old reference books may use this term, but it has long been defunct because the Temminck's cat is not closely related to cougars (pumas) and plainly belongs with the *Felis* or *Profelis* genus.

Temminck's cat is also known as the Asian golden cat, golden cat, Asiatic golden cat, Temminck's golden cat, rock cat (northern subspecies), yellow leopard (northern subspecies), fire cat, and fire tiger.

Behavior

Little is known of the Temminck's cat's behavior in the wild. It prefers to remain on the ground, most of the time avoiding climbing trees, although it sometimes does climb them in order to have an elevated view of its surroundings. The cats hunt in pairs, although it is not certain whether or not the pairs are bonded males and females. However, it is known that the male helps in the rearing of the young. The adults' tails are carried curled up when walking, with a pale underside showing; it is possible that the bobbing tale of a walking adult helps kittens keep track of their parents and to follow them.

The typical prey for the Temminck's cat are small mammals, including small deer, most notably the muntjac, and birds. They also prey on domesticated animals: sheep, goats, young water buffalo, and chickens. They probably have dens in hollows of trees, but may also reside in rocky shelters or even caves.

The Temminck's cat has an even disposition and may not regard humans as enemies. There are records of kittens being adopted and raised as pets and remaining loyal and gentle with their owners when they became adults. Temminck's cats kept in zoos also seem to be calm, tractable, and even friendly.

Habitat

Temminck's cat seem to prefer rocky,

forested terrain. The forest may be very dense, but the cats seem to favor woodlands with low undergrowth and open spaces. They live in temperate and tropical regions.

Distribution

During the Pleistocene epoch the ancestral golden cat ranged as one species through Africa and across southern Asia into Indochina. The climate for its territory was warm and wet, and tropical forests covered its range. As the climate of the Middle East changed to arid, the golden cat was separated into two groups, each of which evolved into a separate species, the African golden cat and the Asian golden cat (Temminck's cat). The Temminck's cat has long ranged through the forests of Nepal, northeastern India, through most of southern China, Indochina, and into Malaysia, the island of Borneo, and other islands in Indonesia, especially Sumatra. This range only began to shrink significantly in the late 1960s as local cultures began exploiting their forests for lumber, the human population boomed. Wherever forests are clearcut, the Temminck's cat ceases to exist. It is possible that a good breeding population still exists in Burma — at least the locals report seeing the cats. Another such population may be in China, but information on the cat in China is scant.

Its numbers in the wild are not known and it may already be headed toward extinction.

Threats

The Temminck's cat is most threatened by deforestation of its habitat. Loggers are primarily responsible for the clearcutting of forests that destroys the animal's environment, although expanding human populations have displaced the cats as well. The hunting of them for collecting their coats is a problem, mostly in China, but it does not represent as significant a threat to the cat as loss of habitat does. It may soon disappear altogether from Sumatra due to logging.

Conservation and Recovery

Although the Temminck's cat adapts well to zoos, it has not been widely targeted for captive breeding. One problem with breeding this animal for return to the wild is the lack of information about the cat's biology and behavior. Without knowing the cat's instinctive behavior, breeding and food requirements in the wild, recovery plans cannot be formulated with any certainty of success.

Tiger Cat

Felis [=Leopardus] tigrinus

Luiz Claudio Marigo

Status	Endangered
Listed	March 30, 1972
Family	Felidae (Cats)
Description	Light brown coat with dark brown stripes and spots, pale underparts, and dark rings on the tail.
Habitat	Forest floors.
Food	Mammals, birds, lizards, insects.
Reproduction	1 or 2 kittens after gestation of 74 days.
Threats	Humans hunting them for their furs and habitat loss.
Range	Costa Rica, Central America, Brazil, Argentina.

Description

Adults tiger cats, *Felis tigrinus*, are between 15.5 and 22 inches from tip of nose to tail, with the tail measuring between 10 and 16 inches. They weigh between 4.5 and 6 pounds. At birth, they weigh about 2 ounces. They are weaned between 4 and 5 months, and they reach sexual maturity after 2 years. They have life spans of roughly 20 years.

Their fur is short but thick, with a light brown coat covered with dark brown, sometimes black, stripes and blotchy spots. Their tails have dark rings around them and dark tips. Sometimes their fur is entirely black.

Complicating description of the tiger cat is much disagreement among naturalists over its taxonomy. Some assert that the cat has two, three, or four subspecies; others assert that the supposed subspecies cannot intermate, making them two, three, or four separate species that have yet to be scientifically described and assigned to their proper genera. If the latter assertion is true, then humanity may never know what these tiger cats were because two or three of the (possibly) separate species are probably beyond recovery. The U.S. Fish and Wildlife Service presently recognizes only one species, in which all tiger cats belong, and most scientific evidence, scant though it is, supports this view.

The tiger cat is also known as the little spotted cat, ocelot cat, and oncilla.

Behavior

The tiger cat is a good climber, and it

prefers birds as prey and plucks them clean of their feathers before eating them. It also eats small mammals and lizards. Its hunting behavior is largely unknown. It is fierce and known to kill animals larger than itself.

Little is known of its social behavior, but it seems that the tiger cat lives in pairs and mates for life, an unusual trait for a member of the *Felidae* family.

Habitat

The tiger cat prefers forests and lives in dense tropical rain forests on lowlands to high cloud forests on mountains.

Distribution

The tiger cat's past range has included Costa Rica, extended southward through Central America, then westward to northern Bolivia and south and eastward along the eastern Andes extending all the way to the coast, through Brazil and into northern Argentina. Its present range may be similar, although it is not actually known where any of the tiger cats may still survive. Naturalists speculate that it survives as a tiny population spread far apart throughout most of its traditional range.

Threats

The tiger cat is very rare throughout its range. As ocelots became scarce from humans relentlessly hunting them for their skins, hunters turned to the tiger cat because its similar coloring satisfied the desires of the international market in animal furs. In the 1970s, tens of thousands were killed each year, and in the early 1980s, nearly 100,000 were killed annually. This destruction has made the cat very rare; the continuing destruction may soon wipe it out. Habitat loss is not as important as the fur trade in making the tiger cat a severely endangered species because some of its populations have lived in remote mountainous areas on the eastern side of the Andes. Even so, loss of forest lands is a factor in the species' losing battle for survival.

Conservation and Recovery

Although the need to protect the tiger cat is urgent, little has been done to protect its range and little has been done to stop the voracious commercial hunting of the animal. Naturalists need to uncover at least one viable population (more if they hope to clarify whether the tiger cat is one or several species); the nations in which the animal occurs need to enact and enforce laws against hunting, killing, and trapping the animal. The tiger cat's population may be so sparse that not enough males and females can get together to perpetuate the species; in this case humans may have to intervene and transport individual cats to safe areas where they can form breeding populations.

The tiger cat is protected in CITES, Appendix I: Trade Prohibited.

Fishing Cat

Felis [=Prionailurus] viverrinus

Roland Wirth

Status	Unknown
Listed	IUCN Red List
Family	Felidae (Cats)
Description	Short, rough, light brown base coat covered with dark spots.
Habitat	Swamps, marshes, and forests.
Food	Fish, crustacea, small mammals, birds, snakes, frogs, and insects.
Reproduction	1 to 4 kittens after gestation of about 63 days.
Threats	Habitat destruction, poisoning by people, hunting for its coat.
Range	Indochina, India, Indonesia (Java, Sumatra), China.

Description

The adult fishing cat, *Felis viverrinus*, weighs between 12 and 26.5 pounds, with a head-and-body length between 22 to 33 inches and a tail length between 8 and 12.5 inches. It stands 15 to 16 inches high at the shoulder. It is heavily, powerfully built. Its coat is pale brown with numerous dark brown or black spots, with rings around the tail. Six to eight dark lines begin at the top of the nose, extend over the forehead and down the back of the neck, and two wavy lines mark each cheek. The back of each ear is pale to dark brown with a white spot in the middle. Its hair is short and bristly.

The fishing cat's figure shows adaptations for living in and near water, as well as for fishing. Its paws have webbing, probably to aid in swimming (not all naturalists agree that the webbing is a significant adaptation). Its claws are not fully retractable and suited to quick swipes-and-grabs in water to snag fish. Its head is large, sleek, somewhat flattened, elongated, and narrow, adaptations that allow it to dart its head into water and slip quickly toward underwater prey.

The fishing cat is also known as machbagral, and tarai.

Behavior

If acquainted with humans as kittens, fishing cats may be friendly with people they know. Otherwise, fishing cats are ferocious and dangerous. Even for *Felidae,* fishing cats are especially powerful and are known to be able to drive off a pack of dogs; one in captivity broke out of its enclosure into one holding a female leopard and killed the leopard, which was twice its size. They can do significant harm to humans or other large animals that they deem threatening.

In captivity, males help females care for and rear their kittens, and it is likely that they do the same in the wild. Whether or not fishing cats mate for life is unclear, at present. They seem to able to mate and produce young year round. Gestation is about 63 days; litters consist of one to four kittens. The kittens' eyes open in two weeks; they are weaned in four months.

Fishing cats live near water, and their diet consists primarily of fish and underwater animals such as snails. They are patient hunters and will crouch or sit next to a body of water while carefully gazing into the water for signs of their prey. A fish that swims into range is scooped up quickly by one of the cat's forepaws and held close, then eaten. The cats also feed on crustacea near the shore by scooping them up with their paws or dipping their heads into the water and grabbing the prey in their mouths. Fishing cats also swim after prey. When they do, they bite the fish and haul it to shore in their mouths. When hunting on land, they seem to stay on the ground and to favor small prey.

Habitat

A plentitude of fresh water is essential to the fishing cat's survival, and it is therefore found in watery areas or areas with large rivers or lakes, such as highland forests. Most of their habitat consists of marshes and swamps. They are found in mangrove swamps in particular, as well as reed forests.

Distribution

The fishing cat once had a very large range that included Pakistan, India and its coastal islands, the southern Himalayas, most of southern China, all of the southeast Asian mainland, and Sumatra and Java in Indonesia. It no longer exists in Pakistan, but may be found in remote northeastern India near the coast. It has what may be a healthy population in southwestern India, and may still be found on Sri Lanka, near India's southern coast. Once a common sight in China, its present status in that nation is somewhat clouded, but it seems now to be rare. It lives in small, widely spread pockets in Indochina and southeast Asia; it is likely that these pockets are disappearing as the cat's habitat is logged and its waters fouled. There is disagreement among authorities about the fishing cat's status on the Malay Peninsula, but it seems to be extinct in that region. It is possible that Indonesia may harbor some of the cats on the island of Java, although deforestation of that island has left a very small range for the cat. The island of Sumatra offers better hope for the cat's survival in Indonesia because some large swampy areas are still preserved.

Threats

Because the fishing cat is very dependent on fresh water, pollution of rivers, lakes, marshes, and swamps can hurt it greatly; much of its habitat in China, India, and southeast Asia has been poisoned. Logging of its forest ranges and the filling in of marshes and swamps to accommodate human communities and farms has shrunk much of its ancient range so that it now lives in pockets scattered though southern Asia. Local people sometimes fear it and other times regard it as a pest that threatens their livestock (although this threat is unlikely, given its instinctive eating habits); they therefore kill fishing cats. Hunting for its valued fur has resulted in the cat's outright extinction in most of its old territory, with only India seeming to having the potential for a secure population — although poaching threatens even the fishing cats in India's wildlife preserves.

Conservation and Recovery

The U.S. Fish and Wildlife Service has not listed the fishing cat as endangered or threatened, but it is listed in CITES, Appendix I: Trade prohibited, meaning that the animal is thought to be endangered worldwide. The IUCN lists the cat's status as unknown because while it is known to be under great threat to its survival, not enough is known of its population in the wild to determine whether it is endangered, threatened, or rare. The listing in CITES means that it is illegal in most nations to kill fishing cats or trade in their body parts, including their coats. Conservation efforts need to include identifying populations, providing them with enough habitat to support good-sized breeding populations, and putting a halt to poaching. Indonesia, Malaysia, and India have moved toward taking these steps, although at present India appears to be the only nation that may have a good breeding population left. Only a few fishing cats are held in captivity — not enough for a successful breeding program.

The cat is rare everywhere and could be extinct by the turn of the century.

Margay

Felis [=Leopardus] wiedi

C. Allan Morgan

Status	Endangered
Listed	March 30, 1972
Family	Felidae (Cats)
Description	Spotted wildcat resembling an ocelot but with shorter and rounder head and longer tail; has large brown eyes, body color contains patterns of bright cream yellow and jet black spots.
Habitat	Tropical and subtropical forests.
Food	Rats, squirrels, birds.
Reproduction	Mating from October to January producing 1-2 young.
Threats	Hunted for pelts.
Range	Central America, Mexico, Northern Argentina, Paraguay, Uruguay.

Description

The Margay, *Felis wiedi*, grows to a length ranging between 18 to 28 inches. Its tail length ranges from 15 to 20 inches. Its eyes are large and brown. Body color occurs in patterns of bright cream yellow and spots that are jet black. The margay has often been compared with the ocelot; the pelts of these two species look similar. However, the head of the margay is shorter and rounder and its tail is longer.

Behavior

The margay may purr, mew, snarl, growl, grunt, hiss, yowl, or scream when marking their ranges or finding mating partners. Mating may occur at anytime during the year but generally happens from October to January. After mating, young are born 2 to 4 months later. Females den in hollow trees, burrows of other species, or among dry reeds. Litters may range from 1 to 2 young. Females do all of the rearing, rarely letting males get near the kittens. The kittens stay with the mother playing games of stalk-and-pounce and accompanying their mother on hunts. When sufficient hunting skills have been learned, the young will wander off to find their own hunting grounds.

The margay is nocturnal, hunting at night and resting during the day. The margay feeds on rats, squirrels, and other small animals which may include birds. It is an avid hunter. The margay's limbs are highly flexible such that its hind foot can rotate 180 degrees inward. This allows the margay great agility when climbing trees and when hunting. Individuals hunt alone by hiding until an unsuspecting animal passes. They will allow their prey to pass and slowly begin to creep up on them. When stalking, the margay will begin swiftly at first and then stop. They will watch, laying flat against the ground under cover. Then, they creep again, and stop. The closer they approach, the slower they move. When close enough to their prey, the margay springs upon it with their sharp teeth and strong claws. Killing occurs with the bite of powerful jaws. Because they possesses no flat-topped teeth for chewing, margays cannot grind meat. Thus, they swallow without chewing.

Habitat

The margay lives in tropical and subtropical forests of South America. It requires a habitat which will provide hunting grounds and areas for a hidden den such as hollow trees, burrows, or dry reeds.

Distribution

Currently, margays in the wild are un-evenly distributed throughout their historic range. Few are seen in the wild. In the past, the margay ranged from the extreme southern area of Texas south through Mexico and Central America to Paraguay, Uruguay, and northern Argentina.

Threats

The margay is endangered primarily because it has been hunted beyond its population numbers' capacity to sustain itself. Since the pelt trade of larger cats has been highly regulated and almost completely halted, smaller species of cats, including the margay, have been hunted to fill the demand. Many margay pelts are shipped with ocelot pelts. Even experts cannot distinguish between the two species once they have been skinned. Little is known of the numbers shipped or killed each year. However, 80,000 ocelots were killed every year in Brazil before 1970. In 1968, 128,966 skins were brought into the United States and 133,069 in 1969.

Conservation and Recovery

The margay is secretive in the wild and is difficult to observe. Because of this and the remoteness of its habitat, experts are unsure of how to best protect the species from the factors that threaten it.

Gulf Coast Jaguarundi

Felis [=Herpailurus] yagouaroundi cacomitli

Felis yagouaroundi   C. Allan Morgan

Status	Endangered
Listed	June 14, 1976
Family	Felidae (Cats)
Description	Small weasel-like cat with short legs, a small, flattened head, a slender, elongate body and a very long tail.
Habitat	Chapparal, mesquite thickets near streams.
Food	Birds and small mammals.
Reproduction	Litter of 2 to 4 kittens twice a year.
Threats	Predator control, habitat loss.
Range	Mexico

Description

The Gulf Coast jaguarundi, *Felis yagouaroundi cacomitli,* is a small weasel-like cat with short legs, a small, flattened head, a slender, elongate body and a very long tail. The ears are short and rounded, the coat is unspotted, uniform in color, varying from either blackish to brownish gray or from foxy red to chestnut. The two color phases were once thought to represent two distinct species; the gray one called "jaguarundi," and the red one called "eyra." However, these are the same species and both color phases can be found in the same litter.

This species is also known as eyra (obsolete), otter cat, ghost cat, weasel cat, onza, or leoncillo.

Behavior

Specific data on reproductive seasons are not known. Various studies suggest that there is no definite breeding season; others say there are two breeding seasons per year (spring and fall). The twice-per-year breeding seasons suggest they may yield two litters per year. Gestation in captive cats range from 72-75 days. Litter sizes have been reported from 2 to 4 kittens, with a possibility of 1 to 4.

Females are responsible for all parental care. Kittens are rarely left alone for long periods. The mother brings birds to the den for the kittens to feed on. Kittens eventually accompany the mother on hunting trips. Females have been observed to abandon dens with kittens when discovered by humans or dogs. More research is needed to accurately define parental care.

Lack of modern, quantitative data about the *cacomitli* subspecies' ecology is responsible for conflicting information regarding their activity patterns. Opinions vary from mainly diurnal, to primarily nocturnal but frequently active by day, to active anytime during a 24 hour period. Others believe it hunts in the morning and evening and is much less nocturnal than most cats.

Documented prey include rabbits, rats, mice and birds, especially ground nesters and domestic poultry. Some authorities believe birds are preferred over mammals. Gallinaceous birds such as quail, chachalacas, guans and wild turkeys were especially selected by *cacomitli*.

Habitat

Gulf Coast jaguarundi habitat (especially in south Texas) includes dense, thorny thickets of mesquite (*Prosopis glandulosa*) and stunted acacias (*Acacia spp.*) known as chaparral. Less than 1% of the land area in south Texas supports this extremely dense chaparral. Similar habitats have been identified in the northeastern Mexican states of Tamaulipas and Veracruz. E. R. Ricciuti believes their habitat in the arid areas of northern Mexico also include dense chaparrals of scrub oak on low mountain slopes.

The *cacomitli* subspecies almost always inhabits areas with dense cover. Den sites include dense thickets, fallen logs grown over with grass and shrubs, hollow trees, ditches with overgrown shrubs, or thick, grassy clumps creating "forms" in the protective cover.

Distribution

Historically, the Gulf Coast jaguarundi was never widespread or abundant in Texas. Limited information indicates this species occurred in the counties of Cameron, Willacy, Hidalgo, and Starr. Some evidence suggests their occurrence on Laguna Atascosa National Wildlife Refuge (NWR) and Santa Ana NWR. The Gulf Coast jaguarundi has apparently disappeared from Texas altogether. This means that Mexico is presently the animal's primary refuge.

Threats

This subspecies is hunted in some areas where there are conflicts with poultry. Loss of Gulf Coast jaguarundi habitat has been cited as a concern in Costa Rica, Venezuela, and probably other areas in Latin America. However, F. Goodwyn, Jr. found the subspecies in Mexico used dense habitats interspersed with open areas. Similarly, in Costa Rica, they utilized "altered habitats" and for this reason, these cats were not considered endangered in that country. Fertile soil types required to grow the dense vegetation preferred by the Gulf Coast jaguarundi are also conducive to crop cultivation. Consequently, intensive clearing of this brush for the past 60 years has caused even more concern for their survival. Forest clearing (or brush) for agricultural purposes and general development has resulted in vegetation composition changes.

Conservation and Recovery

The Gulf Coast jaguarundi has already been exterminated in the United States. It seems to require a mixture of dense forest or brushland and open lands in order to hunt, secure its prey, and care for its young, with the open lands offering hunting opportunities and the densely vegetated lands offering security. In its range in Mexico, most of the open and forest lands have been converted to agriculture, and the Gulf Coast jaguarundi is regarded as vermin because it preys on farm animals, especially poultry. Mexico protects the animal under law, listing it in *"Especies de Fauna en Peligro de Extincion en Mexico, 1982"*; even so, people need to be educated in the rarity of and need for protecting the animal in order for it to avoid being killed when found on farms. It is likely that the jaguarundi does not recognize that its traditional hunting grounds have been changed to farms, and it probably preys on the animals it finds there just as it would wild animals in unconverted open lands. What little densely vegetated lands that remain for the Gulf Coast jaguarundi need to be preserved because they likely are essential to the cat's reproduction. A mysterious animal, the jaguarundi requires more study so that its habits and its needs can be properly understood, thus enabling Mexico to create and preserve an ideal environment for it.

Jaguarundi

Felis [=Herpailurus] yagouaroundi fossata

Joe Maynard, Exotic Feline Breeding Compound

Status	Endangered
Listed	June 14, 1976
Family	Felidae (Cats)
Description	Slender body with dark red to black coat.
Habitat	Brushlands and woodlands, and the lower reaches of mountains.
Food	Small animals and fish.
Reproduction	1 or 2 kitten after gestation of about 75 days.
Threats	Loss of habitat and hunting.
Range	Mexico and Nicaragua.

Description

The *fossata* subspecies of the jaguarundi, *Felis yagouaroundi fossata*, is known by only a few examples and skulls collected years apart since the 1920s. For many years, scientists ridiculed claims for discovery of a new species of cat when remains of *fossata* were presented to them, and thus examples of its skull were neglected, lost, or discarded. Once the jaguarundi species was accepted as genuine, scientists were confused by observations of the *fossata* subspecies in its natural habitat and thought it might be an entirely new genus. During the 1990s, *F. y. fossata* has become generally accepted as a very rare subspecies of jaguarundi, although not all naturalists may agree with this.

An adult *F. y. fossata* has a slender body, with a head-and-body length of 21.5 to 26 inches and a tail length of 13 to 24 inches. It weighs between 12 and 22 pounds. It is dark gray with a lighter shaded underbody; other colors, shades of red, gray, and black, are likely. It has no other markings such as stripes or spots, although its young probably have spots when born. Like other jaguarundi, its forelegs are slightly shorter than its hind legs. Its head is narrow, with small, rounded ears — adaptations for a brushy habitat through which it races at high speed.

Behavior

This elusive animal may be the most solitary of the subspecies of jaguarundi. It has been so little observed that its behavior is very much a mystery, but when seen it is alone. Individual *F. y. fossata* probably are territorial. They live in brushlands and woodlands and prey on small animals. They seem to be the most shy of humans of the subspecies of jaguarundi, but will hunt the poultry kept by humans. In this, their hunting behavior resembles that of the other subspecies of jaguarundi: careful, patient watching of the prospective prey, a leap onto the prey when it wanders within range of the cat's hiding place, a bite on the bird's neck, and a forceful tug on it into protective cover — all in one rapid movement. It seems to hunt strictly for food and will not kill unless hungry.

Habitat

The jaguarundi has been sighted in rocky areas of Mexico, as well as brushlands. It may prefer to live near water and is reputed to be a good swimmer. *F. y. fossata* may not be as fond of water as its related subspecies; it may even avoid swimming when it can. Although it is primarily a ground hunter, it may sometimes sleep in trees, and like other jaguarundi it probably kills birds roosting in trees at night.

Distribution

The *F. y. fossata* is a mysterious animal, and one of its mysteries is its range. Scientists missed opportunities to study the animal in the first several decades of the twentieth century, when much of its range might still have been intact (they dismissed it as being a cougar). It has been found in southern Mexico and Nicaragua, but may have ranged (and still range) farther.

Threats

For *F. y. fossata*, loss of habitat is probably its biggest threat. It seems to prefer the same habitat that humans like for farming. So as humans have cleared brushlands and woodlands for their farms, they have probably pushed *F. y. fossata* out of its natural range. The problem for naturalists, here, though, is that the cat's preferred habitat is not entirely known. Further, the size of its population is not known, and what would be a normal population for a given territory is not known. It is possible that the *fossata* has always been very rare, or it is possible that human beings have made it rare by reducing its hunting range.

Conservation and Recovery

The jaguarundi have been blessed with coats that human beings do not want to wear or for home decoration, thus hunting by humans is not a great problem for it. Sportsmen have shot it while hunting, mistaking it cougars. For the *F. y. fossata* subspecies, killing by humans has usually occurred when an individual cat was stalking domesticated poultry, and primarily because the human involved was frightened by it. Apparently, the cat can put on a fearsome show of ferocity when it confronts a human being. However, it is probably like other jaguarundi and runs away from humans whenever it can.

Panamanian Jaguarundi

Felis [=Herpailurus] yagouroundi panamensis

Joe Maynard, Exotic Feline Breeding Compound

Status	Endangered
Listed	June 14, 1976
Family	Felidae (Cats)
Description	Dark red, reddish brown, gray, or black, slightly lighter on the underbody than the rest of the body; an individual animal's color is always uniform.
Habitat	Lowland brushlands and woodlands; possibly mountain foothills.
Food	Small animals of almost any kind, including fish.
Reproduction	Gestation period of about 70 days, resulting in litters of two to four kittens.
Threats	Loss of habitat and human persecution.
Range	Costa Rica, Nicaragua, Panama.

Description

An adult Panamanian jaguarundi, *Felis yagouroundi panamensis*, has a slender body, with low shoulders and high haunches. It is possible that males are slightly larger than females, but the subspecies has not been studied enough to determine this. An adult has a head-and-body length of 22 to 31 inches, with a tail length of 13 to 24 inches, and it has a shoulder height of 14 inches; it weighs between 10 and 20 pounds. It has a uniform color of dark red, reddish brown, gray, or black, with an underbody that is lighter than

the rest of the coat; the color variations from one individual animal to another do not represent different subspecies — a single litter may produce four kittens that are individually dark red, reddish brown, gray, or black. Like other jaguarundi, it has a stooped appearance because its forelegs are slightly shorter than its hind legs. Its head is narrow, with small, rounded ears — adaptations for a brushy habitat through which it races at high speed.

The reason it has two scientific names, one putting it in the genus *Felis* and the other putting it in the genus *Herpailurus* is that the jaguarundi has only thirty-six chromosomes, whereas other cats have thirty-eight; thus some naturalists argue that the species needs it own genus *Herpailurus*, separate from the one for other small cats. Others point out that the jaguarundi behaves like other cats, has a biology like other cats, and looks like other cats, and thus they classify it with other cats; besides, some deem the chromosome count as suspect and await further scientific confirmation that the number of chromosomes of jaguarundi really is thirty-six. Probably the most interesting aspect of the controversy over the jaguarundi's chromosomes is that its different number of chromosomes may mean that it is a protocat— an evolutionary link between modern cats and their remote ancestors.

Behavior

The *panamensis* subspecies of jaguarundi is territorial, with adults having ranges that they patrol. However, these ranges are not exclusive of other *panamensis* adults; territories greatly overlap one another. Much about the social life of *panamensis* has yet to be accounted for; for instance, their mating behavior is obscure. They seem to be solitary hunters, but otherwise they hunt somewhat like cheetahs, relying on a terrific burst of speed to snare an animal close upon which they had carefully crept. Their hunting style is very patient, with a willingness to stalk and observe prey for hours. Once the prey is caught, the jaguarundi bites on its neck, either breaking the neck or suffocating the prey. The prey is then dragged quickly and powerfully into underbrush, where the jaguarundi may feed unobserved. Although it is primarily a ground hunter, it may sometimes sleep in

trees, and like other jaguarundi it probably kills birds roosting in trees at night. Small animals of any kind, and fish as well, are prey for the jaguarundi.

Habitat

The *panamensis* is a good swimmer that prefers to live near open water. It favors regions with ample ground cover, either open brushlands or woodlands with brushy undercover.

Distribution

The *panamensis* subspecies of jaguarundi has been driven out of most of its traditional range by expanding human agriculture, but is known to live in areas on the edge of farms that grow grains, and it may still be found in areas as yet undisturbed by farms or settlements in Costa Rica, Nicaragua, and Panama.

Threats

Loss of habitat is probably the greatest threat to the survival of *panamensis* throughout its Central American range. As humans permanently expand into once wild areas, the jaguarundi loses the brush in which it hides, breeds, and raises its young; the wild prey of the jaguarundi is also restricted, with rodents and other animals that are regarded as pests being subject to extermination, and other animals, such as ground-nesting birds, being driven away. Although the fur coats of jaguarundis are not coveted by humans, *panamensis* is still subject to hunting by humans. It apparently makes no distinction between wildfowl and domesticated birds, and thus farmers treat it as a threat to their farm birds. Further, the jaguarundi can be frightening to humans, which encourages people to hunt them as threats to humans, although the jaguarundi is unlikely to try to attack a human, even in defense of its young. When surprised by humans, the jaguarundi puts on a terrifying display of ruffed fur, growling, bared fangs, and bared claws, but this display is very likely a result of the jaguarundi being terrified of the human that has surprised it; it seems that *panamensis* avoids humans if it possibly can.

Conservation and Recovery

The preferred habitat for *panamensis* is not entirely known. However, it is reasonable to believe that it needs some lowland brush-lands and woodlands to be preserved in order for it to survive. In Costa Rica, most of this land is gone, having been converted to agriculture in the last thirty years; Nicaragua still has some ideal lands left in the east and northeast, and some of these lands may be preserved because of government agreements with local Native American tribes to leave their lands in peace; in Panama, the best hope for the jaguarundi subspecies that is named for it is probably in the north.

Sinaloan Jaguarundi

Felis [=Herpailurus] yagouaroundi tolteca

Felis yagouaroundi   C. Allan Morgan

Status	Endangered
Listed	June 14, 1976
Family	Felidae (Cats)
Description	Small weasel-like cat with short legs, a small, flattened head, a slender, elongate body, and a very long tail.
Habitat	Chaparral, mesquite thickets near streams.
Food	Birds and small mammals.
Reproduction	Litter of 2 to 4 kittens.
Threats	Predator control, habitat loss.
Range	Mexico, and possibly Guatemala.

Description

The Sinaloan jaguarundi, *Felis yagouaroundi tolteca*, is a small weasel-like cat with short legs, a small, flattened head, a slender, elongate body, and a very long tail. The ears are short and rounded. The coat is unspotted, uniform in color, varying among individual animals from blackish to brownish gray and from foxy red to chestnut.

Behavior

The early 1800s Swiss naturalist Rengger observed the Sinaloan jaguarundi in Paraguay and formulated the following account:

The mother seldom leaves her offspring alone for long periods of time. As the young grow, birds are brought to the den for consumption by the kittens. Eventually, young accompany their mother on hunting trips. However, the mother will not defend her kittens from intrusions by humans or dogs and she runs from her den once discovered by an intruder.

No detailed analysis of the Sinaloan jaguarundi's food habits has been reported. However, some anecdotal information from naturalists and trappers has surfaced in the popular and semitechnical literature. Rabbits, rats, mice and birds (especially ground nesters) have been cited as prey taken by this subspecies. Some authorities believe birds are preferred over mammals. Gallinaceous birds such as quail, chachalacas, guans, and wild turkeys seem especially selected by the subspecies. Sinaloan jaguarundi are notorious predators on domestic poultry in Mexico and in most of Central America.

Lack of modern, quantitative data about this subspecies' ecology is responsible for conflicting information regarding *F. y. tolteca* activity patterns. Conflicting reports state that it is (1) primarily nocturnal but frequently active by day, (2) active anytime during a 24-hour period, (3) mainly diurnal, hunting in the morning and evening, and is much less nocturnal than most cats.

Gestation for captive Sinaloan jaguarundi lasts from 72 to 75 days. Litter sizes have been reported from 2 to 4 kittens, with a possibility of 1 to 4.

Habitat

The Sinaloan jaguarundi is found in a variety of habitats: Costa Rica — primary and secondary forest, and overgrown and grazed pastures at elevations from sea level to 8,000 feet; and Venezuela — semiarid thorny forest, deciduous forest, humid premontane forest, upland dry savanna and swampy grassland. Some authorities believe it prefers localities near streams, but this may be related more to the fact that dense vegetation accompanies waterways and riparian communities because of favorable water and nutrient conditions. The subspecies seems to prefer the edges of forest and brush communities rather than deep interiors, but almost always inhabits a region of dense cover. These fields are not necessarily connected with particular species of brush, but generally require an area of rich vegetation and thick undergrowth which provides this dense cover.

Distribution

The Sinaloan jaguarundi was once found in Arizona, Mexico, and Guatemala. It has disappeared from Arizona and may no longer inhabit Guatemala.

Threats

The Sinaloan jaguarundi is still hunted in some areas where there are conflicts with poultry. It also has an aesthetic value as a part of the natural heritage of biotic diversity throughout its historic range.

Fertile soil types required to grow the dense vegetation preferred by this subspecies are also conducive to crop cultivation. Consequently, intensive clearing of this brush for the past 60 years has cost the Sinaloan jaguarundi much of its habitat. Changes in land use probably have had more detrimental effects on the animal than has direct mortality caused by humans.

Conservation and Recovery

The Sinaloan jaguarundi is one of the least known cats on the continent of North America. Its life history and population are not well documented. All four subspecies of jaguarundi (*cacomitli, tolteca, fossata,* and *panamensis*) are listed as endangered by the USFWS and are in Appendix I: Trade Prohibited of the CITES. The species *Felis yagouroundi* is listed in Mexico's *"Especies de Fauna en Peligro de Extincion en Mexico, 1982"* (a recommendation to CITES I, Reyes, August 1982) and in Guatemala's list under *"Fauna en Vias de Extincion, 1967."*

Clouded Leopard

Neofelis nebulosa

N. n. brachyura   Bruce Bunting

Status	Endangered
Listed	June 2, 1970
Family	Felidae (Cats)
Description	Long, bushy tail and short legs; gray to yellow fur with large splotchy cloudlike markings.
Habitat	Tropical forest.
Food	Birds, monkeys, pigs, cattle, young buffalo, goats, deer, porcupine.
Reproduction	2 cubs after gestation of 88 days.
Threats	Hunted for pelts; loss of forest.
Range	Nepal; southeast China; Asia, Sumatra and Borneo.

Description

The clouded leopard, *Neofelis nebulosa*, is well adapted for moving easily through the trees. This small leopard, weighing 33 to 77 pounds, has a long, bushy tail for balance. The tail measures 21 to 35 inches and is almost equal in length to the head and body of 24 to 42 inches. Its legs are short with flexible ankles, and the paws have broad pads for moving easily through tree branches.

The clouded leopard's fur is grayish or yellowish with large splotchy cloudlike markings that have a dark margin and a paler center. The head, legs, and tail are spotted. A melanistic (black) variety may have been observed in Borneo. The canine teeth of the clouded leopard are exceptionally long.

The female normally bears 2 cubs after a gestation of approximately 88 days. After about five months, the cub is weaned from the mother. The cub's coat is initially black in the patterned areas, and the coat changes to the adult colors in about six months.

Four subspecies of *Neofelis nebulosa* are recognized: *Neofelis nebulosa nebulosa* (south China and southeastern Asia); *Neofelis nebulosa brachyura* (Taiwan; possibly extinct); *Neofelis nebulosa diardi* (Borneo); and *Neofelis nebulosa macrosceloides* (Nepal to Burma).

Behavior

Although its feeding habits have not been studied in detail, the clouded leopard has been reported to feed on birds, monkeys, pigs, cattle, young buffalo, goats, deer, and even porcupines. As can be seen from their prey, clouded leopards seem to hunt both in the trees and on the ground. Reputedly, the clouded leopard can hang by one hind foot and wait in ambush for potential prey.

The clouded leopard is usually nocturnal, although recent studies suggest it is more active during the day than previously reported.

Habitat

The clouded leopard lives in the tropical forests of southeastern and south-central Asia at an elevation up to 8,000 feet. Generally, this cat is considered highly arboreal. However, recent studies suggest it spends a good portion of its time on the ground, using trees primarily as resting sites.

Distribution

The clouded leopard has been found in southeastern and south-central Asia from Nepal through southeastern China to the Malay peninsula, and on Taiwan, Hainan, Sumatra, and Borneo. Currently, the species may have disappeared from Hainan, and was last found in Taiwan in 1983 in the most inaccessible parts of the island's central mountain range.

Threats

The clouded leopard has been ruthlessly hunted for its pelt. Up to the 1980s, its beautiful fur could still be bought openly in Japa-nese department stores, at prices exceeding $100,000. The clouded leopard has also been hunted for the medicine and culinary trades. Also, the loss of forest to agriculture increasingly limits the available habitat for this rare species. As the clouded leopard's population dwindles and becomes more fragmented, the species becomes more susceptible to disease and natural catastrophe.

Conservation and Recovery

The clouded leopard has been listed in CITES, Appendix I: Trade Prohibited since July 1, 1975. The treaty seems to have been effective in cutting down on the trade in the clouded leopard's fur, although unscrupulous dealers and buyers still pay top dollar for the cat's skins in Europe and Japan. The appetite for exotic fare in Southeast Asian folk medicine is ferocious and threatens the clouded leopard everywhere. If the clouded leopard is to survive, the trade in its body parts for medicine must be ended; the nations such as China and Taiwan where its parts are marketed need to enforce the provisions of the CITES and end the importation of the clouded leopard's parts and end the marketing of the parts once they enter the nations.

Loss of habitat is a serious problem for many animals that share the clouded leopard's range. The best hope for survival of such animals is the creation and maintenance of national parks in which wildlife and their environment would be protected. Nepal, Malaysia, and Indonesia each have wildlife reserves that might remain large enough and undisturbed enough to preserve the clouded leopard, but it is not known for sure whether the animal actually lives in any of the parks.

Asiatic Lion

Panthera leo persica

Bruce Bunting

Status	Endangered
Listed	June 2, 1970
Family	Felidae (Cats)
Description	Smaller and slimmer than African lions; tawny brown, with dark tufts on the ends of their tails. Males have dark manes.
Habitat	Small patches of forest.
Food	Prefers large game.
Reproduction	2 to 4 cubs after gestation of 100 to 116 days.
Threats	Loss of habitat; human hunters.
Range	Northwestern India.

Description

The Asiatic lion, *Panthera leo persica,* looks much like African lions, except that it has a small mane, has more conspicuous tufts of hair on its elbows, and has a thicker overall coat. The tuft at the end of its tail may be larger. It also has a more conspicuous fringe of skin along its belly.

Adult males tend to be much bigger than females. Males may measure 6 feet from tip of nose to the tail; females may measure about 5 feet. Their tails are 2.25 to 3.5 feet long. Males may reach 170 pounds, with females as much as 50% smaller.

Behavior

Asiatic lions live in groups, except for young males who have left their parents' pride and have yet to find one of their own, although these young males often form what some naturalists call "coalitions." The groups, like those of other lions, form around a core of females, and the group as a whole shares a large territory. Males will form close bonds with one to four other males, often related by birth, and will fight cooperatively to protect the females and the young of their group from marauders. Males who succeed in taking over a group of females, usually by ousting the resident males in a bloody fight, will often kill the group's cubs. However, confrontations between individual males rarely lead to physical conflict; after some posturing, the smaller lion concedes and leaves. Hunting tends to be a group affair, and the females of a group do most of the work, although males do sometimes hunt, kill, and drag away game themselves.

Habitat

The Asiatic lion now lives in a forest with some open areas. There they hunt wild game and make use of the trees by sometimes climbing into them to rest.

Distribution

In historical times, the Asiatic lion once ranged from Turkey, throughout the Middle East, and into India. It is now found only in the Gir Forest Sanctuary, partly because a British Viceroy once declined to hunt down the remaining lions (then about twelve in number) and kill them for sport, and partly because enlightened local government chose to give it legal protection.

Threats

There are at present three principal threats to the survival of the Asiatic lion. One is loss of habitat: The Asiatic lion was at one time a wide-ranging species that could be found in open lands as well as woodlands. Now, all of its open-land range is gone. Most of it has been taken over by humans for settlements, farming, and ranching. In what open lands that remain in the Asiatic lion's traditional territory, the Asiatic lion has been exterminated by hunting and there is no realistic chance of its ever reestablishing itself in those areas. The small patch of forest in which it survives is threatened by encroaching agriculture, although the Indian government is doing a good job of protecting it. A great danger to the forest is fire, which could destroy it in a day, taking with it the lives of the lions within.

Humans have long hunted the Asiatic lion for sport, taking the species just about as close to extinction as any species can go and yet be recovered. Lion parts are used in Asian folk medicine, and the Asiatic lion is threatened by poachers who would profit by selling the lion parts to medicine dealers. This particular threat to the Asiatic lion has been well controlled by India's forest rangers, but the poachers are kept at bay only by constant vigilance and vigorous enforcement of the laws protecting the lions and their forest.

The third principal threat is the lack of genetic diversity. In any mammal, lack of genetic diversity makes its species very vulnerable to disease. Asiatic lions, which once bred by the thousands, were reduced to twelve or fewer animals; this means that the genes of thousands of members of the species have been altogether lost, along with any disease resistance that they had encoded in them. A parasitic infection or a virus could kill all of the surviving Asiatic lions.

Conservation and Recovery

From near extinction, the population of the Asiatic lion has risen to more than 300, up from a low of about 12. This is near the maximum number their current range can support. They were given refuge in the Gir Forest Sanctuary in the state of Gujarat in northwestern India in 1966. Here, they have become a tourist attraction.

Although humans hunted the Asiatic lion to near extinction, the Indian government has had success in protecting the lions from poachers. Once a threat to livestock, the lions were killed by farmers, but in the Gir Forest, they are far enough removed from farmland that farmers need not fear them.

Jaguar
Panthera onca

Ron Singer, USFWS

Status	Endangered
Listed	March 3, 1972
Family	Felidae (Cats)
Description	Short bristly tail with irregular blotches and black rosettes.
Habitat	Tropical and subtropical forests; mangrove swamps; rain forests.
Food	Otters, deer, wild pigs, turtles, crocodiles, ground-nesting birds.
Reproduction	Litter size ranges from 1 to 4 cubs.
Threats	Excessive and illegal hunting.
Range	Southeast U.S.; Mexico; Guatemala; Colombia to Argentina, Amazon basin into central Brazil.

Description

The jaguar, *Panthera onca,* is the largest and most robust of the American cats. Adults extend from 5 to 7.25 feet in length. The tail is short and bristly. Females on average are smaller than males. Ground color varies from pale yellow to rusty red dorsally, paler on the sides, and white on the underparts and inner surfaces of the legs. Markings are irregular blotches and rosettes, the latter centered with black spots. Young are more heavily spotted, and their coats are woollier. Both black and albino individuals occur occasionally.

Behavior

The breeding season is year-round in tropical areas of the range. In the more northern areas, breeding takes place in December and January with births in April and May. Females are polyestrous and males fight for first breeding rights. Gestation lasts from 93 to 113 days. Litter size ranges from one to four, with an average of two. The growth rate is not well known, but 8-week-old cubs will weigh from 4.5 to 6.5 pounds. Young stay with the mother for about 2 years, at which time sexual maturity is reached. Both parents help rear young, but the bulk of the burden is on the female. The family unit is maintained until the young are at least a year old. Record longevity in captivity is 20 years.

The jaguar is solitary and somewhat territorial in its habits, except during the breeding season. Little is known about its territorial behavior beyond the fact that it will mark trees. It requires dens in rocky caves or dense thickets.

The jaguar will hunt both day and night, but sleeps a significant portion of the day. Principal foods are peccaries and capybaras (*Tayassu sp.*) (*Hydrochoerus sp.*). It will also take tapirs (*Tapirus sp.*), agoutis (*Agouti sp.* and *Dasyprocta sp.*), otters (*Lutra*), deer, small crocodilians, turtles and their eggs, large ground-nesting birds, and occasionally livestock. It stalks prey until close enough to pounce, then drags the kill to the nearest thicket to be eaten. Remains are usually not covered.

Habitat

The jaguar appears to require areas with cover. It inhabits tropical and subtropical forests ranging from mangrove swamps to rain forests. At the southern extreme of the range open savannas and deserts are used. Chaparral and timbered areas are preferred at the northern extreme of the range. It appears to have a preference for areas near water but has been reported from deserts.

Distribution

The jaguar was formerly distributed throughout the tropical lowlands of Mexico, Central America, and South America to about 40 degrees south latitude. The former U.S. distribution included southern California, New Mexico, southern Arizona, and possibly Louisiana and Colorado.

Fair numbers of jaguars remain in eastern Campeche, Selva Lacandone, eastern Chiapas, and eastern Oaxaca in Mexico and western El Peten in Guatemala. It is scattered and considered a pest in Argentina. North of Mexico, it occurs extremely rarely in Texas, Arizona, and New Mexico. No current population estimates are available. There are no viable breeding populations in the U.S. and it exists there as only an occasional stray.

Threats

The jaguar is valued for its pelt and as a game animal. Deliberate persecution, excessive and illegal hunting, over-exploitation by the fur industry, and predator control activities have extirpated the jaguar from much of its original range and seriously reduced numbers in most of the rest. Timber and brush clearing have degraded and destroyed habitat to the point where reestablishment of populations in the northern part of the range is doubtful. Mining and oil exploration and development have made formerly remote Central and South American areas more accessible to human activity and subsequent illegal killings.

Conservation and Recovery

The IUCN is surveying this species' status in Latin America; in a cooperative venture, the U.S. Fish and Wildlife Service and the Direccion General de la Fauna Silvestre of Mexico with support from the National Wildlife Federation, the National Audubon Society, and the Texas and New Mexico Departments of Game and Fish, are surveying the population status in Mexico.

The jaguar is protected in the U.S. and most of the Central and South American countries within its range, but laws are not adequately enforced. Colombia still allows hunting of all field species. Protection in some Central and South American countries is provided in National Parks. Importation of skins to the U.S. is prohibited except by permit. However, illicit commerce to European and Asian markets is common. Brush clearing in national wildlife refuges in the Lower Rio Grande Valley of Texas has been stopped to preserve rapidly disappearing brush habitat.

Leopard

Panthera pardus

Charles R. Belinky

Status	Threatened in Gabon, Republic of Congo, Uganda, Kenya. Endangered in the rest of Africa and all of Asia.
Listed	June 2, 1970
Family	Felidae (Cats)
Description	Short, muscular, extremely strong legs; a series of black dots form a discontinuous border.
Habitat	Tropical rain forest desert and temperate forests; high mountains.
Food	Antelope, rodents, birds, monkey, fish, domestic animals.
Reproduction	Litter size ranges from 1 to 4 cubs.
Threats	Hunting; loss of habitat.
Range	Gabon, Congo, Republic of Congo, Uganda, Kenya, and Sri Lanka

Description

The powerfully built leopard, *Panthera pardus*, stands almost two and a half feet tall and weighs up to 180 pounds, with the female weighing only slightly less than the male. The length of the adult male varies from 35 to 59 inches, with a tail length between 24 to 35 inches. The leopard has short, muscular, extremely strong legs. The paws are large with sharp claws, five on the forepaws and four on the hind paws.

A leopard usually has cinnamon, ocher, or yellowish fur that is lighter on the flanks. The spots, or rosettes, are darker areas surrounded by a series of black dots that form a discontinuous border. The dark spots alternating with lighter areas render the shape of the body less distinct, masking the animal's outline. The back of each ear is black with a central white spot. A melanistic version of the leopard (called the black panther) can be found throughout its range, especially in the humid rain forests of southeastern Asia.

Behavior

One of the most silent animals in existence, the leopard walks almost on tiptoe, placing the back paws exactly where the forepaws were, so that it can move over uneven ground without making noise. This large cat can briefly run at speeds of over 37 miles per hour. An excellent climber, it can descend head first from a tree. It is a strong swimmer but is not as fond of the water as the tiger.

The females give birth to one to four cubs after a gestation period of approximately three and a half months. The cubs have dull gray fur with barely visible spots when they are born. The female hides the cubs at first in a quiet cave or hollow tree. After about two years the cubs are almost fully grown, and they go off and hunt by themselves.

These animals live in large, partially overlapping home ranges. Juveniles remain as transients in the area they are born, until a home range becomes available due to adult mortality. Otherwise, these animals are solitary except when mating; although there have been reports of males remaining with females after mating to help rear the young. Like most cats, the leopard uses scent and claw marks to stake out their territory. To communicate, the cat makes a deep, rasping coughing noise.

Being a widespread species, the leopard has a variable diet. It appears to be more opportunistic than other cats, feeding on antelope, rodents, birds, monkey, fish, domestic animals, and sometimes even fruit.

The leopard captures its prey either by surprise in an ambush or by using ruses and tricks to attract the prey's attention. After catching its meal, the leopard usually drags the prey to a tree or other safe spot away from hyenas, vultures, and other scavengers. Such is the strength of a leopard that it can ascend a tree carrying a carcass larger than itself. When using a tree for a safe spot, this muscular cat wedges the prey among the branches and starts to feed. Any meat left is saved for other meals.

Leopards mainly hunt at night. However, recent studies suggest that this behavior is the result of being hunted by humans, which has made the animal insecure during the daytime when humans are nearby. Its behavior when humans are far away may vary from a strictly nighttime hunting pattern.

Habitat

This widespread species can be found in virtually every habitat from tropical rain forest to desert to temperate forests to high mountains in Africa and southern Asia. Primarily, though, they favor forests and plains abundantly supplied with trees and vegetation, offering both a wide variety of prey and sufficient cover.

Distribution

Leopards were once widespread throughout most of central and southern Africa. The species can still be found in most of this historical range, although the population is dwindling, especially in southern Africa. Further, leopards were once widespread throughout most of West and North Africa, except for the innermost parts of the Sahara desert. In Asia, leopards were found in parts of the Middle East, the Indian subcontinent, Southeast Asia, and northeast China. Now, however, leopards are rare in much of West and North Africa as well as in most of Asia.

Numerous subspecies have been described for the leopard. Many races are based on variations within a single population and thus are probably not valid. Some subspecies, however, show variations correlated to climate and habitat differences. The subspecies of the leopard that are recognized, especially in captive populations are: Javan (*melas*), Amur (*orientalis*), Indian (*fusca*), North Chinese (*japonensis*), Somali (*nanopardus*), Zanzibar (*ardersi*), Sinai (*jarvisi*), Sri Lankan (*kotiya*), Barbary (*panthera*), Persian (*saxicolor*), Arabian (*nimr*), Anatolian (*tulliana*), Caucasus (*ciscausasica*), and Indochinese (*delacouri*).

Exact estimates of the populations of leopards in central and southern Africa are not easy to obtain because of the difficulty involved in carrying out an accurate census. The numbers in central Africa, however, seem to be relatively high with 20,000 animals reported in Republic of Congo (formerly Zaire) alone. Unfortunately, in South Africa, reports state that much of the species has been eliminated.

It is known that the numbers are dwindling rapidly in much of their West and North African and Asian ranges. Only about 400-600 individuals are known to survive in Sri Lanka, and the future of the leopard there looks bleak.

Threats

The leopard population has been greatly reduced because of demand for its beautifully spotted fur and killing for sport. Additionally, humans have increasingly been moving into the savannahs that are rich in the leopard's prey in order to farm and raise cattle. As the humans push out the wild ungulates, the leopard turns to domestic animals for food thereby provoking humans into killing it.

Conservation and Recovery

The banning of trade in leopard fur through national laws and international agreements seems to have reduced the number of animals killed for their fur. The leopard is listed in CITES, Appendix I: Trade Prohibited as of July 1, 1975. In the *IUCN Red Data Book*, the subspecies *panthera, orientalis, nimr, tulliana,* and *jarvisi* are listed as endangered; all other subspecies are listed as vulnerable.

Tiger

Panthera tigris

Bruce Bunting

Status	Endangered
Listed	June 2, 1970
Family	Felidae (Cats)
Description	Relatively large head; the rounded, small ears are black.
Habitat	Wet evergreen, semi-evergreen, moist thorn, and dry deciduous forests to hilly country.
Food	Animals of any size.
Reproduction	2 to 6 cubs after a gestation of 98 to 110 days.
Threats	Hunting; destruction of habitat.
Range	Russia, India, Iran, Turkey, China, Indonesia

Description

The tiger, *Panthera tigris*, is the largest member of the cat family, weighing 286 to 600 pounds. Females are slightly smaller, seldom exceeding 300 pounds. The head and body measure 55 to 109 inches long, with the tail measuring 23 to 27 inches in length. This large, muscular animal has powerful forequarters and a relatively large head, especially in the male. The tiger has the longest canines of any living member of the cat family. The feet are large, with five toes on the front and four on the back. The long claws, measuring 3 to 4 inches in length, are usually retracted and are only bared when catching prey or in defense. The rounded, small ears are black with a central white spot.

The tiger's tawny coat with black, usually vertical, stripes effectively camouflages the animal in the forest and tall grasslands. Considerable variation in color and length of fur occur among the different subspecies. Size also varies according to latitude, with the smallest tiger occurring at low latitudes in Indonesia and the largest at high latitudes in Manchuria and Siberia.

Behavior

Tigers are generally solitary animals living in nonoverlapping home territories. Usually, the animals keep 1 to 3 miles apart.

However, if game is plentiful, they may stay together for short periods.

Tigers are excellent swimmers, regularly crossing rivers and lakes to explore new hunting grounds. Infrequently, the animals have been known to climb trees. They like to den in caves, hollow trees, and dense vegetation. Each animal may have several favorite den sites within its territory. They can jump horizontally over 30 feet. The tiger roars and purrs like many of the other big cats.

Females bear two to six cubs after a gestation period of 98-110 days. The cubs, blind at birth, stay with their mothers for two to three years. The mothers teach their cubs to hunt at two months of age, and they can hunt on their own by seven months of age. Cub mortality rate is very high and only one or two usually survive. Tigers reach sexual maturity at three or four years.

Tigers prey on animals of any size, from baby elephants to the smallest rodents. In India, they mainly prey on deer; although they occasionally kill rhino calves, wild pigs, and porcupines. The Siberian tiger's diet consists mainly of wild pig and Manchurian wapiti.

From countless stories and legends, tigers are known to occasionally kill humans. Despite the fearsome stories, most of these large carnivores avoid humans and do not normally consider them prey. Usually man-eating occurs when the animals do not have an adequate natural food supply and are encroached upon by humans in an area where the tiger still retains an adequate breeding population. In these areas, mothers have been known to teach their young that humans are legitimate prey.

Tigers hunt mainly at night, starting at dusk when the wild ungulates are most active. During the day, they rest in the shade, sometimes lying in a quiet pool of water to escape the heat, although they may be more active during the day in the northern part of their range, especially during winter.

As tigers cannot run great distances, they stalk close to their prey and then rush to pull the animal to the ground with their teeth and claws. The tiger strangles larger animals by biting the throat and breaks the necks of smaller ones. When tigers kill large animals, they cannot eat all the meat in one sitting. They may camp near the kill for several days until all the meat, including the bones, is gone. When they are away from their kill, they cover the remains with grass or debris. Tigers usually eat about 12 pounds per meal, but they may eat as much as 60 pounds at a time.

Habitat

A wide-ranging and versatile species, the tiger has exploited many different habitats throughout southern Asia. Its main requirements for survival are some form of plant cover, a water supply, and sufficient prey. In tropical Asia, they can live in rain, wet evergreen, semi-evergreen, moist thorn, and dry deciduous forests as well as mangrove swamps, thick grasses, bamboo thickets, savannahs, and tamarisk shrublands. They prefer hilly country with a dense cover of trees and shrubs in the western part of their range. In portions of central Asia that were in the former Soviet Union, they can be found in the "tugai" habitat; the dense tangle of tall grass, reeds, shrubs, and trees found along riverbanks and floodplains. Their habitat varies from conifer forest to barren rocky mountains in the northern and eastern parts of their range.

Distribution

Eight subspecies have been described for *Panthera tigris*, two of which are probably extinct and one that is certainly extinct:

P. t. tigris (Bengal tiger), Indian subcontinent

P. t. altaica (Siberian tiger), Siberia and Manchuria

P. t. virgata (Caspian tiger), Iran and Turkey

P. t. amoyensis (Chinese tiger), South China

P. t. sumatrae (Sumatran tiger), Sumatra

P. t. sondaica (Javan tiger), Java

P. t. balica (Bali tiger), Bali (extinct)

P. t. corbetti (Indochinese tiger), southeast Asia

Threats

For centuries, humans have heavily hunted tigers for sport, because of their reputations as man-killers, and for their pelts. The fur of the tiger is very valuable. As recently as the 1980s, tiger coats could be bought openly in Japanese department stores for over $100,000. Some Indian maharajahs and European hunters were known to kill hundreds of tigers each.

However, the greater threat to this species' future survival is the destruction of its habitat. The human population has expanded into traditional tiger habitat by logging the forests and eliminating natural prey. This forces the populations into almost constant conflict with humans.

Conservation and Recovery

The exportation of tiger skins has been prohibited by law, although this measure is far from adequate. More successfully, many wildlife preserves have been set up to protect this magnificent animal. India has doubled its population of tigers through an effective system of reserves. However, many reserves hold too few tigers to maintain viable populations.

In zoos, captive breeding programs are becoming increasingly important. Here, too, maintaining genetic diversity is a problem. For example, there are about 600 captive Siberian tigers in zoos, descended from only 25 individuals. This excessive inbreeding makes the Siberian tiger population extremely susceptible to such genetic problems as lethal genes and low birth rates. However, the Siberian tiger is more fortunate than the extinct Bali tiger (*Panthera tigris balica*), and the probably extinct Caspian tiger (*Panthera tigris virgata*) and Javan tiger (*Panthera tigris sondaica*), which were not bred in captivity.

Siberian Tiger

Panthera tigris altaica

USFWS

Status	Endangered
Listed	June 2, 1970
Family	Felidae (Cats)
Description	Light yellow coat with broad black stripes; the underside from neck to hind legs is pale, sometimes white.
Habitat	Cold coniferous forests to temperate deciduous forests.
Food	Prefers large prey such as deer and wild pigs, but will eat small animals such as birds and frogs.
Reproduction	Litters average 2 to 4 cubs after gestation of 90 days.
Threats	Deforestation of its habitat by logging; poachers.
Range	Russia (Siberia); China (Manchuria)

Description

The Siberian tiger, *Panthera tigris altaica*, is one of the largest existing predators on land; its adult males can weigh over 700 pounds (the largest recorded tiger weighed 845 pounds). Females weigh much less, but at 450 pounds or more, they are still impressively large. Siberian tigers may be as long as 12 feet from tip of nose to tail, although this figure is disputed, but specimens of more than ten feet have been found. This means that the Siberian tiger is larger than existing Bengal tigers (reports of huge Bengal tigers from the past are now discounted). The tail may be as much as 4 feet long. Again, females are smaller than males.

Its fur also distinguishes the Siberian tiger from other subspecies. It is 2 inches long on the back, and during winter reaches 4.5 inches on its underside, and it is thicker than the fur on other tigers. The head of the Siberian tiger features a broader nose than found on other species of tiger.

The Siberian tiger is also known as the Manchurian tiger, amur tiger, and amba, and has been treated taxonomically as *Panthera tigris amurensis, Panthera tiger corensis, Panthera tiger mandshurica,* and *Neofelis tigris altaica.*

Behavior

The Siberian tiger is territorial. An adult tiger of any subspecies, male or female, marks out a large territory for itself, and Siberian tigers mark out the largest territories of all, perhaps because food is not as plentiful in its habitat as it is for other subspecies of tiger, and perhaps because its huge size requires more food. A male may have a territory of 360 square miles (sometimes as much as 1,080 square miles). He will probably mark this territory with urine and scent glands, as well as with dung. Females have smaller territories which may overlap as territories for some of the other subspecies do. It is possible, according to some early and somewhat dated research that Siberian tigers form social bonds, and that a family consisting of a male and female and cubs would share a single territory. What is more likely is that one male's huge territory encompasses the territories of several females, similar to the behavior of the Bengal tiger.

Mating is seasonal, perhaps a product of the cold climate. This is unique among tigers, although it is possible that Siberian tigers in captivity in warm climates will mate year round. As it is, the wild Siberian tiger mates in winter to produce young in spring. The loud roars of the tigers may sometimes signal female receptiveness for mating. A female's scent markings will also indicate to a male whether she is in estrus. Males will fight determinedly for the right to mate with an available female, and they can seriously injure one another. Once a male has secured the right to mate, its problems are not over; once mating is completed the female often turns and attacks its partner, driving him away, and sometimes cutting him badly. The resulting cubs will remain with their mother, traveling with her once their eyes open. They are weaned at about 6 months of age and will reach sexual maturity at about 4 years of age. The young leave their mother's territory at between 2 and 3 years of age. With a gestation period of only three months, the Siberian tiger is capable of replenishing its numbers.

Tigers are built for hunting, and Siberian tigers spend much of their waking time tracking down prey. They hunt at night, carefully creeping up on their prey and then pouncing. Their jaws are very powerful, so that when they latch on to the prey they seldom let go. The Siberian tiger's great weight probably helps it pull down an animal struggling to escape. It dispatches its prey with a bite to the neck — often breaking it and thereby ending the struggle — and closes off the prey's windpipe, suffocating it. Like other tigers, it may take days to eat a large animal, and it will eventually consume everything, including the bones. Their preferred prey consists of wild pigs, sika deer, and red deer. Other than man, the only predator that conflicts with the Siberian tiger is the brown bear, which is known to give up its kill to a Siberian tiger rather than fight.

Habitat

The Siberian tiger inhabits both coniferous and deciduous forests with a wide variety of trees and fauna. The climate is very cold in winter, during which the tiger is active, leaving distinctive footprints throughout its territory. The warm months remain cool in its northern range, but become temperate in the lower part of its range in Manchuria. Before the twentieth century its habitat was even more varied and included flatlands and mountainsides (up to 12,800 feet), mostly forests, but grasslands, too. It has always shown a preference for cool weather. In its present range, winter temperatures can fall below -40 degrees Fahrenheit, although -4 degrees is more common.

Distribution

The Siberian tiger once roamed a vast forestland in central to eastern Asia. The range extended southward to Beijing, northward to Lake Baikal, and due east from each. Now it is found south of the Amur River. Little is known of its movements when its range was at its peak. It is a mysterious animal that has wanted nothing to do with human beings and has avoided them. Only in recent years has the Siberian tiger been giving up the secrets of its life in the wild, as Russian and international scientists cooperate to study it. Presently, fewer than 20 roam the temperate forests of northeastern Manchuria. The remaining tigers occupy a forest along Siberia's southeastern coast.

Threats

The Siberian tiger is rapidly nearing extinction, in spite of an impressive international effort to save it. In the 1970s, the former Soviet Union made an effort to protect it, and its heavily forested territory in the far east of Siberia was protected by law and by forest rangers. Typical of the practices of the Soviet Union, foreigners were unwelcome in the tiger's national preserves. In the late 1980s, American researchers from the University of Idaho were allowed to participate with Soviet scientists in studies of the elusive animal. When the Soviet Union fell apart, the Siberian preserves became the responsibility of Russia, one of several republics to emerge from the Soviet Union. There was chaos and lawlessness for a few years. In desperate need of foreign currency for its cash-starved economy, Russia began logging its eastern forests and selling the wood abroad. This logging daily marches toward the coast, reducing the Siberian tiger's range and the range of elk and other prey favored by the tigers. The trees are important sources of food for the large herbivores that comprise the bulk of the Siberian tiger's diet. Further, poaching became common. The Siberian tiger had made encouraging gains in the 1980s; its numbers rose to more than 500, perhaps as high as 600, in the range under the control of the Soviet Union. That number has shrunk to perhaps 150, and is shrinking so fast that international observers fear that it will be hunted into extinction by 1999. Russian scientists are even less sanguine and fear that the tiger will be wiped out by 1997.

All subspecies of the tiger are under pressure from hunters who sell the cats for use in folk medicines in China and Taiwan. A single Siberian tiger sells for more than $30,000, dead or alive. Its parts are believed to be powerful aphrodisiacs, and to ease or cure a wide variety of ailments. Its fat may be the most familiar to Westerners because it is supposed to be the main ingredient in "tiger balm." The demand for the tiger products exploded in the 1970s, and the demand now far outstrips the number of tigers available.

Thus, makers of the folk medicines have used substitutes in their products and passed them off as having been made from tiger parts.

Although trade in tiger parts is supposed to be outlawed by international treaties, the Siberian tiger continues to be killed and shipped to Chinese, Taiwanese, Japanese, or Korean manufacturers. Poachers are said to use the latest equipment, including American-made off-road vehicles, to outrace forest rangers to living tigers and then, with a new tiger carcass, to outrace them out of forest preserves, possibly into China. This killing has not only reduced the number of Russian Siberian tigers, but has reduced the Manchurian population of the Siberian tiger to fewer than 20 in the wild. In 1994, the United States invoked trade sanctions against Taiwan for its continued ignoring of treaties that obligate it to reduce the trade in tiger parts in its territory. China narrowly escaped similar sanctions by offering evidence that it had made a good-faith effort to curtail the importation of tigers and tiger parts into its territory. In 1992, China had asked CITES for an exemption from the international agreement banning trade in tiger parts, asserting that the killing for sale of tigers in China was an internal matter. Its apparent change of policy may stem from a desire to appear to be a responsible member of the international community and thereby gain trade advantages and even the Olympic Games.

Conservation and Recovery

In the early 1990s, organizations such as the National Geographic Society and the National Fish and Wildlife Foundation provided funds to help Russia research and preserve its Siberian tigers. In the mid-1990s,

the Russian government provided funding for several teams of park rangers for the forests in which the Siberian tiger lives. Some of these rangers were drawn from the military and operate helicopters as part of their effort to track down poachers. However, overall their equipment is not as good as that used by poachers, making law enforcement difficult. During the 1990s, American cooperation in studying the Siberian tiger has increased, with scientists using sophisticated electronic collars to keep track of tigers in the wild. (These collars offer no protection from poachers, who kill the cats and toss the collars away.) Once among wildlife's most mysterious creatures, the Siberian tigers are beginning to be understood. At one time, almost nothing was known about what they did in warm months when there was no snow on the ground to leave tracks in. The collars help to reveal where the tigers go in relatively warm weather, and on-site research is beginning to reveal the animals' natural history.

Many zoos around the world are cooperating in a vast captive breeding program for Siberian tigers. There are now more Siberian tigers in captivity than in the wild, but as of 1990, these tigers — about 600 — were all descended from a core group of 25, which made their gene pool too small for long-term survival. The poor genetic diversity made them especially susceptible to diseases that seemed not to affect wild tigers. Thus, in the mid-1990s, Siberian tigers in the wild were captured and used to breed with captive Siberian tigers; the resulting offspring have been bred to yet other captive tigers in zoos around the world, increasing the gene pool for captive Siberian tigers and improving the hopes for preserving it in zoos even after it disappears from the wild, which it seems likely to do, although Russia's natural reserves offer some hope that the wild Siberian tigers will survive.

In November 1996 World Wildlife Fund reported that the population of Siberian tigers had risen from 250 animals in 1985 to around 430 animals in 1996, a 72% increase. This improvement was a result of strict poaching enforcement by the Chinese government, and by radio tracking, which provided data for helping animals and discouraging poachers. Still, poaching remains the most serious threat; one tiger was actually killed in a zoo and the poacher was caught (and later executed) for carrying off the carcass.

Chinese Tiger

Panthera tigris amoyensis

Barry Driscoll

Status	Endangered
Listed	June 2, 1970
Family	Felidae (Cats)
Description	Light yellow to reddened yellow coat with widely spaced broad black stripes that are fewer in number than on other tiger subspecies.
Habitat	Temperate forests, frequently on mountainous terrain.
Food	Prefers large prey such as deer and elk.
Reproduction	Gestation lasts about 110 days; litters have 2 to 4 cubs.
Threats	Humans represent its only threat.
Range	China

Description

Studies of tiger skeletons suggest that the Chinese tiger, *Panthera tigris amoyensis,* is the most ancient of the modern subspecies of tiger. The ancestral tiger evolved in northern Siberia, which may explain why even tropical modern tigers retain some adaptations for cold weather and prefer wallowing in cold waters to moving about during the day. About 10,000 years ago, the glaciers of a new ice age forced the ancestral tiger southward into the ranges of modern tigers. The Chinese tiger's lineage likely dates back almost to that time 10,000 years ago and can give modern humans their best idea of what the first tigers were like.

The Chinese tiger's fur is longer than that of other tiger subspecies except for the Siberian tiger. Its black stripes are broad and fewer in number and more widely spaced than on other subspecies. Its undercolor tends to be paler than that found on other tigers, but it has a smaller white area on its underside.

It is a medium sized tiger, midway between the largest tiger, the Siberian (*Panthera tigris altaica*), and the smallest tiger, the Bali (*Panthera tigris balica*). This means that adult males may be over 8 feet from tip of nose to tail, with tails of about 3 feet in length, and they may weigh 600 pounds. As with other tiger subspecies, females tend to be significantly smaller than males, 7 feet in length not including the tail of perhaps 3 feet and weighing 400 pounds.

Behavior

Little is known about the behavior of Chinese tigers either in the wild or in captivity. They probably are territorial, with the adult males establishing territories of about 40 square miles each. Females have smaller territories that fit into the large male territories, so that there may be 3 or 4 female territories to each male territory. It is possible that as with the Bengal tiger the females' territories overlap. The territories, whether male or female, are marked by urine, scent glands, and possibly dung. A male patrols his territory constantly in order to deposit his markers, or else other males may try to expand into it by depositing their own markers. An absence from a given part of a territory of two weeks may result in the loss of that part of the territory.

Females may be receptive at any time of the year. How long estrus lasts is unclear. Females seem eager to mate and can be as aggressive as female Bengal tigers. Foreplay includes the tigers batting one another with their forepaws. The female makes progress by nudging the male to an upright stance; by rubbing her flanks against his, the female may bring the male to full arousal. She then crouches on the ground, he then takes his position and grasps the back of her neck with his teeth. Coitus takes about 15 seconds. As with other tiger subspecies, the female ferociously attacks the male after coitus, usually swiping at him with her claws. In spite of the violent end of coitus, the pair may mate several more times, each time becoming less energetic (this is implied from Bengal mating

behavior; that the Chinese tigers do this seems likely but is not a certainty). Pregnancy lasts about 110 days (some naturalists would place the days closer to 105), typically resulting in 2 cubs, although there have been reports of as many as seven.

The rearing of young is likely to be similar to that of the Bengal and Indochinese (*Panther tigris corbetti*) tigers because of similarities in their habitats. In any case, the details are vague. The cubs are weaned when they are 3 to 6 months old. They reach sexual maturity when between 3 and 4 years old. The almost mature cubs may remain in their mother's territory for a few more years, or they may become "transient" like some Bengal males, meaning that they move from territory until they reach the fringe of the Chinese tiger's range. As they grow larger and stronger, they may eventually carve out territories of their own or take over abandoned ones. It is unclear whether males will fight each other for territories; it is possible that transitions of authority are peaceful, with one tiger yielding to another by moving away. Similarly, it is unclear whether females physically conflict over their territories. There is evidence that female territories may overlap and that females may tolerate one another's company.

Chinese tigers devote much of their waking time to hunting, most of which probably occurs at night. Their hearing is good; their night vision is excellent (superior to that of a human being, possibly as good as that of a domesticated cat). Tigers are built for ambushing their prey. They carefully creep up on their prey and then pounce when their prey wanders within reach. This suggests that the Chinese tiger is an intelligent animal, capable of outwitting its prey. Although a bit boxy in their shapes, the Chinese tigers have the typically powerful hind legs found in other tigers, providing great thrust when they leap at their prey, which has a good chance of being knocked down by the tiger's body blow. Their jaws are very powerful; they lock their teeth onto the neck of their target and probably suffocate it by forcing its windpipe closed. If the Chinese tiger is like other tigers, then it may take days to eat a large animal, and it will eventually consume everything, including the bones. Their preferred prey consists of large animals of 100 pounds or more.

Habitat

The Chinese tiger inhabited temperate and subtropical forests until very recent times. The climate may be cold in winter, especially on the mountains where the few remaining tigers live. The warm months are temperate; in the southern range when the Chinese tiger had its heyday, the weather would be hot and humid. Historically, it seems to have preferred the drier climates of its northern range. In any case, it is likely (but not certain) that it no longer inhabits the tropical forests along the borders of southeast China.

Distribution

The Chinese tiger once ranged in forests in central to eastern and southeastern China. It is now found in stray individual animals scattered in China's Fukien province, southern Szechwan, and the Yangtze River valley. The species was pressed into mostly mountainous areas over thousands of years as humans expanded their populations and turned forests into open farms. Even so, there were thousands of them apparently thriving

in the early 1950s, and their reduced range and numbers are due primarily to humans hunting them.

There may be no more than 40 Chinese tigers alive in the world today. Indeed, the number is likely to be fewer. In the 1950s, the Chinese tiger numbered over 4,000 animals in the wild, a healthy figure given its range and its place at the top of its habitat's food chain.

Threats

In the 1950s, the Chinese government declared tigers pests and urged that they be killed. This policy probably resulted in the extermination of China's Caspian tigers (*Panthera tigris virgata*) in the northwest. Siberian tigers in Manchuria are down to about 20 and are rapidly nearing extermination. The Chinese tiger was relentlessly hunted down and killed by professional hunters and local farmers. Its body parts may have helped to fuel the boom in folk medicines made from tigers that began in the 1960s or 1970s.

Conservation and Recovery

The Chinese government seemed to reverse its longstanding policy when it joined the CITES treaty, which bans the international sale of tigers and tiger parts, and the IUCN (The World Conservation Union), which advocates the preservation of tigers as endangered species. Countries who violate their CITES and IUCN obligations may be subject to international sanctions that may involve banning of purchasing products from or selling products to the offending nation by other members of CITES or IUCN and the imposition of tariffs on some of the offending nations' exports. However, in 1992, China asked for an exemption from the CITES rules, asserting that what it did with tigers in China was an internal matter. This brought China close to having international trade sanctions invoked against it. In 1994, the United States invoked these sanctions against Taiwan, a center for the buying and selling of illegally killed tigers, but China narrowly avoided the sanctions by demonstrating good faith efforts to protect its tigers. How long China will continue to show good faith is uncertain; tigers continue to be dreadfully abused within their territory. The reversal of policy may be part of an effort to appear to be a responsible member of the international community, thereby gaining trade advantages and possibly even the Olympic Games.

In China, the tigers are protected by law, and naturalists from other nations who have been allowed to observe China's efforts to save the Chinese tiger subspecies say that those efforts have been great, even Herculean. But the habits of generations of persecution die hard, and poachers continue to kill Chinese tigers, whose carcasses may fetch poachers tens of thousands of dollars apiece. Sometimes horrifying stories of abuse of the tigers have appeared in China's own press as well as abroad. For instance, in June 1996, animal rights activists complained about a tiger held captive in a nightclub in Shenzhen. When police raided the nightclub, they found a declawed tiger chained in a cage. A sign urged patrons to dance with the tiger, while the animal was poked with an electrified prod to make it move with the beat of the music. This young animal (perhaps three years old) has been placed in a wild animal park. In another report, a zoo in Nanchang had fastened a tiger so that it could not move, next to a table. For about 60 cents, patrons could pose with the immobile animal, even sit on its back, and be photographed.

The Chinese tiger's survival depends on efforts by people throughout the world. Efforts are hampered by China's reluctance to allow foreigners to be involved in what the government considers internal, and therefore national, affairs. On the other hand, the Chinese tiger has not attracted the international interest of people the way the Siberian tiger has. The Siberian tiger is the largest of all cats, which adds to its mystique. On the other hand, the Chinese tiger is an animal of mystery and ancient lineage that could appeal to people if a good publicity campaign on its behalf were waged, especially by the Chinese themselves. Chinese scientists might benefit from infusions of money from abroad the way Russian scientists have. At present, Exxon Corporation is providing money for tiger research, including studies of the Chinese tiger, and it provides a clearinghouse for information on tigers.

The Chinese tigers are now very few in number, and that number may be declining. Some naturalists have given it up for extinct. There do not seem to be enough Chinese tigers in captivity for a successful breeding program, although one probably should be attempted. Still, the Chinese tigers that survive live in rugged, difficult to travel on, terrain, and a concerted effort to preserve and study them could possibly save this valuable natural resource from extinction.

Indochinese Tiger

Panthera tigris corbetti

Alan Shoemaker

Status	Endangered
Listed	June 2, 1970
Family	Felidae (Cats)
Description	Darker yellow coat than other tigers, with short black stripes.
Habitat	Tropical forests.
Food	Prefers large prey.
Reproduction	Gestation lasts about 110 days; litters have 2 to 4 cubs.
Threats	Loss of habitat.
Range	Burma, southeastern China, Malaysia

Description

The Indochinese tiger, *Panthera tigris corbetti,* was only identified as a separate subspecies in 1968 and there is very little information about it from before that date. Because of the warfare that has marred the years since 1968, researchers have had much difficulty in gaining access to its range.

Its coat is distinctive among tigers because of the spots. It has black stripes that point down from its back, and these stripes break apart into spots on its sides. The background of the coat is a darker yellow than what is found on the other subspecies of tiger. Its underside is paler than the rest of its coat. The Indochinese tiger's coloration could be an adaptation to its densely vegetated environ-ment. The stripes would break up its outline when it moved, and the spotting could resemble the dappled patterns on the forest floor, especially when the tiger is at rest.

The Indochinese tiger is a medium-sized subspecies, close to the dimensions of the Chinese tiger (*Panthera tigris amoyensis*). Males are about 6 to 7 feet long not counting the tail, with a 3 to 3.5 foot long tail. Females are slightly smaller, being 5 to 6 feet long, with a tail of about 3 feet. Males weigh about 550 pounds, with females weighing perhaps 300 pounds. Not enough examples of the Indochinese tiger have been studied to create a picture of the extremes in its size, large and small.

The Indochinese tiger is also known as Corbett's tiger.

Behavior

The Indochinese tiger's behavior patterns are at present mysterious. It seems to be territorial, with males and females following the typical territorial pattern of other tigers: The males have relatively large territories and the females have smaller ones, probably within male territories. The size of the territories is open to speculation, but males may utilize up to 40 square miles.

Swimming seems to be a favorite pastime of Indochinese tigers, and they prefer to be near water, although they can be found in relatively dry mountainous areas. When they make a kill, they tend to drag it near water and will break off feeding for frequent drinks, much as Bengal tigers (*Panthera tigris tigris*) do. Hunting is done in the typical tiger manner: stalking, creeping near the prey, waiting in hiding, then ambushing the quarry. A powerful bite to the neck suffocates the prey by closing its windpipe. Indochinese tigers are known to hunt large animals such as deer, wild pigs, and tapirs. Whether or not it takes advantage of its habitat's numerous small game is not clear, but it likely follows the pattern of the Siberian tiger (*Panther tigris altaica*) and only eats small animals when it cannot find big ones. A tiger may eat a large kill over several days; when it leaves its not-yet-consumed prey, it covers it with leaves and debris. When finished, it will have eaten everything, even the bones. It does not seem to hunt domesticated animals, but this could change if human communities encroach on its present range.

Mating patterns for the Indochinese tiger are uncertain, but likely resemble those of the other tropical tigers. This would involve a courtship that could last weeks, as with Bengal tigers, aggressiveness on the part of the female when she is ready to mate, and vigorous but short coitus (about 30 seconds), after which the female would take a powerful swipe at her partner, which he must dodge or be significantly hurt. The pair may mate several more times during the day. The gestation period is about 105 days, resulting in the birth of 2 to 4 cubs. They would be weaned in 3 to 6 months and become sexually mature in 3 to 4 years. Young probably remain with their mothers, although whether they would travel with her on her hunts is not known.

Habitat

The Indochinese tiger inhabits temperate to hot and wet tropical forests, from southeastern China, through central and western Indochina to the southern end of the Malay Peninsula. Its northern range is less densely forested than its southern range; its diet varies with the game available in a given area.

Distribution

The Indochinese tiger's traditional range is hard to determine because it was only identified in 1968. The range likely encompassed all of Indochina except for the southern reaches of Vietnam. The Indochinese tiger likely competed with the Chinese tiger for territory in southeastern China. At present, it still has a large portion of its range intact. Absent from Laos and Vietnam because of human hunters, it still may be found in far southeastern China, through Burma and Thailand, and into Malaysia, where significant portions of its range are legally protected.

Experts in tigers differ greatly over the

Indochinese tiger's numbers. Some say that the Indochinese tiger is near extinction, but the tiger's status in Malaysia and Thailand seems to belie this. One estimate places its numbers at about 1,500, which is good enough for a stable breeding population. It is probable that no Indochinese tigers inhabit Cambodia, Laos, or Vietnam, although there may have been three individual Indochinese tigers in west-central Vietnam in the 1980s.

Threats

Hunting remains the greatest threat to the survival of the Indochinese tiger. Burma does not protect the Indochinese tiger and does not allow outsiders to check on its status. Cambodia may have a hundred or so tigers left, but they are being hunted to extinction. Indochinese tigers may still inhabit southeastern China, but that nation's decades-long persecution of tigers has probably left its numbers very small, perhaps less than a dozen.

Conservation and Recovery

The Indochinese tiger is doing better in Malaysia and Thailand than elsewhere. Malaysia has an extensive system of natural reserves, but it has significant problems with the poaching that threatens all subspecies of tigers with extinction. Thailand's wilderness areas seem to have hundreds of Indochinese tigers living in them, but poaching is a problem. Thailand has not committed enough resources, particularly in personnel, to maintain its wild reserves. Expanding human settlements also are shrinking the tiger's range in Thailand.

Because of pressure brought by conservation organizations during the renewal of the country's Most Favored Nations status, China has shown signs of taking conservation of tigers seriously since 1996.

American zoos have made the Indochinese tiger a special project and are receiving cooperation from Malaysia and Thailand in an effort to create a good breeding program designed to maintain the populations in those countries' reserves. The American Zoo and Aquarium Association is trying to gather 75 to 80 Indochinese tigers and breed them, with an eye to preserving the subspecies should it be hunted to extinction in the wild and to assisting breeding programs in Malaysia and Thailand.

Javan Tiger

Panthera [=Neofelis] tigris sondaica

WWF/Helmut Diller

Status	Endangered (Probably extinct)
Listed	June 2, 1970
Family	Felidae (Cats)
Description	Second-smallest tiger with fewer markings on its forelegs.
Habitat	Tropical rain forests.
Food	Prefers large prey such as deer and wild pigs.
Reproduction	2 to 4 cubs after gestation of about 105 days.
Threats	Loss of habitat and poaching.
Range	Indonesia (Java)

Description

The Javan tiger, *Panthera tigris sondaica*, is either the smallest or second smallest of the tiger subspecies. (The extinct Bali tiger may have been smaller.) Adults are about 5 feet in length with 2 to 2.5 foot tails. They stand about 2.5 to 3 feet at the shoulder. Males weigh about 400 pounds, and females weigh 250 to 300 pounds.

It has the longest cheek whiskers of all tigers. Another distinguishing trait is its small mane across the back of its neck. Its undercoat is dark cinnamon, and its sharply delineated, closely packed stripes are a deep black. Its forelegs have few markings.

Behavior

The Javan tiger is a solitary animal that lives most of its life apart from others of its kind, except for mating or rearing young. They may be territorial, the way Bengal tigers (*Panthera tigris tigris*) are, but with its habitat reduced severely, there is no way to really determine this by observation because there is not sufficient room for a tiger to have and maintain an exclusive territory. If the Javan tiger survives as more than one animal, they are likely forced together in what would be for them an unnatural manner. Other subspecies of tiger, when crammed together in zoos, seem tolerant of one another, with few violent clashes; thus, it is possible that Javan tigers survive together in a small area.

Its mating practices are largely unknown. It probably would be able to mate year round like other subspecies of tiger except for the Siberian (*Panthera tigris altaica*). Whether males would fight for the right to mate with a female in estrus is open to conjecture. More likely would be the long courtship pattern of the Bengal tiger, with the female taking an active role in selecting a mate. Coitus would be quick and violent and would probably take place several times during the day. Pregnancy would last approximately 105 days and result in the birth of 2 to 4 cubs. The cubs would be weaned at between 3 and 6 months, and they would be sexually mature in 3 to 4 years.

The Javan tiger is almost certainly a nocturnal hunter. Researchers have noted that some groups of tigers that are diurnal in activity become nocturnal when human beings are around; this change in individual behavior has been similarly noted in some other species of cat, such as servals (*Felis serval*). With humans almost everywhere on Java, nocturnal hunting would be the Javan tiger's best hope for survival. Further, the cats have been seen on the move at night in watery areas. The Javan tiger favors areas with a high density of water, and spends much of its time swimming. It is a very good swimmer, and has been observed swimming in the ocean.

As a solitary hunter, the Javan tiger very likely follows the stalk-and-ambush techniques of other tigers. It would hear or smell potential prey, follow it slowly, creep up near it, and then leap upon it from cover, latch its jaws on the quarry's neck, and then crush the neck.

Habitat

This species inhabits rain forests, of which little remains on Java.

Distribution

The Javan tiger occurs in the forests of Java. If it survives, it could only be in five small wildlife reserves. To venture into the open lands created by human habitation would almost certainly mean extinction.

Threats

The Javan tiger has fallen victim to expanding human populations, poor planning, and poachers. As its forest habitat has been destroyed by logging, expanding communities, and agriculture, it has been forced into small reserves to sustain it.

Conservation and Recovery

Although Indonesia has in the 1990s begun to establish good, scientific programs for the study and protection of its wildlife, it all probably comes too late for the Javan tiger. Most naturalists agree that the Javan tiger is extinct, although there is much disagreement about when this would have happened. Some sources say that the last Javan tiger was seen in 1972. Yet, researcher John Seidensticker saw the spore of five tigers in the Meru Betiri Reservation in 1976. Still other naturalists say that the tiger survived well into the 1980s. There are still reports of sightings of Javan tigers in particularly difficult to access corners of Java, so a few may have managed to survive by staying well away from humans. Another trait of the tiger may also mean that a few survive: the Javan tiger was known to swim in the ocean, and a few may have migrated to other islands. Plainly, the hope that Javan tigers survive is very small; most naturalists believe the last of the Javan tigers were killed by poachers. None survive in captivity.

Sumatran Tiger

Panthera [=Neofelis] tigris sumatrae

Dick George, Phoenix Zoo

Status	Endangered
Listed	June 2, 1970
Family	Felidae (Cats)
Description	Long, broad, full black stripes, and its base coloring is dark reddened orange.
Habitat	Tropical forest and swampy areas.
Food	It prefers large prey such as deer and wild pigs.
Reproduction	Gestation lasts about 105 days; litters have 2 to 4 cubs.
Threats	Loss of habitat to logging, to agriculture, and to expanding human communities; poaching.
Range	Indonesia (Sumatra)

Description

The Sumatran tiger, *Panthera tigris sumatrae*, is one of the smaller tiger subspecies. Adult males are larger than adult females. The full-grown male Sumatran tiger is between 5.5 and 7 feet long from tip of nose to tail, with the tail adding another 3 feet. The male weighs between 450 and 550 pounds. An adult female is about 5 feet long from tip of nose to tail, with the tail adding another 2.5 to 3 feet. She weighs 300 to 350 pounds.

The whiskers of the Sumatran tiger are long. Its head is blocky; in profile it lacks the slanted nose and forehead of the other subspecies and instead has a boxlike angle where its nose meets its forehead. Its coloration is dark. The color of its base coat varies from a dark reddened yellow to a dark reddened orange. The stripes are black, packed close together, and long. Its fur is short and smooth, but not glossy.

Behavior

The Sumatran tigers have only recently become the subject of careful scientific observation, so much of their behavior is presently a mystery. They are territorial, with males having larger territories than females, and with the females' territories occurring inside male territories and overlapping one another. The tigers mark their territories with urine and scent glands, as well as with dung.

Mating may occur year round. The loud roars of the tigers may sometimes signal female receptiveness for mating. A female's scent markings will also indicate to a male whether she is in estrus. Males will fight determinedly for the right to mate with an available female, and they can seriously injure one another. Females seem to be able to choose which males to mate with, somewhat the way Bengal tiger females do. Coitus is brief (about 30 seconds) and vigorous, but the animals may mate several times in one day. The resulting cubs will be 2 to 4 in number and will remain with their mother for 2 to 3 years.

Sumatran tigers seem to prefer to hunt at night, carefully creeping up on their prey and then pouncing. As with other subspecies of tigers, they prefer large animals such as deer and antelope. When they pounce they try to bite their quarry's neck; their jaws are very powerful, so that when they latch on to the prey they seldom let go. The bite closes off the prey's windpipe, suffocating it.

Habitat

The Sumatran tiger inhabits tropical forests, usually near water. It is a very good swimmer and cools itself during the day and pursues prey across water when hunting. Much of the Sumatran tiger's old range has been destroyed by clear-cutting logging; often what is left is unsuitable for agriculture and

Indonesia has tried to regrow the forests on such land, but without success. The forests do not reclaim territory lost to logging. Grasses replace the trees, but the Sumatran tiger finds open grasslands to be unsuitable habitat and tries to remain within tree cover.

Distribution

In ancient times, the Sumatran tiger may have roamed almost all of Sumatra. Humans pushed the tigers out of some areas with their settlements and farms. In the last two decades, logging has eliminated most of the tiger's habitat, leaving it in northern Sumatra and southwestern Sumatra, mostly in parks and reserves, although as many as 100 may still be found in unprotected regions.

Experts on tigers disagree markedly about how many Sumatran tigers presently exist in the wild. Attempts to count them have not been particularly successful, perhaps because the tiger does not like the company of humans and is able to use waterways and underbrush to elude humans. The Indonesian Department of Forest Protection estimates that about 400 Sumatran tigers exist in the wild, which would be down from the 1,000 Sumatran tigers reported in 1978.

Threats

Loss of habitat is the greatest threat to the well being of the Sumatran tiger, and there is probably no longer enough forest to support numbers greater than 800. Poaching is also a significant problem. All subspecies of the tiger are under pressure from hunters who sell the cats for use in folk medicines in China and Taiwan.

Conservation and Recovery

Indonesia's Ministry of Forestry has established a Sumatran tiger studbook, which is used to keep track of the Sumatran tigers in captivity and their lineage. The Sumatran tigers in captivity, about 240, are descended from 37 animals. Zoos throughout the world are cooperating with Indonesia and are participating in efforts to properly breed them. Indonesia has also created the "Indonesia Sumatran Tiger Masterplan," which outlines courses of action for preserving the animal both in captivity and in the wild and for increasing the tiger's gene pool, which with inbreeding could lose its diversity. Indonesia plans to preserve the Sumatran tiger in two wildlife reserves and five national parks on the island of Sumatra. Naturalists familiar with the international efforts to preserve the Sumatran tiger are impressed with Indonesia's aggressive approach to preserving the subspecies and hope that the Indonesian plan not only succeeds in maintaining a healthy Sumatran tiger population but becomes a model for the preservation of other endangered animals.

Bengal Tiger

Panthera tigris tigris

Panthera tigris   Bruce Bunting

Status	Endangered
Listed	June 2, 1970
Family	Felidae (Cats)
Description	Yellow-orange coat with black stripes; the underside from neck to hind legs is pale, sometimes white.
Habitat	Temperate to tropical forests; tolerates cold climate.
Food	Prefers large prey.
Reproduction	2 to 4 kittens after gestation of about 105 days;
Threats	Deforestation; poaching.
Range	Bangladesh, Burma, India, Nepal

Description

The Bengal tiger, *Panthera tigris tigris*, is only slightly smaller than the Siberian tiger. Adults average about 8 feet 10 inches in length, weighing as much as 550 pounds for males and 300 pounds for females. Their tails are about 3.5 feet long. Although there have been reports of Bengal tigers 12 feet long and weighing half a ton, scientific evidence does not support such claims. Before India's independence tigers were hunted as menaces to the human population and for sport. Sport hunting often involved British overlords and rajahs. Riding atop the backs of elephants, they would shoot tigers that were driven toward them by hundreds of men on foot, beating the bushes. When the trapped tiger was finally killed, it would be measured. Sometimes the measurer would painstakingly trace measuring tape along all the curves of the tiger's body. Further, measuring tapes and sticks for tigers killed by aristocrats often only had 10 or 11 inches in a foot. This would make the measurements of the tigers much longer than they actually were. Besides, tigers killed by more than one aristocrat during a hunt would have to vary in size according to the importance of the hunters who shot them; for instance a British governor's would have to be larger than that of a rajah, and the measurements had to be altered accordingly. All this means is that all recent, much more scientific measurements place the Bengal tiger as the second largest subspecies of tiger, after the Siberian tiger. It is possible that the Bengal tiger population once had larger members and that merciless hunting has eliminated their genes from the gene pool, but this is only speculation.

The Bengal tiger is what people usually visualize when they here the word *tiger*. It has a large head and large paws. Its fur is orangish and features sharp black stripes. Its hair is relatively short; its whiskers bristle and droop.

The Bengal tiger is also known as the Indian tiger, royal tiger, and the royal Bengal tiger.

Behavior

When people visualize the Bengal tiger, they often imagine a fearsome, ferocious beast, and for once a stereotype has truth in it. The Bengal tiger is a patient, careful, solitary hunter that uses the cover of its forest domain to creep up on its prey. When the prey approaches, the tiger leaps for its neck and with a powerful bite, breaks the neck or crushes the windpipe, suffocating the quarry. Some Bengal tigers are known to hunt human beings in this manner. One should note that the tigers avoid the company of humans and try to stay far away from them. The problem of man-hunting tigers may arise when human populations press in on tiger habitats and the tigers are unable to move away. One study of tigers in Bangladesh indicated that two thirds of the animals avoided human beings, but that one third was taught by its mothers how to hunt human beings. The threat to human life should not be exaggerated; there are few tigers and nearly all of them want nothing to do with humanity. On the other hand, one of the problems in preserving the Bengal tiger subspecies in particular is that it and humans are incompatible and cannot share the same territory. Take away a tiger's habitat and its natural prey and the tiger is left to starve or to hunt human livestock or humans themselves. This is a problem the Indian government in particular has long sought to address by separating the habitats of people and tigers, but a huge and growing population has made some conflict between tiger and humans inevitable.

The Bengal tigers are territorial animals, but are unusually so. Even though animal territories usually mean conflicts and even physical battles between intruder and territory holder, the Bengal tigers are tolerant of the presence of one another in close proximity. Some males wander from territory to territory, sometimes taking one over, but usually moving after a few weeks or even months, without the resident male putting up a fuss. Although solitary animals, Bengal tigers have been observed in loose groups, usually by much-coveted cold water rivers or lakes, not socializing with each other, but accepting of each other's presence. Conflicts often seem to be resolved in mysterious ways. A resident territory holder may be persuaded to give up its territory without visible signs of confrontation. It just leaves. It is possible that smaller Bengal tigers instinctively yield to larger ones.

An adult tiger of any subspecies, male or female, marks out a large territory for itself. A male may have a territory of several square miles. He will probably mark this territory with urine and scent glands, as well as with dung. Females have smaller territories which may overlap as territories for some of the other subspecies do. One male's huge territory encompasses the territories of several females.

Bengal tigers love water, and the choicest territories tend to have large streams and ponds. They are excellent swimmers and may spend an entire hot day immersed in cool water. They leave the water to hunt at night.

Mating may take place at any time of the year. Bengal tigers seem to court one another, with the female often taking the lead. The pair may associate with one another for months before the female is in estrus. Once in estrus, she arouses the male by rubbing his flanks with her head. Mating is a noisy affair, with load roars, growls, and grunts. The male will bite along the female's neck. The sexual act lasts only 30 seconds, after which the female turns and swings a forepaw, claws extended, at her mate. If she hits him, which she sometimes does, he can be badly scratched. A tiger pair mate many times during a day, although the acts become less energetic. The resulting cubs will remain with their mother, traveling with her once their eyes open. They are weaned at about 6 months of age and will reach sexual maturity at about 4 years of age. The young leave their mother's territory at between 2 and 3 years of age.

Habitat

The Bengal tiger inhabits forests with a wide variety of trees and fauna. In the northern part of its range, the climate can be very cold. In the southern part of its range, the climate can be very wet and rainy, as well as very hot. Bengal tigers seem to like cool water, suggesting their ancestry was a cat that evolved (as most naturalists believe) in a colder climate, to the north. Tigers may have first entered India only as recently as 10,000 years ago.

Distribution

The Bengal tiger once ranged from Nepal, throughout India, and into southeast Asia. For thousands of years, large, very dense forests protected most of them from human beings, and for much of that time, human beings tried to stay away from them. The enormous expansion of human populations in the tiger's traditional range over the last few centuries pushed it out of much of its ancient territory. Loss of habitat must have begun shrinking its numbers significantly in the nineteenth century. As human populations moved into formerly wild territory, tigers became more accessible and they became subject to harvesting for a vast folk-medicine industry, which in the late twentieth century exploded in size. Further, the tigers became subjects for sport hunting, in which hundreds would be killed in a single expedition. All this has resulted in the Bengal tigers retreating to several preserves in Bangladesh, India, and Nepal.

Threats

With no more than 4,000 individuals remaining in the wild, the Bengal tiger is threatened by poachers, and a severe natural event such as a forest fire or flood, could wipe out the animal. Even so, of all the tiger subspecies, the Bengal tiger has the best hope for survival.

The forces working toward the Bengal tiger's extinction are formidable. The tigers need forests for their habitats; they only move into clearings when forced to or when in pursuit of prey. Logging has deforested much of its past range. Forests have also made way for agriculture. The human population in the

Bengal tiger's range has exploded; it shares its range with about a billion people. As the last of the old forests are harvested, the hopes for the Bengal tiger's survival die.

Hunting is another great problem for Bengal tigers. People fear them because they kills some humans every year when they become desperate for food. In addition, all subspecies of the tiger are under pressure from hunters who sell the cats for use in folk medicines in China, India (where the fat in particular is prized), Korea, and Taiwan. Their parts are used in concoctions that are believed to act as powerful aphrodisiacs and to ease or cure a wide variety of ailments. The demand for the tiger products exploded in the 1970s, and the demand now far outstrips the number of tigers available. Thus, makers of the folk medicines have begun to using substitutes in their products and passing them off as having been made from tiger parts.

Conservation and Recovery

India has had some notable success in alleviating the pressures on its native tigers. It has established preserves that are well managed and protected. In general, the best preserves are located well away from human habitations. When humans live nearby, confrontations inevitably arise, but India has done a good job of educating its citizens about the tiger and its plight.

The trade in tiger parts is outlawed by international treaties and laws in Bangladesh, India, and Nepal (Burma is uncooperative). The international community has thus far imposed sanctions only on Taiwan for violating the CITES prohibition on trading in tigers and their parts, although China has come very close to having sanctions imposed on it.

In India, the tigers are being treated as valuable natural resources, and local peoples are seeing economic benefits from the tiger preserves, from tourists and from tax money spent in their regions to maintain the preserves. Of the subspecies of tiger, the Bengal is the only one to actually increase its numbers significantly over the last twenty years. Once fewer than a thousand, they have grown to perhaps four thousand in number. The exact figure is in dispute, with many conservationists insisting that the Indian government is inflating the figures.

Beyond government efforts, the Bengal tiger has benefitted from millions of dollars in private spending to study and preserve them. India itself has several well-financed charitable trusts dedicated to the scientific study and preservation of the Bengal tiger in the wild. Americans have contributed much to the effort to save the Bengal tiger, with organizations ranging from charitable foundations to big corporations (most notably Exxon) contributing money, researchers, and publicity.

Many zoos around the world are cooperating in a vast captive breeding program for tigers. In particular, the American Zoo and Aquarium Association has pooled information on captive tigers and is organizing their keeping and breeding in an effort to keep various subspecies alive and distinct from one another. Bengal tigers figure heavily in their plans, and are being carefully bred in captivity. A significant danger in captive breeding is that the gene pool will be too small and the animals will become inbred and susceptible to even minor diseases. The breeding program is designed to overcome this danger by carefully tracking mates and their progeny, so that the widest possible gene pool is retained. Another, perhaps intractable, problem is that captive-bred animals may lose their wild behavior. For instance, Bengal tiger females are known to teach their young how to hunt. Animals bred in captivity may go untaught and the behavior learned over many generations of tigers would be lost.

Caspian [=Turanian] Tiger

Panthera tigris virgata

Status	Endangered (Probably extinct)
Listed	June 2, 1970
Family	Felidae (Cats)
Description	Close dark brown stripes.
Habitat	High forests
Food	Prefers prey over 100 pounds such as deer and water buffalo.
Reproduction	2 to 6 cubs after gestation of about 105 days;.
Threats	Loss of habitat; hunting.
Range	Afghanistan, China, Iran, Russia, Turkey, Mongolia

WWF/Helmut Diller

Description

The Caspian tiger's, *Panthera tigris virgata*, coat's base is light yellow to reddish yellow, like that of Bengal tigers (*P. t. tigris*; see separate entry), with dark brown stripes. Its stripes are longer and narrower than those of Bengal tigers, and the stripes are packed close together. It has warm and cold weather coats, with the cold weather coat featuring hair of 1.2 inches along its back. It has a slight mane on its neck and has long whiskers.

It is medium-sized tiger; adults are 6 to 8 feet in length from tip of nose to tail, with tails adding about 3 feet. They stand about 3 feet high at the shoulder. Adult males weigh about 500 pounds, with females being smaller at about 400 pounds. It has a long-legged, narrow build.

Behavior

The Caspian tiger lives (or lived) in an area of the world that has been inhospitable to peaceful scientific study for decades. Thus, knowledge of the Caspian tiger's behavior in the wild is sketchy. It was territorial, with males having large territories of perhaps 60 square miles. Females had smaller territories within male territories.

The Caspian tiger is an opportunistic hunter, and stories of its hunting humans are likely to be true, although typical of other tigers, it avoided humans as much as it could. Its prey would be the large animals of its region and large domesticated animals where farmlands bordered on its range.

Habitat

Although its ancient range would have had varied habitats from cold desert steepes, to snowy coniferous forests, to dry, hot mountains, to dry deciduous forests, it survived into modern times mostly in high mountains and plateaus in central Asia, in wooded areas not frequented by human beings.

Distribution

The Caspian tiger once roamed a vast region in central Asia. In recent times, its range included northwestern China, southern Russia, northern Iran, Afghanistan, and eastern Turkey, stretching from Turkey into Mongolia. There is little hope of its now inhabiting any of its former range.

The last Caspian tiger was killed in 1933 and one was captured in 1947. Since 1953 there have been no reported sightings.

Threats

In Turkmenia, the tiger's decline was caused both by hunting and by clearing the dense vegetation for cotton farming. Burning the thickets forced the tiger to abandon the region. In northern Iran hunting and forest destruction were also the reasons for the tiger's decline.

Conservation and Recovery

Before the overthrow of the shah's regime, the Iranian government tried to protect the wildlife in Iran's north, and there were a few indications that the Caspian tiger survived in that region at that time. It is almost certainly eradicated from Iran and Russia, today. Poaching and the war between the former Soviet Union and the Afghan rebels probably resulted in the end of hopes for the Caspian tiger's survival.

Although zoos around the world have had specimens of the Caspian tiger, they were not well-cared for or were interbred with other subspecies of tiger. A few breeders hope that through careful breeding of the descendants of the original captive Caspian tigers the gene pool for the animal can be recovered. This is likely a hopeless effort; the wild animal with all its thousands of years of acquired behaviors cannot be recovered in this way. There is only the faintest of hopes that the Caspian tiger survives somewhere, and nearly all experts on tigers agree that the Caspian tiger is extinct.

Snow Leopard

Panthera uncia

Bruce Bunting

Status	Endangered
Listed	March 30, 1972
Family	Felidae (Cats)
Description	Slightly smaller than the common leopard, weighing from 55 to 165 pounds; general coat is colored a pale charcoal to creamy smoke-gray above and white below, with solid black spots on the head, neck, and lower limbs; the black ears have a central white spot.
Habitat	Rocky slopes.
Food	Wild goat, deer, gazelle, boar, small mammals, birds; domestic animals.
Reproduction	Females bear two or three cubs after a gestation period of approximately 99 days.
Threats	Trapped for pelts; hunted to protect livestock.
Range	Mongolia, India, Bhutan, Afghanistan, Kazakhstan, Tadzhikistan, and Nepal.

Description

The snow leopard, *Panthera uncia*, is slightly smaller than the common leopard, weighing from 55 to 165 pounds. Head and body length is 39 to 51 inches, with the tail almost equal in length, 31 to 39 inches. This animal has one of the most beautiful coats of all the great cats, especially in winter. The general color is a pale charcoal to creamy smoke-gray above and white below. It has solid black spots on the head, neck, and lower limbs and rosettes on the back, sides, and tail. The black ears have a central white spot. In winter, the fur is unusually long with blurred rosettes, especially on the lower parts. The underfur is thick and woolly. In summer, the fur is shorter and the rosette pattern more distinct.

The snow leopard's short muzzle has the effect of making the head appear disproportionately small. The long, bushy tail is used by the animal as a counterbalance when jumping. The snow leopard also wraps the tail around its body for warmth during the cold mountain weather. For jumping in the mountains, the animal has relatively long hind legs compared to the forelimbs and, according to reports, can make leaps of up to 40 feet.

Behavior

The snow leopard, unlike other great cats, does not roar. The loudest noise it makes is a long drawn out moaning call during mating. Grunting, meowing, and moaning sounds are also made by this large cat during various social and sexual contacts.

Snow leopards live in overlapping home ranges, with areas shared by individual cats of both the same and different sexes. Generally these cats stay apart; although pairs may share a range. In Nepal, a study estimated that the home ranges of 5 individual cats averaged approximately 7 to 24 square miles in area.

Females normally bear two or three cubs after a gestation period of approximately 99 days, usually from April to June or July. Newborns open their eyes after seven days. Their coat is thick and woolly and more intensely colored than adults, with black bands on the hind portion of the back. The cubs usually stay in an inaccessible, small cave or rock crevice lined with the mother's fur. When the cubs are about three months of age, the mother teaches them to hunt. The cubs remain with the mother throughout the following winter, until the birth of the next litter.

Snow leopards prey on bhural (blue sheep), wild goat, deer, gazelle, boar, serow, goral, takin, and other small mammals and birds. They also sometimes prey on domestic animals and have even been known to attack cattle in their pens. In one instance, the animal reportedly killed and ate a two year old bear. However, snow leopards are not as aggressive as some large cats and rarely attack humans. Based on information from zoos, they eat about 4 to 7 pounds of meat per day.

When hunting, these large cats sometimes stalk their prey and then make a sudden rush to pull down their quarry, and other times they wait in ambush beside a game trail and use their great leaping ability to spring upon a passing animal.

As observed in zoos, the snow leopard is active at night and early in the morning, with only short periods of activity during the day. In the wild, the snow leopard has been observed mainly at dusk and at night, with occasional observations during the day.

Habitat

Snow leopards live in the rocky slopes of the central Asian mountains. During the summer months, they can be found at elevations between 8,900 and 19,700 feet. These large cats stay in the high alpine meadows and rocky areas, just below snowline, where their prey can be found. During the winter, they follow their prey down to the lower valleys to an elevation of approximately 5,900 feet. However, this is not a set pattern because sometimes, depending upon location and prey, snow leopards may stay all year at low elevations, or reportedly they may stay permanently at higher altitudes.

Distribution

The snow leopard inhabits the highland steppes of Central Asia. These animals have been found in the mountainous regions of Afghanistan, Kazakhstan, Tadzhikistan, India, Nepal, Bhutan, the Tibetan Plateau, China, and Mongolia. Reports of the animal in central and northeastern China and Sakhalin are dubious. Confusion with long-haired leopards may account for records from central China, the Amur region, and the Persian mountains.

Threats

The snow leopard has been ruthlessly hunted for its long, beautiful fur. This animal is generally trapped in winter when it comes down to lower elevations where it is easier to catch. Sport hunting also threatens the snow leopard. Predominantly pastoral countries such as Mongolia have encouraged hunting to protect their livestock from the large predator. The animal continues to be hunted in China even though it is officially protected there. Additionally, prey species have dwindled because of human population pressures, further decreasing snow leopard populations for lack of food.

Conservation and Recovery

Reserves have been set aside for this rare animal in Kazakhstan, India, and other countries. However, poaching may still continue in these areas because of inadequate supervision. In the wild, a total of 3,000 to 10,000 individuals have been estimated to exist. As another recovery measure, the snow leopard is currently being bred in captivity, where about 378 individuals are held. The snow leopard was listed in CITES, Appendix I: Trade Prohibited as of July 1, 1975. In the *IUCN Red Data Book,* the snow leopard is listed as endangered as of 1978.

Dogs, Foxes, and Wolves
Family: Canidae

Dhole (*Cuon alpinus*)

Ron Garrison, San Diego Zoo

General Characteristics of the *Canidae*

There are 35 species of *Canidae* divided into 10 subfamilies: the *Canis* subfamily includes the gray and red wolf, coyote, dingo, domestic dogs and jackals; the *Vulpes* subfamily includes all the vulpine foxes; and the *Dusicyon* subfamily includes the African wild dog, dhole, and maned wolf. The *Canidae* species' original habitat was open grasslands, and their speed, agility, and tooth structure evolved as hunters in this terrain. The smallest species of the wild *Canidae* is the fenne fox, which weighs only one pound; the largest is the gray wolf, which can weigh 175 pounds. The Canids proved to be highly adaptable to habitat and food sources, and ranged out to almost every habitat type. Depending on their diet, canids are either highly social, living and hunting in packs, such as the African wild dog, or solitary, such as some wolf species.

Once the most widespread mammal in the world, only two species of wolves survive today: the gray wolf and the red wolf. Persecuted by humans in the early to mid-1900s, most wolf species became extinct, often as a result of government-sponsored eradication programs. Even the red wolf is believed to be extinct in the wild. (See the *Beacham's Guide to Extinct Species of Modern Times, Vol. I* for data on extinct wolves).

Wolves are able to subdue prey up to 10 times their size, and the size of a species is generally related to the size of prey in its habitat. The smallest and lightest colored of wolf species are found in semi-desert regions; forest-dwelling wolves are larger because the prey is larger; and the largest wolves occur in the tundra where they prey on such large animals as caribou and moose.

African wild dogs have a short, powerful muzzle and exceptionally sharp teeth ideally suited for scavenging meat close to the bone that might be abandoned by the original predator. The typical pack size is 7 to 8 individuals but may vary from 2 to 20 adults plus another 10 pups. The home range of the African wild dog is large, up to 600 square miles, and the pack can cover up to 30 miles a day. The home range of packs overlap. If two packs encounter each other, the smaller pack relinquishes the territory. Packs hunt at least once a day, in the cool hours around dusk and dawn. The pack can successfully attack large prey, such as gazelles, impalas, and greater kudu, that may weigh up to 600 pounds, but the African wild dog also preys on mammals as small as 10 pounds. When attacking much larger prey, several pack members attach themselves to various body parts, such as the tail and lips, while the rest of the pack dismembers the underbelly. All members of the hunting party share the kill, and pups are allowed to eat first.

All males remain with their natal pack throughout their lifetime. Young females leave their natal pack with their sister littermates to seek another pack with non-related males. When they reach sexual maturity at 14 to 30 months, the females become aggressive as they compete for mating rights. Males, which outnumber females by 20%, protect and nurture the young, and the females compete with each other for the parenting help of the males.

Wild dogs have become endangered because of persecution by humans and by diseases, such as distemper, that can quickly spread through a pack.

The dhole has also been persecuted by humans because it is such a vicious killer. The pack will dismember its prey, as large as a deer, in seconds after the kill. Individuals eat very fast in order to gain their fill before another pack member can take it away. They consume the vital organs and any fetuses first. They are also able to scavenge food from leopards and tigers even as the big cats are feeding on their own kill. They can also move in on a kill made by a human and destroy the meat before the hunter can retrieve it. Very resourceful and brave, dholes have become endangered because of habitat destruction and by eradication programs.

The maned wolf is not a true wolf, and more closely resembles a red fox than a wolf. It has long legs and a slight body compared to the wolf's compact, powerful body and legs. Maned wolves prey on smaller animals, such as rabbits, rodents, armadillos and birds, and will occasionally eat fish, insects and reptiles. Fruits, in season, comprise about half the diet. Maned wolves also attack livestock the size of a lamb. Individuals forage alone, usually at night, and they capture prey by pouncing on it.

The maned wolf is considered endangered throughout its range, especially in Brazil. The species is captured for sale to zoos and is killed by farmers protecting livestock. They are also killed for their body parts which are said to be medicinal or bring good luck. However, disease is the primary killer of maned wolves. They are susceptible to the parvo virus, the giant kidney worm infestation, and to cystinuria, an inherited metabolic disease.

Simien Fox

Canis simensis

W. Erikson

Status	Endangered
Listed	March 30, 1972
Family	Canidae (Canine)
Description	Resembles a dog with a wolf-like head; ears are straight and pointed; coat is generally reddish with pale yellowish-brown underfur; the chin, insides of the ears, chest, and stomach are white.
Habitat	Montane grassland.
Food	Mainly diurnal rodents; may hunt hares.
Reproduction	Births occur in May or June.
Threats	Hunted for fur; increase in cultivated lands.
Range	Ethiopia

Description

The Simien fox, *Canis simensis*, looks like a dog with a wolf-like head. The long, pointed muzzle and teeth, particularly the last upper premolars, are especially wolf-like. The ears are straight and pointed. The Simien fox's head and body measure 39 inches and the tail measures about 10 inches. The animal stands approximately 23 inches at the shoulder. The Simien fox has long legs, especially the rear ones.

The beautiful coat is generally reddish with pale yellowish-brown underfur. The chin, insides of the ears, chest, and stomach are white. There is also a distinctive white band around the lower part of the neck. The thickly furred tail is reddish colored close to the body.

Canis simensis has sometimes been placed in the separate genus or subgenus, *Simenia*. Two distinct subspecies of *C. simensis* are recognized: *C. s. simensis* and *C. s. citernii*. Other common names for the Simien fox are the Simien jackal and the Abyssinian fox.

Behavior

In general, Simien foxes hunt singly or in pairs; although small packs of up to 7 members may come together at dusk or dawn. It is not known whether or not these animals are territorial, but urine markings are frequent and some animals avoid others. The species has a tendency to wander over relatively large areas. To communicate, they have two types of vocalizations: a sharp "weeah-weeah" used as a call; and a disconcerting series of short barks used for alarm or aggression. While pairs appear to form in January, births do not occur until May or June.

Unlike the more varied diet of other carnivores, Simien foxes mainly eat diurnal rodents, especially *Tachyoryctes* and *Otymys*. Sometimes they may hunt hares or, rarely, they may prey upon ovines or small ungulates.

Simien foxes hunt mainly during the day when their prey is active by meandering through areas with large populations of rodents, checking out holes and listening carefully. If a likely prey is found, they creep slowly toward the quarry making a final quick dash to capture the animal. However, in the north and other areas where human disturbance is great, the species hunts almost entirely at night.

Habitat

The Simien fox is presently found in the montane grassland and moorland of the Ethiopian highlands at altitudes of 9,800 to 13,000 feet high. In the Bale mountains of south-central Ethiopia, most animals could be found in grasslands supporting large rodent populations. They were uncommon in scrub and did not seem to inhabit forest at low altitudes.

Simien foxes do not seem to shelter in dens, even during the coldest times of the year. Instead, they sleep in the open or in places with grass slightly longer than usual.

Distribution

The Simien fox is one of the rarest carnivores in eastern Africa. Only about 40 individuals of the northern subspecies, *C. s. simensis* still exist in the wild. The southern subspecies, *C. s. citernii* is in better shape with 450 to 600 individuals.

In 1930, the Simien fox was found throughout Ethiopia. Now, however, they are only found in two small, disjunct areas. The rarer northern subspecies, *C. s. simensis*, is still located in the Simien zone and in the hills of Bwahit, Silki, Kidus Yared, and Ras Deyen. The more widespread southern subspecies, *C. s. citernii*, ranges from the Bale mountains, the Sanetti hills, in the valley of Ueb, and on the Gaysay mountains.

Threats

The beautiful fur of the Simien fox is highly prized in the Ethiopian market. As well as being hunted for their fur, local humans hunt the Simien fox to protect their flocks. Unfortunately, the local herders mistake it for the jackal and erroneously believe it kills domestic animals. The increase in cultivated lands has disrupted the species' habitat and decreased the population of its' main food source, rodents.

Conservation and Recovery

Attempts are being made to protect this rare African species. The capture of this animal has been banned, except for scientific purposes, by the African Convention. National parks and preserves have been set up for this species. However, problems have been encountered in protecting the Simien fox in these areas because grazing is still allowed. Ironically, the species is better protected in the unofficial national park of the Bale mountains than the official national park of Simien.

The Simien fox is classified as endangered by the IUCN as of 1978. The species is also placed in Class A of the 1969 African Convention prohibiting capture, except for scientific reasons. Ethiopian law also protects this rare animal.

Maned Wolf

Chrysocyon brachyurus

Louisville Zoo

Status	Endangered
Listed	December 2, 1970
Family	Canidae (Canine)
Description	Long limbs, narrow body, foxlike head with a slender muzzle and large, erect ears.
Habitat	Grasslands, savannas.
Food	Rodents, birds, reptiles, insects, fruit, and other vegetable matter.
Reproduction	2 to 5 young after a gestation of 65 days.
Threats	Hunting, burning of grasslands.
Range	Brazil, Bolivia, Paraguay, Argentina, and the llanos of Colombia.

Description

The maned wolf, *Chrysocyon brachyurus*, looks like a red fox on stilts. The long limbs, narrow body, and pacing gait are all adaptations to life in grasslands. The head is fox-like with a slender muzzle and large, erect ears. The fairly long fur is generally golden-red with white fur on the throat and tip of the tail and black fur on the lower parts of the legs. The erectile mane on the back of the neck and top of the shoulders is also black. This large South American canid weighs approximately 51 pounds and measures 57 inches long from the head to the tail.

Monogamous, mated pairs share a home territory averaging 17 square miles, although they normally don't associate except during breeding season. In captivity, they can be kept together without strife except for an initial period of fighting to establish a hierarchy. Fathers regurgitate food for their young in captivity and may have a significant parenting role in the wild. These animals communicate by a deep-throated single bark heard mainly after dusk, a high-pitched whine, and an agonistic growl.

Mating depends on the season, with breeding occurring in October through February in the Northern Hemisphere and from August through October in South America. After a gestation period of approximately 65 days, females give birth to 2 to 5 young with a maximum litter of 7 young recorded. The black-furred pups are born with their eyes and ears closed and weigh about 0.75 to 0.95

pounds. They grow rapidly, opening their eyes after 9 days and getting their adult fur color by ten weeks. However, they do not develop the long adult legs until one year of age.

The genus *Chrysocyon* contains one species, *C. brachyurus*, and is distinguished from other *Canidae* by its golden-red fur and shoulder height of approximately 35 inches. Differing from other South American canids, the genus *Chrysocyon* has a sagittal crest with a prominent ridge on its skull.

Behavior

This omnivorous animal eats rodents, other small mammals, birds, reptiles, insects, fruit, and other vegetable matter. The diet changes with the seasonal availability of foods. Not an especially swift runner, the maned wolf usually stalks and pounces on its prey like a fox, instead of pursuing the prey for long distances. It is normally active at night with peaks of activity occurring at twilight.

Habitat

The maned wolf lives in the grasslands, savannahs, and swampy areas of central South America. The animal nests in thick, secluded vegetation.

Distribution

Historically, the maned wolf occurred in central and eastern Brazil, eastern Bolivia, Paraguay, Argentina, and Uruguay as well as a disjunct population on the llanos of Colombia. Today, the species occupies most of this range except that it no longer occurs in Uruguay and south of the La Plata River in Argentina. The maned wolf has extended its range to include the recently deforested Zona de Mata of central Brazil.

Threats

The maned wolf has been hunted because of an unjustified belief that it kills domestic animals, especially chickens. Annual burning of grasslands also threaten the maned wolf; although the conversion of rainforest to rangelands has increased its range.

Conservation and Recovery

A successful captive breeding program has been developed with the population increasing from 59 individuals in 1959 to approximately 100 in 1980. The wolf has been successfully managed in captivity with large enclosures for each pair, privacy during the breeding season, and a high protein, low fat diet.

Dhole [=Asiatic Wild Dog]

Cuon alpinus

Ron Garrison, San Diego Zoo

Status	Endangered
Listed	June 2, 1970
Family	Canidae (Canine)
Description	Resembles a dog with shorter skull; upper parts generally rusty-red, and the underparts are pale.
Habitat	Mountainous alpine regions and dense forest; thick jungle.
Food	Large animals.
Reproduction	Litter size averages 4 to 6 pups after gestation of 60-63 days.
Threats	Loss of prey and habitat.
Range	India, Malaysia, Thailand, and Indonesia (Java)

Description

The dhole, *Cuon alpinus*, superficially resembles a dog, genus *Canis*, but the skull has a shorter and broader rostrum. The usually larger male weighs 33 to 46 pounds, and the female weighs 22 to 37 pounds. The dhole stands 16 to 21 inches high at the shoulder. The head and body measure 34 to 44 inches with the bushy tail measuring 16 to 20 inches.

The fur color varies, but the upper parts are generally rusty-red, and the underparts are pale. The tip of the tail is black. In the northern parts of its range and at higher altitudes, the dhole has longer, redder, silkier fur in the winter. The summer coat is duller with shorter, coarser, and sparser hair. At least in captivity in Moscow, the dhole sheds its fur between March and May.

C. alpinus is the only living species of the genus *Cuon*. This species contains 2 subspecies, *C. a. alpinus* and *C. a. hesperius*. Other common names for the dhole are Asiatic wild dog and red dog.

The taxonomic association of *Cuon*, *Lycaon*, and *Speothos* into a single subfamily, *Simocyoninae*, has been questioned by Kleiman, who suggested that these monotypic genera appear more closely related to other *canid* genera than to each other. Clutton-Brock provides further support for this view. These authors analyzed 37 *canid* species using a variety of morphological, ecological, and behavioral traits. When all traits were considered, *Cuon* more closely resembled *Canis*, *Dusicyon*, and *Alopex* than either *Speothos* or *Lycaon*. However, when only cranial and dental characteristics were considered, *Cuon* more closely resembled *Speothos* and *Lycaon*.

Behavior

Dholes usually live in packs of 5 to 12 individuals. Sometimes, especially when only large ungulates are available for prey, related packs congregate to form larger groups, or clans, of up to 40 members. These greater numbers are needed to kill the big ungulates. The large clans usually break up into the smaller packs when the large prey have fawns. The pack appears to consist of a mated pair and their offspring. Social behavior within a pack has not been studied in detail, but the pack seems to have a dominant leader with the others showing submissive behavior. To communicate, the dhole uses a wide range of short yaps, growls, whines, whimpers, howls, and even whistling noises. These sounds are similar to the vocalizations of domestic dogs, except dholes do not have loud, repeated barks.

After a gestation period of 60 to 63 days, an average 4 to 6 pups are born. Several females with litters may share the same den, with pack members bringing the young food. The pups leave the den after 70 to 80 days and start to kill at 7 months of age. Dholes live to be 15 to 16 years of age in captivity.

Dholes mainly prey on large animals. In India, they kill sambar, chital, buffalo, swamp deer, nilgai, wild pig, wild goat, wild sheep, gar, and other mammals. Dholes prey on reindeer, wild sheep, wild goat, and badger in Russia. Small rodents and hares may also be eaten. On occasion, Dholes may eat carrion, and rarely, domestic animals. Reportedly, this species may prey on tigers, leopards, and bears, but this has not been well documented.

Tracking their prey by scent, Dholes pursue quarry by sight. The animals usually separate one animal from the herd as likely prey, and then the whole pack surrounds and attacks the prey. One report had Dholes stampeding herds of gaur and buffalo, and then attacking the calves.

The dhole is usually active in the early morning and evening; although it occasionally hunts at night.

Habitat

Throughout its range, the dhole lives in a wide variety of habitats. In Russia, the species inhabits mountainous alpine regions and dense forest. It is found in more open country in Tibet and Ladak. In India, the species lives almost exclusively in dense forests and thick jungles at an altitude up to 6,900 feet. In Thailand, they prefer dense montane forests at elevations of up to 9,800 feet. Usually, the dhole avoids deserts.

The type of den used by the dhole includes burrows excavated by the animal, other animal's burrows, and rocky crevices. One elaborate earth den was found, with six entrances leading to a long series of interconnecting tunnels and four large chambers. Several generations of dholes probably dug this extensive system.

Distribution

In the past, dholes ranged from the Tyan-Shan mountains, Altai mountains, and the Maritime Province of Russia southward to India (but not Sri Lanka), the Malay Peninsula, and on the islands of Sumatra and Java. Although the present range has not been studied, remnant populations are known to exist in India, Malaysia, Thailand, and Java.

Threats

Dholes have been intensively poisoned and killed even though they rarely take domestic livestock and have only once attacked a person. However, local humans consider dholes a competitor for game. This dislike of the species is not universal. Indeed, some villagers in India welcome the animal and follow it in order to take its kill.

Along with direct persecution, the elimination of the species' natural prey and destruction of its habitat has seriously endangered the dhole. Other threats include diseases contracted from domestic dogs, and continued poisoning by cattle ranchers.

Conservation and Recovery

The dhole occurs in well protected areas in the Chitawan National Park in Nepal and the Corbett National Park in India, although these populations have experienced an inexplicable decline.

Mexican Prairie Dog

Cynomys mexicanus

(*Cynomys parvidens*) close relative   USFWS

Status	Endangered
Listed	June 2, 1970
Family	Sciuridae (Burrowing squirrels)
Description	Coarse, reddish-brown pelage mixed with black, white, and yellow hairs.
Habitat	Plains and valleys at elevations of 5,200 to 7,000 feet.
Food	Grasses and associated vegetation.
Reproduction	One litter a year of up to 6 young after gestation of 34 to 45 days.
Threats	Loss of its original habitat to agriculture and livestock grazing; eradication programs; restricted range.
Range	Northern Mexico

Description

The Mexican prairie dog, *Cynomys mexicanus*, has a coarse, reddish-brown pelage mixed with black, white, and yellow hairs. The area around and below the eye has concentrated black hairs. Males, which are larger than females, weigh up to 3 pounds and grow to 16 inches in length. It has short ears and a short tail tipped with black.

Behavior

The Mexican prairie dog feeds on grasses and associated vegetation.

All prairie dogs burrow extensive tunnels with several entrances. The depth of the burrow reaches 3 feet, where subtunnels radiate out like spokes. Typically, a prairie dog "town" houses a few dozen individuals, but in conducive topographies extensive burrows may house several hundred individuals. Prairie dogs live in family groups comprising a male, one or several reproductive females, and the offspring. The mating season for the Mexican prairie dog, which extends from January through June, is much longer than its North American cousin's, which lasts about one month. The female may produce one litter a year of up to 6 young after gestation of 34 to 45 days. The young, which are completely furred at birth, are helpless until they are weaned in 6 to 7 weeks.

Unlike prairie dogs that occur in colder climates, the Mexican prairie dog is active throughout the day.

Habitat

The Mexican prairie dog inhabits plains and valleys at elevations of 5,200 to 7,000 feet.

Distribution

The Mexican prairie dog occurs in a very restricted range in Coahuila and San Luis Potosi in northern Mexico. It is known from a single colony discovered in 1881, which subsequently dispersed into several smaller colonies. When it was discovered, *C. mexicanus* was considered abundant. Remains of North American species of prairie dog have been found in *C. mexicanus'* limited range, but the North American species disappeared after the last ice age.

Threats

The Mexican prairie dog has lost much of its original habitat to agriculture and livestock grazing. They have also fallen victim to eradication programs because they eat cultivated farm crops, and because their burrows caused accidents to farmers and livestock.

Conservation and Recovery

Because all prairie dogs are considered to be a pest to farmers and livestock, there is little sympathy to preserve their habitat. In the U.S., education programs explaining the importance of prairie dogs to the ecosystem have engendered some preservation sentiment; perhaps because the Mexican prairie dog's range is so restricted a similar educational effort is possible in Mexico.

African Wild Dog

Lycaon pictus

Rick Weyerhaeuser

Status	Endangered
Listed	January 23, 1984
Family	Canidae (Canine)
Description	Coat varies in color; fur is short and sparse making its black skin visible.
Habitat	Savannas and other similar type open areas.
Food	Carnivore, hunting zebra, springbok, antelope; rodents and other small mammals.
Reproduction	Gestation of 70-73 days.
Threats	Disease; hunting; distemper.
Range	Burundi, Togo, Mozambique, Cameroon, Congo, and Uganda.

Description

Lycaon pictus, commonly known as the African wild dog, stands about 24 to 30 inches tall, weighs 37.5 to 79.4 pounds, has a head-body length of 29.9 to 43.3 inches, and tail length of 11.8 to 15.8 inches. This species' pelage is extremely variable in color; the fur is short and sparse, with a unique irregular pattern of white and yellow blotches on each individual; the black skin is often visible.

In 1820, Temminck formally described this species as *Lycaon pictus*. It is also commonly known as the hunting dog or painted dog.

Behavior

The African wild dog is an opportunistic carnivore. It has been observed hunting zebra, springbok, antelope and other game animals, as well as rodents and other small mammals. It is known to hunt in the morning and again in the evening hours.

Historically, this dog traveled in packs of hundreds of individuals. Then the herds of springbok and other game were destroyed. Today the African wild dog lives in groups consisting of up to 20 individuals. The pack hunts large prey such as zebra and antelope. This canine will also hunt for rodents and other small animals.

This species is extremely swift and has incredible endurance. The African wild dog has been recorded chasing its prey at speeds of up to 31 miles per hour for over 3 miles.

Each pack is led by a dominant male and female, who breed once a year. The impregnated female selects a den below ground where the pups are born. The pups are weaned at about 10 weeks, at which time they emerge from the den and begin eating solid food. At 3 months the pups begin to roam with the pack, which protects them until they reach sexual maturity at 12 to 18 months.

African wild dogs seem to possess the capability of learning non-instinctual information from their elders, and passing it along to their young. Some packs, for example, are able to kill zebras, while other packs will not attempt it. This learned ability extends to knowledge of water holes, density of prey, and range boundries.

Habitat

Although the African wild dog inhabits savannas and other similar type open areas, it has been recorded from the Sahara Desert to the snows of Mount Kilimanjaro.

Distribution

Historically, this species ranged throughout all of Africa. Today, it is restricted to a few isolated populations distributed along its historic range. In 1984 sightings and confirmed occurrences of the African wild dog were reported from Burundi, Togo, Mozambique (possible), Cameroon, Congo, and Uganda.

Threats

The African wild dog's decline is attributed to anthropogenic persecution and disease. As man reduced the size of this species' primary food source, this most likely had interspecific effects and attributed to the population's decline. This species was also directly killed by man in a response to human tendency to distrust and fear large carnivores. The dogs were killed as many ranchers believed them a threat to their livestock. This is quite similar to the response wolves received in the United States.

It is also believed that this species was affected by distemper. This disease was introduced into East Africa in 1906.

Conservation and Recovery

The African wild dog is distributed through Serengeti and Kruger National Parks. These parks are not only a haven for this species but a protected and managed grassland/savannah biome. The criteria for National Park recognition and management is primarily for protection of the diversity of ecosystems. National parks are relatively large areas which contain representative samples of major natural regions, features or scenery where plant and animal species, geomorphologic sites, and habitats are of special scientific, educational, and recreational interest. These parks contain one or several entire ecosystems that have not been altered by human exploitation and occupation.

Hyenas
Family: Hyaenidae

Brown Hyena (*Hyaena brunnea*)   Assiniboine Park Zoo

General Characteristics of the *Hyaenidae*

The five subspecies of *Hyaena hyaena* have been integrated into two distinct groups. The northern subspecies group consists of *H. h. barbara* from the western part of North Africa, *H. h. syriaca* found in Asia Minor, and *H. h. hyaena* from eastern India. The southern group consists of *H. h. dubbah* found in northeastern Africa, and *H. h. sultana* from the Arabian peninsula.

Hyenas have large ears and eyes, and a large head with powerful jaws and large, bone-crushing teeth. Their digestive system permits them to consume the remains of prey that other animals cannot eat, including the bones, horns, hooves, ligament and hair. Hyenas will hunt individually or in packs to bring down prey five times their size. When forced to feed rapidly, a group of hyenas can devour an entire zebra, bones and all, in 15 minutes. The two hyena species that are endangered, the brown and striped hyena, are primarily scavengers, unlike the spotted hyena which hunts its prey. The brown and striped hyenas eat insects, small animals, eggs, fruits and vegetables. They are ineffective hunters, but as scavengers they can steal and store sources of food. Their attainable food supply is often widely scattered so that brown and striped hyenas may have territories of up to 200 square miles, which they mark with a pastelike substance secreted from an anal pouch.

Hyenas cooperate in raising their young, which includes communal suckling and providing food to group members. Although brown and striped hyenas do not feed together, they will share large prey and the communal feeding of the young provides the most efficient use of food resources.

Hyenas communicate with each other through whoop calls that can be heard several kilometers away. Every hyena has a distinctive voice, and by repeating the whoop calls individuals can locate one another. Individuals will approach each other only if they recognize the call; otherwise, they approach a strange voice in a group.

Brown Hyena
Hyaena brunnea

Assiniboine Park Zoo

Status	Endangered
Listed	June 2, 1970
Family	Hyaenidae (Hyena)
Description	Sloping back and solid head with long, pointed ears; generally brown fur except for lighter fur on the lower parts, and nearly white fur on the neck and shoulders.
Habitat	Woodland savannah, grassland, and semi-deserts.
Food	Large and small mammals, birds, eggs, insects.
Reproduction	Litters of 2-5 young are born after a gestation period of 3 months.
Threats	Hunted by settlers.
Range	Namibia, South Africa, Botswana, Zimbabwe, Mozambique, Orange Free State, and Natal.

Description

The brown hyaena, *Hyaena brunnea*, is a medium-sized carnivore (about 88 pounds) with well-developed forequarters, weak hindquarters, and a sloping back. The animal measures 35 to 39 inches in total length. The solid head has long, pointed ears and strong teeth. The brown hyena has four toes on each foot with non-retractile claws and stands on the phalanx instead of on the whole surface of the foot. The anal glands are a complex structure that secrete a white liquid and are used by the brown hyena to mark its territory.

The brown hyena has generally brown fur except for lighter fur on the lower parts, and nearly white fur on the neck and shoulders. A few stripes mark the hindlimbs. The animal has a long grayish mane along the middle of its back. The fur is thin with little underfur in the summer and is thicker in the winter.

H. brunnea is one of two members of the genus Hyaena. The other species, *H. hyaena* (striped hyena), is smaller with dark stripes on its body and legs.

Behavior

For a given area, the animals are usually organized into a clan, sometimes numbering as many as 300 animals, although they usually forage alone. A clan typically consists of a dominant male, 3 to 4 subordinate males, 4 to 6 adult females, and associated young animals. The animals in a clan use a wide variety of ritualized behavior to maintain the stable hierarchy. Each clan maintains a territory of approximately 105 square miles with a central breeding den.

Mating is thought to occur mainly from May to August, with 1 to 5 young born after a gestation period of about three months. Mating males are usually wanderers that do not remain with the group. The cubs are born with eyes closed and ears bent forward. Their fur is the same color as the adult's, except shorter. After about eight days, the cubs open their eyes. The den may contain several different litters at one time, and a mother will nurse any hungry cub, not just her own. The cubs emerge from the den after about 3 months but don't leave the vicinity until they are about 14 months old. The female usually has her first litter in her second year and has the next litter between 12 to 41 months later.

The brown hyena mainly scavenges on large mammals, including domestic animals, killed by other carnivores. It will also hunt small mammals, birds and their eggs, and insects. In coastal areas, this animal also feeds on dead crab, fish, and seal. Despite widespread belief, it normally doesn't eat live domestic animals. Fruit, such as tsama melon and gemsbok cucumber, is a very important part of the brown hyena's diet because it provides almost 90% of the water needed by the animal. The brown hyena will drink from surface water, if available.

Normally, the brown hyena forages for food alone. At a large carcass, several animals may congregate with each one taking turns breaking off a piece of the meat. Then each individual takes the meat away to either eat in seclusion or back to the den to feed the cubs. Excess amounts of food are typically stored under a bush or in a clump of grass. Hyenas are voracious foragers and usually dominate competing animals, forcing much larger hunters, such as leopards, cheetahs and jackals to retreat.

The brown hyena is only active during the cool nighttime hours. During the heat of the day, it rests in shelters dug out of the ground among rocks.

Habitat

The brown hyena prefers arid open habitat, such as open scrub, woodland savannah, grassland, and semi-desert. It avoids forests where the spotted hyena is more prevalent.

Distribution

The brown hyena is found in Namibia, Botswana, western and southern Zimbabwe, southern Mozambique, Natal, Orange Free State, and South Africa. They are now apparently extinct in the extreme southern Cape. There are no population estimates, but there are approximately 650 individuals in the Gemsbok reserves.

Threats

The brown hyena has been ruthlessly hunted by settlers to protect their livestock.

As recently as 1976, the brown hyena was listed as a harmful animal in South Africa.

Conservation and Recovery

The brown hyena is protected from hunting, except with special authorization, by the 1969 African Convention. The species is completely protected in the national parks and reserves where it is found, including the Kalahari Gemsbok and Gemsbok National Parks, the Central Kalahari Game Reserve, the southern Namib Desert, and Etosha National Park. It has been reintroduced into the St. Lucia and Itala Games Reserves in Natal.

Educating the public is an important conservation activity. The hyena is a poor hunter who seldom kills a live animal. It feeds only on carrion and provides an ecological service to its range.

Barbary Hyena

Hyaena hyaena barbara

Alan Shoemaker

Status	Endangered
Listed	June 2, 1970
Family	Hyaenidae (Hyena)
Description	Bristly gray or gray-brown fur with dark stripes on its limbs and back.
Habitat	Mountainous areas and plateaus.
Food	Dead carrion, small mammals, reptiles, birds, insects, and fruit.
Reproduction	1 to 5 young after gestation of 90 days.
Threats	Hunted for food, for medicine, for sport, and to protect livestock; destruction of habitat.
Range	Algeria, Tunisia, and Morocco

Description

The barbary hyena, *Hyaena hyaena barbara*, weighs about 60 to 199 pounds and measures about 51 to 59 inches long from its head to its long, thick tail. The front legs of this dog-like animal are slightly longer than the back limbs, causing the body to slope down at the rear. The neck is large and muscular with a solid jaw and strong teeth. *H. h. barbara* has very large ears and a well developed sense of smell.

H. h. barbara, a subspecies of the striped hyena (*Hyaena hyaena*), has bristly gray or light gray-brown fur with transverse dark-brown or black stripes on its limbs and back. The stripes can run together, forming large blotches. In the summer, the fur is shorter and the stripes are more pronounced than in the winter.

The long, distinct mane has hairs growing up to 12 inches long. Depending on the mood, parts of the mane can be erected. A frightened animal erects the whole mane, but not the hairs on the tail. An aggressive animal erects the mane hairs of the mid-back and neck, and with increasing aggressiveness, the tail is also held up.

Behavior

The Barbary hyena mainly scavenges on dead carrion, using its powerful jaws to eat every part of the dead animal including most of the bones. Hunting also comprises a large part of its diet; it preys upon small mammals, reptiles, birds, and insects. The Barbary hyena has been known to attack goats and sheep as well as feed on garbage thrown away by humans. In addition, fruit is an important part of its diet.

When hunting for food, the Barbary hyena moves in a zigzag pattern at a rate of approximately 1.2 to 2.5 miles per hour. After scavenging or catching its meal, the animal often brings the food to the den where a large number of bones may eventually accumulate.

The Barbary hyena normally hunts at dusk and is occasionally active at night. During the heat of the day, they rest in natural caves or dug-out lairs.

The Barbary hyena walks on the phalanx of its four-toed paws instead of on the whole surface of the foot. The claws are non-retractable. This animal can walk long distances averaging between 1.2 to 6.2 miles per hour.

Not a particularly social animal, the Barbary hyena usually hunts in pairs, and if groups are formed, they are of limited size and generally between members of the same family. The strong incompatibility between adult females prevents the larger pack formations observed in spotted hyenas.

After a gestation period of approximately 90 to 92 days, females give birth to 1 to 5 offspring. The newborn is born with its ears and eyes closed and weighs approximately 1.5 pounds. At about eight days, the cub usually opens its eyes after it has already started walking. The cub is reared in natural caves or in burrows dug-out or enlarged by the mother before birth. The mother starts feeding the young torn pieces of meat at approximately one month of age. The Barbary hyena starts living independently at about 5 months and usually reaches sexual maturity at 2 or 3 years of age.

Habitat

The Barbary hyena lives in the mountainous areas and plateaus of North Africa (Algeria, Tunisia, and Morocco). They avoid the Saharan desert area because they need surface water within 6 miles.

Distribution

In the past, the Barbary hyena was widely distributed throughout North Africa. Now, however, the species lives mainly in a few mountain ranges (Great and Middle Atlas Mountains, the Taza Mountains, and Urme) of Morocco, Algeria, and Tunisia. The Barbary hyena has also been sighted in the plateaus between Algeria and Tunisia, as well as in some of North Africa's national parks and reserves.

Threats

The Barbary hyena has been ruthlessly hunted to protect livestock, for food, for medicine, and for sport. Destruction of its habitat and natural food sources has also contributed to the decrease in population numbers.

Conservation and Recovery

The Barbary hyena has been protected by law in Morocco since 1955. In 1969, the African Convention established that any member of the *H. hyaena* species can only be caught or killed if special authorization has been granted.

Marsupials
Order: Marsupialia

Quokka (*Setonix brachyurus*)

Perth Zoo

General Characteristics of the *Marsupialia*

Marsupials comprise a diversified group of mammals that include the American opossum, shrews, marsupial mice, numbat, bandicoots, rabbit-eared bandicoots, ringtail possums, kangaroos, rat kangaroos, koala bears, and wombats. Marsupials are known from fossils collected in North and South America and are believed to have occurred in the Western Hemisphere 75 to 100 million years ago; the earliest fossils collected in Australia are from 23 million years ago. It is assumed but not proven that marsupials originated in the Western Hemisphere and radiated to Europe and Australia. Marsupials disappeared from North America 15 to 20 million years ago, and the large, carnivorous marsupials succumbed to carnivorous predators such as jaguars. Small, omnivorous marsupials survived in South

America, and after the two continents were joined, some species, such as the common opossum, recolonized in North America. In Australia, however, where there were no carnivorous predators until human settlement, marsupials thrived and evolved into greatly diversified species.

Marsupials flourished for millions of years in Australia. The first stress that the species endured were climatic changes that reduced favorable habitat. When settlers arrived in Australia, they burned large tracts of land and introduced predators to the ecosystem. Europeans brought sheep, cattle, rabbits, foxes, cats, dogs, donkeys and rats, as well as sophisticated farming practices that resulted in large scale modification of habitat. Nine marsupial species have become extinct (along with numerous bird species); the hardest hit species are the small kangaroos, bandicoots, and large carnivores. Habitat degradation by grazing animals and rabbits have placed heavy pressure on species in the arid regions, such as the greater bilby, bandicoots, and rat-kangaroos. Only the large kangaroos have benefitted from environmental changes; they are able to take advantage of the increased food and water supplies produced by agriculture, and their numbers increased to the point where they were considered a nuisance and were systematically eradicated during the nineteenth and twentieth centuries. Most marsupial species, however, are not pests and their survival is threatened by loss of habitat and alien predators.

Physiology

Marsupials possess many physiological characteristics which set them apart from the placental mammals; primarily the differences are isolated to the urogenital and skeletal systems. Some of these characteristics include a shorter gestation period; short development period; larger ovum with a series of membranes; no chorio-allantoic placenta (excluding the koala and wombat); two uteri and two lateral vaninae; bifid penis which is posterior to the testes (except in kangaroos); a pair of epipubic bones are located on the pelvis; the lower jaw has a distinct interior shelf; the tympanum is covered by an alisphenoid bone rather than by the tympanic bone; the body temperature and metabolic rates are lower.

Marsupials are unusual mammals in their reproductive characteristics. The marsupial egg is more similar to reptiles and birds than to other placental mammals. The young, which are born after a short gestation period, are undeveloped and undergo most of their growth outside of the womb. The newborn "swims" from the birth canal to the pouch, where it latches on to a nipple and remains fully attached for 1 to 2 months. The young are carried in the pouch until they grow to a size where they can become more self sufficient. In some kangaroos, for example, the gestation period may be a month while the development period may last a year. After the young are removed from the pouch, they may remain with the mother and continue to suckle.

With some species of marsupials, such as the Australian *Dasyuridae,* the pouch is merely folded skin around the nipples and does not serve as a carrying case for the young. The newborn hang onto the nipples, more or less suspended, and are carried with the mother until such time as their mouth development allows them to release. The mother then makes a nest for the young so that she can forage on her own without the weight of the young impeding her hunt.

Most marsupials do not live in groups, do not form long-term bonds with their mates, and mate promiscuously. Because the mother is able to feed and protect the young in her pouch, she is less dependent on the male than most animals. This factor, combined with a lack of predation and no contact with human development for 45 million years, provided marsupials with independence, and their social systems developed much differently from most other mammals.

Marsupials have a well developed sense of hearing and smell which serves them well as nocturnal animals. They possess several odor producing skin glands which they use to mark sites and to identify friendly species or individuals.

The jaw and tooth structure of marsupials may have been originally designed to capture insect prey, but as marsupials became herbivores, their specialized teeth were exceptionally well suited to pick leaves or grass that would not have been accessible to species with different teeth structures. This, of course, provided marsupials with a food selection advantage and contributed to the success of the family. Bandicoots and dasyures have as many as eighteen incisor teeth, compared to ten in placental animals.

Kangaroos

The characteristic most often associated with kangaroos is their exceptional ability to hop. All kangaroos have well-developed hind limbs and move bipedally. When moving slowly, kangaroos use all four limbs; however, when moving fast, the body moves forward with springy leaps and the tail is used as a balance. During slow movement a hop is measured at 3.9 to 6.2 feet, but during fast movement a single hop may carry the kangaroo 29.5 or more feet.

The tail is used to counterbalance its upper body during hopping, although kangaroos who have lost their tails have been observed hopping perfectly well. Large kangaroos, such as the red kangaroo, cruise very efficiently at 15 to 20 miles per hour, and because of the elastic energy stored in its tendons, the kangaroo uses less energy as its speed increases, up to about 20 miles per hour. A red kangaroo can accelerate at speeds of 40 miles per hour but it can maintain that speed for only a few hundred yards, while at cruising speed, it can run for hours.

When kangaroos are being chased, speeds of 25 to 30 miles per hour have been recorded. When females with young are being chased many times the young is taken out of the pouch and dropped or is sometimes forced out of the pouch. This is probably to relieve weight. When the young are sacrificed during a chase they rarely survive.

A group of kangaroos is called a "mob". Mobs consist of between 4 to 12 animals. Many references cite many more in a group, but this probably derives from the fact that many groups may aggregate in one particular area due to ecological reasons, like shading and vegetation abundance. It seems that the only natural bond made between kangaroos is that between a mother and her young. In fact, the larger buck from a group or a female may join another group with no opposition.

Kangaroos are generally docile and rarely attack humans or other animals unless cornered. Fighting among kangaroos occurs during competition for females and when an outside male comes into an established territory.

Kangaroos are most active during the early morning and at sunset, and most kangaroo species can be active throughout the night. Smaller kangaroos tend to be more nocturnal and avian kangaroos are very nocturnal.

The food source for kangaroos is associated with their size. The small species, bettongs and rat-kangaroos, are omnivorous but depend on high quality foods such as fungi. The medium-sized species, such as wallabies, will consume a wide variety of leafy vegetation with a low fiber count. The large kangaroos are true grazers and specialize in grass, which they eat while standing in a crouched position. They graze in a semicircle, walking forward as they graze. They use the curved claws on their forepaws for grappling food, and their hand-like paws are adept at holding and manipulating stems. Kangaroos seldom drink water even when it is available. They obtain moisture from vegetation. Kangaroos are also highly opportunistic feeders, including picnic baskets and trash cans in national parks.

Kangaroos have excellent eyesight, with large eyes on either side of the head providing a wide field of vision. They also have good night vision and are keenly aware of motion. They can detect some colors in the red and blue ranges. Their hearing is also acute, and it may be their most important sense for protection against predators. They can rotate the ears independently so that they can assess sounds coming from different directions. They constantly use their ears to monitor their situation, even when at rest.

Smell is a less important sense for defense but plays an important function in social behavior. It helps in identifying individuals and for determining the receptivity of females.

Females have an estrus cycle of 45.6 days. Although many kangaroos have a baby in the pouch and an embryo developing in the uterus at the same time (embryonic diapause), *M. giganteus* rarely exhibits this condition. In females, conception does not generally occur until after the first young has vacated the pouch, at an average age of about 320 days. Usually, the interval between successive births is approximately 1 year. However, if the pouch young dies, the female returns to estrus within approximately 11 days. *M. giganteus* takes a relatively long time to reach sexual maturity with captive males first mating at 42.5 months and females at 21 months. In captivity, this kangaroo has lived to 24 years of age.

In most kangaroo species, the estrus cycle is not affected by the pregnancy, and the female becomes receptive to mating again shortly after the birth of the young. But because the gestation period is so short and the nurturing period is so long, the embryo that is produced remains dormant, entering a state of embryonic diapause because of a hormonal signal produced when the young are still feeding from the mother in the pouch. When the sucking from the young decreases, or if the young are lost, the embryo resumes developing.

The basic social unit for kangaroos is formed around the female and her young. She forms a strong attachment with her young, which continues between the mother and her grown daughters. Male offspring disperse from the maternal group to colonize new reproductive territories, and this is one of the most vulnerable times for the young kangaroo. The subadult, inexperienced male setting through uncharted territory provides a prime target for predators. Males maintain a high degree of tolerance of each other, although conflict is sometimes exhibited in competing for an estrous female. If the conflict is mild, the males will retreat to self-grooming or grazing; more serious conflicts bring up a display of dominance during which one animal, usually the dominant male, scratches the ground, stalks in a crouched position with his rump above his head, and arches his back in an apparent show of superior size. The dominant male may assume the upright, fighting position and claw at the opponent, but even this confrontation may result in the animals' returning to grazing. If the challenge ensues, the combatants stand erect to their maximum height and each claws at the other's head and throat with their forefeet. They throw their heads back to avoid eye damage, and as the fight continues they lean on their tails and begin kicking with both hind feet, attempting to knock the opponent off balance. Fights may last up to ten minutes when the loser withdraws from the action and returns to normal activities. Only minor injuries are ever sustained.

The Great Kangaroos

There are six species of giant kangaroos: the common, black and Antilopine wallaroos, and the eastern and western great kangaroos, and the red kangaroo. When standing, they can reach 7 feet high, and they weigh up to 200 pounds. They are primarily nocturnal, spending most of the day in the shade.

The range of the eastern gray kangaroo covers the eastern one-third of Australia and parts of Tasmania; the western gray's range extends across the southern quarter of the country. Both species occur on the plains of New South Wales and in western Victoria and southeast South Australia. Western gray kangaroos have a natural resistance to fluoroacetate, which is widely used in pesticides, and other kangaroos do not, giving the western gray a food advantage. Except for this natural immunity to fluoroacetate and a different gestation period and pouch life, the two species are very similar. They inhabit semi-arid scrub to forest; they graze in open grassy areas at night; they have five color phases ranging from brown to black; breeding occurs throughout the year but peaks in early summer; they are seasonable breeders and are sexually inactive during the winter; gray kangaroo females weigh up to 70 pounds while large males can weigh 140 pounds. In the wild, gray kangaroos live for 20 years.

Potoroos

Potoroos are small, pointed-nosed rat-kangaroos that are 13 to 16 inches in length and weigh up to 4.5 pounds. They inhabit areas with dense ground cover of shrubs or grasses, and can survive forest fires by taking shelter in burrows. But habitat that has been burned is unacceptable to potoroos and they will relocate to other dense cover.

The female's pouch contains four nipples although only one young is born at a time. The single offspring will remain in the pouch for four months, after which the female produces another offspring. Over her four year reproductive life, a female may produce two or three young a year.

Potoroos feed on roots, tubers, invertebrates and underground fungi that they extract by digging with their short forelimbs. Fungi provide an important food source because of its abundance, high protein, water and mineral content.

Bettongs

Bettongs are the largest member of the rat-kangaroo family, weighing up to 7.75 pounds. Bettongs inhabit arid environments and the habitat types range from dry eucalyptus forests to desert sandhills, but they prefer areas with dense ground vegetation. They build nests out of plant material that they carry in their tails. They spend most of the day sleeping in their nests and forage at night.

A single young is born after a gestation period of about 21 days. The offspring remains in the pouch for 95 to 115 days depending on the species. Sexual maturity occurs in 5 to 12 months. Bettongs may breed throughout the year and may produce several offspring a year.

The burrowing bettong is the only kangaroo that digs and inhabits burrows. It excavates large and complex tunnel systems that can have 120 entrances, providing shelter to several or dozens of individuals. They emerge from their tunnels in the cool of night to feed on roots, bulbs and fungi. Under duress, they are opportunistic feeders and will eat fish or mammals.

Burrowing bettongs were widespread across Australia during the nineteenth century but are now restricted to a few small islands off the northwest continent.

Hare Wallabies

Wallabies and kangaroos are both included in the genus *Macropus*, and the primary difference is in their size. Adults are classified as kangaroos if they weigh more than 44 pounds and if their hind feet are shorter than ten inches.

Hare-wallabies are small kangaroos whose size and appearance resemble hares. During the day they hide under bushes or in grass clumps and when disturbed flee at high speed. They tend to be browsers with grass a part of their diet. They are able to extract water from their food without requiring additional moisture. The eastern hare-wallaby, now apparently extinct, was easy to tame and became a part of the camp life of early explorers. The western hare-wallaby, once common in deserts throughout the western half of Australia, preferred sandy areas covered with spinifex grass which sustained its high fiber diet of seeds, sedges and perennial shrubs. The population of the only remaining colonies on islands off the west coast fluctuate widely with increases occurring after wildfire burns.

The banded hare-wallaby is a gregarious species that congregates in small groups in bushy thickets. Its range extended throughout western Australia but by the twentieth century it had become extinct on the mainland and survives only on two offshore islands. The only hare-wallaby that remains fairly common is the spectacled hare-wallaby, which ranges throughout the northern half of Australia but is declining in Western Australia where the loss of spinifex habitat is contributing to the decline. These wallabies prefer open forests, acacia thickets and spinifex hummock grasslands. They rest by day in shallow depressions concealed by shrubs and browse at night on spinifex grass and shrubs.

Nail-tail Wallabies

Nail-tail wallabies are small, pretty animals about 45 inches long, including the tail, and weighing about 14 pounds. They have a horny spur hidden in the hair at the tip of their tails, whose function is unknown. The incisor teeth are more slender than in other wallabies, which may indicate a specialization in their diet that includes the wiry roots of grass and perhaps *Melaleuca* leaves. They rest in shallow depressions during the day under protective brush. They are extremely shy and usually solitary. When they run, they hold their short forearms out in awkward angles from their body.

The crescent nail-tail wallaby has experienced the most serious decline. Adapted to semi-arid woodlands and desert life, it was common in the central and western parts of Australia, but the last individual was sighted in 1956 and the last dead animal discovered in 1964. It is presumed extinct but its refuge is so isolated that a few individuals could survive. The bridled nail-tail wallaby once ranged over most of eastern Australia but it, too, is believed to have become extinct by 1937, but a small population was found in 1973 in the Duaringa area of eastern Queensland.

When wallabies were common, they were hunted for food by the Aborigines, who considered their meat a delicacy. They were hunted with spears and dogs, and captured in nets stretched across their paths. Predation by foxes is not considered a contributing factor to their decline since wallabies are too large and too fast to be easy prey for foxes. The main reason for the decline of wallabies is the transformation of their habitat into grazing land and wheat fields.

The distribution and numbers of most hare-wallabies have been in serious decline since European settlement, which brought the deterioration of grasslands by trampling sheep and cattle, and by fires that destroyed the species' required underbrush.

Parma Wallabies

Parma wallabies were discovered in 1840 and by 1930 were thought to have become extinct because of habitat alteration and predation by introduced foxes. In 1965, however, a population of several hundred individuals was located after an extensive search on the island of Kawau, off the coast of New Zealand, near Aukland. Other, smaller populations have subsequently been discovered in New South Wales, their original range. Their preferred habitat is wet eucalyptus forests with a thick shrubbery understory and open patches of grass.

Rock Wallabies

Rock wallabies are among the most specialized of the kangaroo family. This agile animal has adapted to rugged rock terrain and has diversified considerably. The rear feet have been modified from other kangaroo species to give the rock wallaby more traction on the slick surfaces of its rock habitat. The long toenails are short. The pad is granulated, and stiff hairs surrounding each hind foot provide better gripping. The long, cylindrical tails are used for balance. Normally curved above the back, the tail is extended out from the body during leaps, and the arms may also be extended forward for additional balance.

Rock wallabies weigh between 2 and 18 pounds; males may be 30 percent larger than females, but the species are otherwise dimorphic. These highly sociable animals live in large colonies in rock outcrops that have deep fissures or caves. Colonies do not migrate and many generations will inhabit the same location. One of the essential habitat requirements is the proximity of feeding areas to the rock outcrop. The primary food source is grass, but rock-wallabies also eat herbs and fruits if available. Because of the extreme daily temperatures in much of the rock wallaby's range, feeding usually occurs in the cool of the early evening. During the hot days and cold nights, the wallaby remains in its rock crevice or cave where the temperature is constant. Rock-wallabies do not require a water supply since they receive their required moisture through the plants they consume.

Reproduction is somewhat different in rock-wallabies than in other kangaroos. Although they can breed on a continuous basis because of embryonic diapause like other kangaroos, the breeding cycle is discontinuous because of seasonal and habitat conditions. The rugged terrain and temperature extremes of the habitat also restrict the young from remaining with the mother, and they are left in shelters rather than clinging to the mother in the pouch.

Some rock-wallaby species have fared pretty well, but a number of species are in decline and many were severely threatened by human predation. Rock wallabies were shot for sport and for their beautiful skins, as well being regarded as pests. By 1912 it was evident that rock-wallabies were being overhunted and various local and state governments passed regulations controlling wallaby hunting, but with their populations reduced, rock-wallabies became susceptible to natural predation. Introduced foxes became the primary threat because they are able to climb into the rock outcrops and pursue the wallabies into their caves. Feral goats, which are also good climbers, compete with rock-wallabies for food and shelter, and the larger goats will displace wallabies from their habitat.

Because of the rugged terrain of some rock wallaby habitats, some species have only been recently discovered, such as the Monjon, the smallest of the rock wallabies, and the Proserpine, both of which were discovered in 1976.

Bandicoots

The bandicoots comprise the second of three main branches of marsupials which occur in Australia. Their evolutionary adaptations have fitted them for digging and living on a variety of diets related to invertebrates, vegetation and roots. There are two main evolutionary lines of bandicoots which are artificially designated within two family levels.

The *Peramelidae* include the spiny furred, ordinary bandicoots and the long eared "rabbit" bandicoots. Members of the *Peramelidae* are found throughout Australia, Tasmania, New Guinea and several adjacent islands. The *Thylacomyidae* are found only in southern and western Australia. Their fossil histories are known, respectively, from the late Miocene and late Pliocene of Australia.

Bandicoots are small rodent-like marsupials with short limbs, a long pointed muzzle and a short neck and ears. These insectivores have small teeth with pointed cusps and strong foreclaws well adapted to foraging in the ground. The rear-opening pouch, usually with eight teats, extends across most the female's underside while she is carrying her young, but it retracts when the pouch is no longer needed. Males are larger than females. Both sexes have a good sense of smell and poor to medium eyesight.

Australian bandicoots are generally divided into two groups: those restricted to dry or arid areas and those that occur in coastal zones. The dry habitat species, which include the desert bandicoot and western barred bandicoot, have suffered major population losses. The range of the coastal species, which includes the bridled bandicoot, is determined by the amount of rainfall, and they may occur far inland if moisture conditions are suitable.

As bandicoot species evolved, some developed longer skulls, longer limbs, shorter tails and enlarged molars, which gave them an increased ability to forage in deeper holes. These species developed in arid areas. The shorter-nosed species occur in areas with tall grass or low shrubbery. They are stockier than the slender long-nosed bandicoots, which also have longer ears and barred body markings. The long-nosed bandicoot prefers bare forest floors or short grassland. Rabbit-eared bandicoots have still longer ears, a longer skull and limbs, and a highly developed inner ear structure. They are the only burrowing bandicoots.

Bandicoots are specialized for feeding on soil invertebrates, but they also seem to be opportunistic omnivorous feeders whose diet includes insects, fruits, seeds, fungi and plant fiber. The diet also includes a high proportion of surface foods. The bandicoot forages over its entire range of 2 to 12 acres, spending little time in one spot, which suggests that it is looking for scattered items rather than large concentrations of food.

The typical gestation period for bandicoots is about 12 days, which is half that of most marsupials. Common litter size is 2 to 4, and up to seven. The young crawl to the pouch and attach themselves to a nipple for 49 to 50 days. Sexual maturity can be reached in 90 days. Females breed throughout the year in favorable climates, and mating occurs when one litter is nearing the end of its pouch life. Weaning occurs 10 days after the young leave the pouch, and the new litter may be born a day or two later. Bandicoots have become uniquely specialized for a high reproductive rate and low parental care. This is achieved by accelerated gestation, rapid development of the young in the pouch, early sexual maturity, and a rapid succession of litters. Because bandicoots are solitary, coming together only to mate, there is no attachment between mother and young, and all contact is lost at weaning.

In spite of their unique reproductive characteristics, Australian bandicoots have experienced the greatest decrease of all marsupials. Bandicoots are extremely dependent on ground cover, and grazing by sheep, cattle and rabbits render a habitat unusable. Introduced predators, especially foxes and cats, find bandicoots easy prey. Bandicoots adapted to areas of heavy rainfall have not been as seriously affected because of the regenerative ability of the vegetation cover.

Possums

The Australian possums, ringtails, pygmy and gliders, are nocturnal animals with large, protruding eyes. Most of the species are quiet and secretive, and occasionally emit soft, twittering sounds. If attacked, they screech loudly. The gliders, of which Leadbeater's is one, are arboreal leaf-eaters (folivores) that require a high fibrous diet. They grind their food finely with well developed molars. Pygmy possums also thrive in the nectar-rich heathlands, shrublands and eucalyptus forests. All of the small possum species are extremely mobile, and in poor seasons many individuals may be found in isolated flowering trees and shrubs, which provide pollen and insects.

These possums have large litters of 4 to 6 young and rapid growth development rates. The competition for mating partners has led to the development of scent-marking glands for use in marking members of the social group, indicating the individual's social status, sex, group membership, and reproductive position.

Eastern Jerboa Marsupial [=Kultarr]

Antechinomys laniger

P. Woolley and D. Walsh, NPIAW

Status	Endangered
Listed	December 2, 1970
Family	Dasyuridae (carnivorous marsupial)
Description	Small, rodent-like, gray and speckled marsupium with white underparts and legs; It has large ears and eyes, a long thin tail, and long hindlegs.
Habitat	Tropical rain forests.
Food	Insects
Reproduction	6 to 8 young
Threats	Soil erosion, dry-land salinization, poor water quality, and rising groundwater tables.
Range	Australia: Queensland, New South Wales, Victoria

Description

The Eastern jerboa marsupial, *Antechinomys laniger*, is fawn-gray to tan above and speckled. This marsupium is rodent-like in appearance and only about 5.5 inches in length whose tail is much longer than its head and body length. Its underparts and legs are white. It has large ears and eyes, a long thin tail, and long hindlegs.

Originally known as the Jerboa marsupial, it is better named the kultarr since its method of locomotion includes all four legs rather than the hopping motion of most marsupials.

Behavior

The kultarr moves using all four legs, bounding from hindlegs to forelegs. It can change directions quickly by pivoting on its forefeet.

The kultarr adopts burrows of other animals, including spiders and mice, and may dig burrows of its own, covered with grass.

This species is nocturnal. It forages at night on insects such as spiders, crickets and cockroaches.

Females produce as many young as they have teats to feed them, either 6 or 8. The mammary glands develop during the breeding season, then regress once the young are weaned, about 3 months after birth. They can leave the pouch after about 30 days, when they are placed in the nest, and eventually accompany the mother by clinging to her back. Mother and young call to each other if lost.

The eastern subspecies is identified as *A.l. laniger*; the western subspecies is *A.l. spenceri*. The two subspecies exhibit different reproduction cycles and inhabit different types of terrain.

Habitat

The kultarr inhabits desert plains and stony terrain marked by grasses and small bushes. The eastern population's preferred habitat is composed primarily of sparsely vegetated claypans among Acacia woodland. The western population inhabits stony scrubland characterized by stumps, tussocks, and cracking soil.

Distribution

The kultarr occurs throughout the southern interior of Australia from eastern Australia through central and western Australia. Although uncommon throughout its range, it does not appear to be endangered, except in southwestern Queensland and in southern New South Wales where it has not been reported since the early 1900s.

Threats

The kultarr does not seem to be affected by human activity except when its habitat is altered for agricultural use.

Conservation and Recovery

Since it is not endangered throughout much of its range, no specific plans have been adopted to protect this species. However, the Australian government has assessed the importance of the nation's natural resources and has embraced a natural resources conservation program that encourages the preservation of habitat.

Gaimard's Rat-kangaroo

Bettongia gaimardi

Dave Watts, NPIAW

Status	Endangered
Listed	June 4, 1973
Family	Macropodidae (Rat-kangaroo)
Description	Rat-like in appearance with long hind feet and well-developed hind limbs, short pelage, ears and snout.
Habitat	Grassland, desert, woodland and open forests.
Food	Bulky foliage and herbs.
Reproduction	1 or 2 after gestation periodof 21 days.
Threats	Clear felling of native hardwood forests; soil erosion, dry-land salinization, poor water quality, and rising groundwater tables.
Range	Australia: Tasmania

Description

Gaimard's rat-kangaroo, *Bettongia gaimardi*, is a rat-like marsupial in appearance with long hind feet and well-developed hind limbs. This species measures 11 to 16 inches in body length with a tail length of 8 to 10 inches. Its weight at maturity is approximately 2 to 7 pounds. The upper parts of adult Gaimard's rat-kangaroo are buff gray to grayish brown and the underparts are grayish-white. The furry tail usually has a white tip. This species has a short snout and ears.

Gaimard's rat-kangaroo is a macropod as it is a member of the kangaroo family and the *Potoroinae* subfamily. Recognizable characteristics of this group are the large hind limbs, long back feet and modified teeth. The rat-kangaroos of Australia are distinguished and placed into five genera: *Bettongia, Caloprymnus, Aepyprymnus, Potorous,* and *Hypsiprymnodon.* Gaimard's rat-kangaroo is known as the Eastern bettong, Tasmanian rat-kangaroo or Tasmanian bettong.

Behavior

The reproduction cycle of Gaimard's rat-kangaroo is a 21 day gestation period with a pouch period of 90 to 115 days resulting in one or rarely two young being born at less than .03 ounces in weight. Young are weaned at 120 to 165 days and are sexually mature between 10 to 12 months. The life span of Gaimard's rat-kangaroo is four to six years. Breeding is continuous, and a female may produce two or three young a year.

Nests usually are constructed of grass and sometimes sticks or bark. Gaimard's rat-kangaroo carry nesting material in the curled-up tips of their tails. These nests are usually located under overhanging bush or at the base of grass tussocks.

Gaimard's rat-kangaroos have specialized teeth for grazing. This species seems primarily herbivorous and feeds on roots, tubers, seeds and legume pods, and especially underground fungi, which the bettong helps to disperse.

This species is nocturnal, resting in its nest during daylight hours. Upon leaving the nest at night, it travels a long distance away before stopping to feed. An individual will return to the same nest for up to a month, and may reoccupy the same nest in the future. Two individuals may occupy the same nest at the same time.

Habitat

Gaimard's rat-kangaroo is now restricted to Tasmania. When it inhabited the southeastern coastal region of the Australian mainland, its original habitat was open grassland but heavy agricultural use of these regions forced it into dry, fire-prone open hardwood forest with a grassy understory in poor soil. Gaimard's rat-kangaroo avoids dense vegetation areas. Its habitat today consists of woodlands with grassland territories with areas up to 337 acres.

Distribution

Gaimard's rat-kangaroo was once plentiful throughout southeastern Queensland, coastal New South Wales, southern Victoria and Tasmania but is thought to have become extinct on mainland Australia during the early twentieth century. It is relatively common throughout its range on Tasmania.

Threats

The primary cause of decline in Gaimard's rat-kangaroo is the clearing of brush for agricultural development. Birds of prey and snakes are common enemies of this species.

Conservation and Recovery

It is thought that Gaimard's rat-kangaroo has thrived on Tasmania because of the low numbers of predator foxes and rabbits, which degrade the grassy habitat which this bettong requires. Tasmania also remains relatively undeveloped agriculturally, and as long as the grassy habitats remain intact, Gaimard's rat-kangaroo will prosper.

Lesueur's Rat-Kangaroo [=Burrowing Bettong]

Bettongia lesueur

Babs and Bert Wells, NPIAW

Status	Endangered
Listed	December 2, 1970
Family	Macropodidae (Kangaroo)
Description	Rat-like kangaroo with a tail as long as the body; yellowish-gray above with light gray underparts.
Habitat	Low bushes or grassy tussocks.
Food	Vegetation
Reproduction	Single young after a gestation period of 21 days.
Threats	Loss of habitat.
Range	Central Australia

Description

Lesueur's rat-kangaroo, *Bettongia lesueur*, also called the burrowing bettong, balances on its large hind feet and tail like a kangaroo. Morphologically, this species resembles a rat, yielding the common name. Measured from the tip of its snout to the base of its tail, this species is 12 to 15 inches long. The tail is about as long as the body. Rat-kangaroos weigh about 2.5 to 3.5 pounds.

The pelage of this rat-kangaroo is yellowish-gray above with light gray underparts. The island populations have plain gray upperparts with lighter gray underparts. Its body is thickset, with short, rounded ears. Its tail is fat but has few hairs.

B. lesueur was originally classified by Quoy and Gaimard in 1824.

Behavior

The burrowing bettong derives its name because it is the only bettong to regularly inhabit burrows. The burrows may be simple, one tunnel structures with two or three entrances, or complex warrens with many tunnels and entrances. One warren was reported to have 120 entrances; a rough guess as to population is that there are half as many residents as entrances. Burrows are constructed in sandy soil or under outcrops of limestone. On Barrow Island burrows are almost always constructed in limestone out-crops on slopes or in the floors of caves. The burrowing bettong will tolerate some other marsupials sharing the warren.

Lesueur's rat-kangaroo is nocturnal. It forages by digging, and its seems to locate food sources through smell, keeping its nose close to the ground. Food sources include seeds, roots, termites, fungi, and the fruit of figs.

Females produce a single young after a gestation period of 21 days. The young re-mains in the pouch for 115 days. The female may breed again once the young leaves the pouch, so she could produce as many as three young a year.

Habitat

Lesueur's rat-kangaroo inhabits wood-lands and semi-deserts on the islands of Bernier, Dorre, Barrow and Boodie off the coast of western Australia.

Distribution

Formerly, Lesueur's rat-kangaroo had one of the most widespread ranges of any of the Australian marsupials, occurring throughout the southeast coast and from the west coast to the eastern cordillera in New South Wales but may not have occurred in the northeastern sector including most of Queensland and part of New South Wales. By 1863 it had disap-peared from Victoria but survived throughout the rest of its range until the 1930s when fox were established. Although the burrowing bettong and rabbits compete for the same food sources, these two species shared burrows and habitat in the areas where food supplies were plentiful.

Today Lesueur's rat-kangaroo is restricted to a few isolated populations in central Aus-tralia and the nearby Barrow, Bernier and Dorre Islands.

Threats

The clearing of the former woodland and desert habitat for grazing and other agricul-tural practices has severely decimated the Lesueur's rat-kangaroo population in much of Australia. Along with clearing the land, Euro-pean settlers also introduced rabbits, to the determent of this rat-kangaroo, for rabbits take over their burrows. Goats also threaten this species by altering the natural environ-ment.

Conservation and Recovery

Australia has been involved in World Wilderness Congresses and has participated in Inverness, UNEP, IUCN, CITES, South Pacific Regional Environmental Program, and Findhorn. In fact Australia was one of the first countries to adopt the World Conservation Strategy and to develop a National Conserva-tion Strategy.

For Lesueur's rat-kangaroo, Australia has designated Bernier and Dorre Islands as a Class A reserve for the conservation of fauna.

Brush-tailed Rat-kangaroo [=Bettong]

Bettongia penicillata

ANCA

Status	Endangered
Listed	December 2, 1970
Family	Macropodidae (Rat-kangaroo)
Description	Yellowish-gray above, paler below with a black crest on the tail.
Habitat	Wondoo forests and brush woodland of southwest Australia; nests consist of dry grass.
Food	Mushrooms, bulbs, tubers, seeds, insects and resin.
Reproduction	1, rarely 2 young after a short gestation; pouch period of 90 to 115 days.
Threats	Loss of habitat due to clearfelling of native hardwood forests.
Range	Southwest Australia

Description

The brush-tailed rat-kangaroo, *Bettongia penicillata*, is unusual in that it stands by balancing on its large hind feet and tail, like a kangaroo. Morphologically, it resembles a rat, yielding the common name. This species measures in body length 11 to 16 inches. The long tail has a measurement of approximately 8 to 10 inches with a body weight of 2 to 7 pounds. The overall coloring is yellowish-grayish that is paler on the underparts. There are noticeable black hairs in rows on its tail. Unworn adult pelage is crisp and sometimes harsh.

The genus *Bettongia* was discovered by Gray in 1937. Four species of rat-kangaroos were described by Ride in 1970 and by Kirsch and Calaby in 1977. The brush-tail rat-kangaroo is also commonly known as the bettong and the woylie.

Behavior

Breeding occurs year round and the female produces young every 100 days over her entire lifespan of 4 to 6 years. The gestation period is 21 days. One, very rarely two, young are born weighing less than 0.03 ounces, after a pouch period of 90 to 115 days, until the next generation of young is born. Females have four mammae and well-developed pouches.

Weaning takes place after 120 to 165 days. The brush-tail rat-kangaroo reaches maturity at approximately 180 days. This species' life span has been documented at four to six years; though in captivity some have survived for eight years.

The main portion of the brush-tail rat-kangaroo diet consists of mushrooms, tubers, roots, seeds, and insects. There have been documented reports of feeding on marine refuse, carrion and meat. This species is a solitary nocturnal mammal that forages between dusk and an hour before dawn, and spends the daylight hours in a nest made of grass or bark built over a shallow depression.

Habitat

The brush-tail rat-kangaroo's range is restricted to a few tracts of open forest and temperate woodlands covered with tussocks and bushes at the extreme southwestern tip of Australia.

Distribution

The brush-tail rat-kangaroo was once abundant across the southern part of Australia, including certain islands and northwestern Victoria. By the end of the nineteenth century it was rare, and by the 1920s it was extinct over most of its range except for the very most southwest tip of Western Australia. Today the brush-tail rat-kangaroo is restricted to a few woodland tracts at the extreme southwestern tip of Australia.

Threats

Although the brush-tailed bettong has not been excluded from its range by agricultural development or grazing animals, it has been severely threatened by the fox.

Conservation and Recovery

Colonies of the brush-tail rat-kangaroo have been reestablished on Francis and Wedge Islands, Australia. Australian National Parks and Wildlife Service protect this species in the Perup and Dryandra forests and in the Tuttanning Reserve.

Queensland Rat-kangaroo

Bettongia tropica

P. M. Johnson, NPIAW

Status	Endangered
Listed	December 2, 1970
Family	Macropodidae (Rat-kangaroo)
Description	Rat-like kangaroo with a small head and body, and crested tail with a black or white tip.
Habitat	Broadleaf evergreen forests.
Food	Herbivorous
Reproduction	One young every 100 days over her entire lifespan.
Threats	Habitat disturbance; predation
Range	Australia: eastern Queensland

Description

The Queensland rat-kangaroo, *Bettongia tropica* is a small rat-looking marsupial. It has a small head and body; its length is about 14 inches. Its tail is crested with either a black or white tip and measures approximately 12 inches. The body color is gray, darker above than below.

Some authorities regard *B. tropica* as a subspecies of *B. penicillatta*, the brush-tailed bettong. Other common names for the Queensland rat-kangaroo are the northern rat-kangaroo and the northern bettong.

Behavior

This species is herbivorous and has a specialized digestive system to digest the vast quantities and variety of vegetation it eats. An important food source is mycorrhizal fungi, as well as the underground portions of cockatoo grass.

The Queensland rat-kangaroo is nocturnal, ranging widely at night. It rests during the day in grass nests constructed in the forest. It may also use hollow logs for daytime shelter. The Queensland rat-kangaroo is solitary, although it will share its nest or hollow with other individuals.

This bettong feeds on the soft spore-mass of underground fungi which it forages from shallow holes. It supplements its diet with cockatoo grass.

Reproduction for the Queensland rat-kangaroo is probably the same as for *B. penicillata*. Breeding occurs year round and the female produces one young every 100 days over her entire lifespan. The gestation period is 21 days. After a pouch period of 90 to 115 days, the next generation of young is born. Females have four mammae and well-developed pouches. Weaning takes place after 120 to 165 days. Sexual maturity is reached at approximately 180 days.

The population growth of this species is related to the abundance of underground fungi, which is partly determined by the frequency of forest fires. The Queensland rat-kangaroo can survive forest fires and apparently has an advantage over other species during periods of frequent fires.

Habitat

Lamb Range, the habitat of one of the two extant populations of the Queensland rat-kangaroo, comprises grassy, open forests and woodlands at elevations of 400 to 1,100 meters, whose tree specimens include eucalyptus and gums. Mount Windsor contains tall, open eucalyptus forests adjacent to rainforests at elevations of 2,900 to 3,900 feet.

Distribution

The Queensland rat-kangaroo is known only from samples collected in Queensland. In 1884 one specimen was found at the Coomooboolaroo Station in Dawson Valley in southeastern Queensland. Other specimens were found in 1922 a few miles south of Ravenshoe, north Queensland. Mount Spurgeon, 48 kilometers northwest of Cairns in north Queensland was the site of other collections in 1932.

In 1976 a few individuals were discovered at Davies Creek, and later expeditions recorded two isolated populations. One east of Mareba (Lamb Range) and the other west of Mossman (Mount Windsor). The Lamb Range population seems to be larger, but populations will fluctuate with the availability of fungi.

Threats

Since the Queensland rat-kangaroo has only been collected six times, the reasons for its rarity are not known.

Conservation and Recovery

The Windsor population falls within the Wet Tropics World Heritage area and the Lamb Range population falls within protected reserves, so species management is possible once the species' relation to fires and the common *rufous bettong* can be determined.

Mountain Pygmy Possum

Burramys parvus

L. Broome, NPIAW

Status	Endangered
Listed	December 2, 1970
Family	Burramyidae (Possum)
Description	Mouse-like possum with fine, dense, short fur; short and somewhat curved claws.
Habitat	Inhabits dense shrub, snowgum trees in alpine and subalpine areas.
Food	Seeds and nuts.
Reproduction	4 young after gestation of 14 to 16 days.
Threats	Introduction of predator species.
Range	Australia: Eastern Victoria

Description

The mountain pygmy possum, *Burramys parvus*, is mouse-like in appearance with fine, gray-brown dense fur that is short and soft. Its underparts are a pale gray-brown to cream; the flanks are bright orange, and are particularly pronounced in males during the breeding season. The tail is long, thin and scaly, and seems to be naked but is actually covered with very fine hair and scales; its body size is approximately 4 to 5 inches in length with a tail length of 5 to 6 inches. Its body weight is 1 to a little over 2 ounces. This species has unusually large premolar teeth. There is a distinct pouch in females with two pairs of mammae. These possums are unique in that they have syndactyl toes.

The *Burramyidae* family consists of mouse-like marsupials with syndactyl toes. In the early 1950s specimens were examined by W.D. L. Ride who determined that *Burramys* actually are a small possum related to *Cercartetus*. In August 1966 a live specimen was found in a ski hut on Mount Hotham, Victoria and upon examination it was identified as *B. parvus*. The mountain pygmy possum is also known as a pygmy phalanger.

Until 1895 this species was apparently extinct and was described only on the basis of jaw and skull fragments found in a cave in New South Wales. In 1952 David Ride discovered that the species was closely related to living species of pygmy possum.

Behavior

The mountain pygmy possum is nocturnal, traveling up to 1.5 kilometers among boulder patches in search of food, particularly in search of the Bogong moth during the summer months. It occupies home ranges that vary in size according to the abundance of food sources. In the most productive habitat, Mount Higgenbotham (Victoria), the overlapping ranges are small and densities are as high as 115 individuals per hectare, compared to 6 individuals per hectare in New South Wales.

During winter some populations experience a state of torpor similar to hibernation during which their body temperature and energy levels are reduced. The species spends six months beneath a blanket of snow in the high altitude heaths of the Snowy Mountains. Unlike other pygmy possums, which build nests in tree hollows, the mountain pygmy possum constructs ground nests which are covered with snow during the winter hibernation.

The mountain pygmy possum forages on the ground and in trees and has a unique diet of seeds, fleshy fruit, plant foliage, and insects, especially caterpillars, millipedes, beetles, spiders and the Bogong moth. The sectorial premolar tooth is adapted for husking and cracking seeds, and it will store excess seeds for winter shortages.

The reproduction cycle of the mountain pygmy possum consists of a gestation period for 13 to 16 days, giving birth to 4 young weighing less than 0.03 ounces at birth. After a pouch period of 22-30 days, the young become independent; they wean themselves at approximately 55 to 60 days and reach sexual maturity at 1 year. Breeding occurs in the spring after the female's second summer. Its life cycle has been documented at over 4 years.

Following breeding, the body weight doubles in anticipation of the winter hibernation. Females hibernate first, at the beginning of the snowfall, but juveniles and males are active for another month or two, especially at the lower elevations. Adults may hibernate for up to seven months; juveniles up to five months.

Habitat

The mountain pygmy possum lives at elevations between 4,200 and 7,140 feet on end moraines of glaciers and between boulders in rocky, brush-covered areas with alpine vegetation associated with snow gum trees. In the winter its habitat is covered with snow for at least 3 months of the year, where it hibernates under the snow cover. The boulders reduce the extreme temperatures and provide sheltered nesting sites. The boulders are used during the summer as aestivation sites by migratory Bogong moths, which form part of the food resources. This is the only member of the pygmy possum that does not live as a forest dweller.

Distribution

This species was found in 1966 in the Alps of eastern Victoria. Today, the mountain pygmy possum's only range is 68 miles outside of Melbourne. It is restricted to four known populations on Mount Kosciusko, Mount Bogong, Mount Hotham (Victoria), and in the Kosciusko National Park. The total population is estimated at 2,600 individuals.

Threats

Victoria's central highland forests were dominated by the mountain ash, the world's tallest hardwood tree. In 1939 a fire destroyed two-thirds of the forests, and the remaining forest has been degraded by excessive logging and inadequate forest management techniques. The area is also being developed as a ski-run and tourist attraction, which will certainly pressure the habitat and both endangered animals, the mountain pygmy possum and Leadbeater's possum.

Conservation and Recovery

The mountain pygmy possum is protected against taking by the laws of Victoria, but only some parts of its habitat are being managed with consideration of its welfare. More effective government management is essential for the species recovery.

This species occurs in such small numbers that inbreeding and loss of genetic viability could be a problem.

Plains Rat-kangaroo
Caloprymnus campestris

Gould illustration

Status	Endangered (Probably extinct)
Listed	December 2, 1970
Family	Macropodidae (Kangaroo)
Description	Rat-like kangaroo with short pelage, short snout, and relatively long ears.
Habitat	Sandridge flats and stony plains.
Food	Probably vegetation.
Reproduction	Single young.
Threats	Primarily predation.
Range	Queensland and South Australia

Description

This small marsupial, *Caloprymnus campestris*, commonly known as the plains rat-kangaroo, is rat-like in appearance with long hind feet and well-developed hind limbs. It hops with an easy stride and can run swiftly for several miles. The forearms are short and weak, and between the forearms is a patch of hairless skin. Its pelage is short and the color is grayish brown on the top of the back and head, becoming brown, then tan as it progresses to the underparts. Its muzzle is short with large upper lips. This species is distinguished by its comparably long ears and tail that is as long as the head and body.

Other common names include the desert rat-kangaroo and buff-nose rat-kangaroo.

Behavior

The plains rat-kangaroo lives in flimsy nests built of leaves, grasses and twigs and located in hollows, preferably under a bush, but often in the open. It is nocturnal.

As the plains rat-kangaroo has not been reported since 1935, its food habits are unknown. However, other rat-kangaroos eat vegetation. This species was not dependent on surface water or succulent plants that would have provided moisture through the vegetation.

Females, who produce one young, have a deep pouch with four teats.

Habitat

The plains rat-kangaroo is known to have inhabited sandridge flats and stony plains bordering the Simpson Desert in the gibber plains of Australia. This habitat is usually only sparsely covered with shrubs, which included saltbrush, emu bush, and corkwood.

Distribution

The plains rat-kangaroo is known from southwestern Queensland and northeastern South Australia. A survey in 1931 found this rat-kangaroo common on only two small flats lying west and east of Cooncheri and a specimen was collected on the low Diamantina in the far northeastern corner of South Australia. First described in 1843 by Gould, this species was not recorded again until 1931 and the last confirmed sighting was in 1935. It is presumed extinct but may survive in the remote parts of its range.

Threats

Since the plains rat-kangaroo has not been recorded since 1935, the reasons it has vanished are not known. However, other rat-kangaroos in Australia are threatened by habitat degradation and the introduction of non-native species such as rabbits and goats.

Conservation and Recovery

Australia has been involved in World Wilderness Congresses and has participated in Inverness, UNEP, IUCN, CITES, South Pacific Regional Environmental Program, and Findhorn. Australia was one of the first countries to adopt the World Conservation Strategy and to develop a National Conservation Strategy. However, no recovery plans have been formulated because no current population is known.

Pig-footed Bandicoot
Chaeropus ecaudatus

ANCA

Status	Endangered (Probably extinct)
Listed	December 2, 1970
Family	Peramelidae (Bandicoots)
Description	Slightly smaller than a rabbit; gray-brown with long slender legs and long ears and a crested tail.
Habitat	Semi-arid woodlands, grasslands and mallee scrub.
Food	Coarse barley and native grasses; perhaps rodents and insects.
Reproduction	Breeding season seems to be in May and June, producing 2 young.
Threats	Habitat destruction; introduction of domestic cats, dogs and foxes.
Range	South Australia

Description

The pig-footed bandicoot, *Chaeropus ecaudatus*, is slightly smaller than a rabbit. The snout is sharp and pointed, giving the head a rather bird-like appearance; ears are very long and point backward. The tail is long and about half the animal's body length which is about 5 to 6 inches. The pouch opens downwards and backwards and there are approximately 8 mammae. The coarse fur is orange-brownish on the back and a pale color below. Its long slender legs have a miniature deer-like appearance.

The common name, pig-footed, is derived from the hooflike claws of the forefoot which were thought to resemble a pig's, although it more closely resembles a deer's hoof. All four legs are well developed, long and slender for speedy locomotion.

Behavior

Because this species is possibly extinct there is little known about its life cycle. Studies have been documented that the breeding season seems to be in May and June, producing 2 young. There is a short gestation period; short development period; females produce large ovum with a series of membranes.

The pig-footed bandicoot was reported to be a strict vegetarian by Krefft, Byrne and Gilbert in about 1857, feeding mainly on coarse barley and native grasses. It was recorded that their specimens did not attack mice or eat meat like other bandicoots. However, the explorer Sturt, on the contrary, noted that they showed a "partiality for flesh, through not flourishing" on such a diet, including insects which the captured specimens were fed by aborigine guides. In captivity it fed on grass, lettuce, roots and grasshoppers.

This species spends the day in a low, covered nest of dried grass and pieces of sticks. At night it burrows its way out of the nest leaving no opening. Its burrow is usually 12 inches long and about 8 to 10 inches deep. Most of the time the burrow is left open.

Habitat

The pig-footed bandicoot occupied sand dunes and sand plains grasslands in the central deserts. In moister climates it occupied grassy plains and open woodlands with a shrub understory.

Distribution

The first specimens were collected in Victoria in 1836. Later, specimens were collected in South Australia, Western Australia, and the Northern Territory. It apparently disappeared from South Australia in the early part of the 1900s but survived in Western Australia until the 1950s. It is assumed to be extinct.

Threats

The decline of the pig-footed bandicoot has been caused by the introduction of domestic livestock that destroyed much of its habitat. Competition of introduced rabbits also contributed to the decline of this species, as well as the feral cat. The introduced fox may have contributed to the final extirpation, although this bandicoot was doomed to extinction by the time the fox and rabbit were established in the bandicoot's range.

Conservation and Recovery

Even though this species is protected in Australia most documentation has noted that it is probably extinct.

Eastern Native-cat [=Eastern Quoll]

Dasyurus viverrinus

Dave Watts

Status	Endangered
Listed	June 4, 1973
Family	Dasyuridae (Carnivorous marsupials)
Description	Sleek, slender marsupial resembling a domestic cat, with a spotted coat; measuring 11-18 inches long from the tip of its snout to the base of the tail.
Habitat	Scrub and rain forest areas.
Food	Carnivorous
Reproduction	5 to 6 young after gestation of 8 to 15 days.
Threats	Epidemic disease.
Range	Australia: Tasmania

Description

The Eastern native-cat, *Dasyurus viverrinus*, has two color phases, one fawn, the other black. All eastern native cats have prominent white spots or blotches on the back and sides of their coat. The coat is usually short, soft and very thick. Measured from the tip of its snout to the base of the tail this species is 11 to 18 inches; tail length is between 7 to 11 inches long. Males weigh approximately 2 to 4 pounds while females weigh 1 to 3 pounds.

The eastern native cat is also known as the Eastern quoll and Eastern Australian native cat. This marsupial is a member of the Dasyuridae family. A significant difference between *D. viverrinus* and other members of the family is that it lacks a first toe on the hind foot while the pads of the feet are granulated.

Behavior

The eastern native cat's diet consists of caterpillars of the butterfly genus *Oncoipera* called Corbie grubs or earthworms. The dasyruidids are the only carnivorous marsupials. At night this species becomes active and moves into pastures to hunt and forage.

Gestation of the eastern native cat is

approximately 21 days with a litter size of up to 30. However, survival is limited to the first 6 young to attach themselves to the mother's 6 teats. Young wean themselves at approximately 8 weeks and become independent by 18 weeks. Documented life span of the eastern native cat has been up to six years.

Habitat

The eastern native cat is most commonly found in dryer forest and open country areas where bush and pasture are interspersed, thus providing accessible hunting grounds and suitable shelter. During the day the eastern native-cat's refuge mainly consists of rock piles and hollow logs.

Distribution

The eastern native cat today is restricted to the island of Tasmania. This species was once known from southeastern Australia, even in suburbs of large cities like Melbourne and Adelaide, and were also found on Kangaroo Island and King Island.

Threats

The eastern native cat has declined extremely since the settlement of Australia by Europeans. Direct human harassment by killing this species for its raids on domestic poultry have almost exterminated the eastern native cat from the mainland of Australia. Destruction of Australia's canopy, and introduction of competitors such as domestic cats and dogs have also contributed to the decline of this species. In the years between 1901-1905 this species suffered from an epidemic dis-

ease. This disease continues to plague the Tasmanian population today. In Queensland, the eastern native cat also is declining due to the toxic cane toad, a South American native introduced in 1935 to control sugar cane beetles. Species are poisoned when they attempt to eat this cane toad.

Conservation and Recovery

The eastern native cat populations occurring on the island of Tasmania are totally protected. This species is actively and successfully bred in captivity.

Australia has been involved in World Wilderness Congresses and has participated in Inverness, UNEP, IUCN, CITES, South Pacific Regional Environmental Program, and Findhorn. Australia was one of the first countries to adopt the World Conservation Strategy and to develop a National Conservation Strategy.

Black Dorcopsis Wallaby

Dorcopsis atrata

Status	Vulnerable
Listed	IUCN Red List
Family	Macropodidae (Wallabies)
Description	Thick black fur; broad feet; drooping muzzel.
Habitat	Mountainous rain forests.
Food	Fruits, buds, and leaves, and possibly insects.
Reproduction	One young.
Threats	Deforestation.
Range	Papua New Guinea: Goodenough Island

Description

The black dorcopsis wallaby, *Dorcopsis atrata*, is considered by naturalists to be one of the more primitive examples of the family of true kangaroos (*Macropodidae*). They may be sexually dimorphic, with males larger than females, although this is not certain. Adults of these rarely observed animals may stand 16 inches high, although the range of height may be 12 to 20 inches. They may be 20 inches in length, with males possibly reaching as much as 28 inches, and females may be as small as 11 inches. Their tails are about 16 inches long. They may weigh about 8 pounds.

They have broad feet. Their muzzle droops somewhat. When sitting or hopping they hold their tail off the ground, sometimes vertically, sometimes horizontally with a curve that points the tip vertically to the ground. Its molars have sharp edges — an adaptation for biting through hard plant stems and branches. Its black fur is thick, an adaptation for the cool climate of the mountains that are its home.

This species is also known as the Black Forest wallaby.

Behavior

The black dorcopsis wallaby was discovered in the 1950s and since then has been little observed. Therefore, much of its behavior is mysterious. Its mating habits are largely subject to conjecture, but pregnancies result in the birth of one youngster, which then spends perhaps 10 months in the pouch. It is weaned after a year and reaches sexual maturity after two years. The black coat suggests that it is a nocturnal animal, with the coat offering camouflage in the darkness.

Habitat

This species inhabits the cool mountain rain forest of Goodenough Island of Papua New Guinea.

Distribution

The black dorcopsis wallaby lives on Papua New Guinea's Goodenough Island. Little observed, it is thought by naturalists to be rare even in its native range.

Threats

So little is known about the black dorcopsis wallaby that developing conservation plans would be difficult. It is thought to be threatened by deforestation of its range by logging and by predators introduced by man, especially dingoes.

Conservation and Recovery

The first step in conserving this species would be to preserve what is left of its habitat; the second would be to properly study its biology and habits in order to establish its requirement for a good breeding population, as well as a good breeding environment.

Leadbeater's Possum

Gymnobelideus leadbeateri

P. R. Brown, NPIAW

Status	Endangered
Listed	May 16, 1986
Family	Phalangeridae (Possum)
Description	Blue-gray to brown above with a dark mid-dorsal stripe from between the eys to the middle of the back; cream to pale gray below.
Habitat	Moist, high-altitude eucalyptus forests with mountain ash trees over 150 years old.
Food	Nectar, insects.
Reproduction	1 or 2 young born in May or June.
Threats	Loss of ancient trees.
Range	Australia: Victoria

Description

Leadbeater's possum, *Gymnobelideus leadbeateri*, is approximately 6 inches long, with a tail about 8 inches long and flattened laterally. It is blue-gray to brown above with a dark mid-dorsal stripe from between the eyes to the middle of the back. It is cream to pale gray below. The club-shaped tail is gray to black, sometimes tipped with white.

Another common name is fairy possum.

Behavior

Leadbeater's possum feeds on wattle or acacia gums, insects and insect exudates. By incising notches in the bark of trees, it enhances the production of gums. The habitat is highly productive, providing plentiful food sources that give individuals excess energy to defend territories.

Leadbeater's possum forms nesting groups comprised of one monogamous breeding pair, offspring, and up to three males. Members of one colony frequently visit other colonies, and often change groups. More aggressive females will attack intruders from other colonies; mothers also force daughters from the colony once they reach sexual maturity. These young females, who are dispersed at 10 months of age, suffer high mortality rates because of being excluded from another established colony. Males do not disperse until 15 months of age, and they are absorbed by other colonies until they mate.

Females occupy large, well-insulated nests constructed in a tree hollow. They actively defend a territory of 2.5 to 3.7 acres in which they exclude other females. Mating is monogamous and the male will help her defend the territory. Additional males are tolerated but do not participate in the pair-bonded couple.

Females produce 1 to 2 young per litter, normally in May or June. The young remain in the pouch for 80 to 93 days. After 111 days, they emerge from the nest to begin foraging alone, and are highly vulnerable to predation by owls. Life expectancy of females in the wild is 1.6 years.

Leadbeater's is the most primitive of the possum species, and it has the least developed of the scent glands, which are used to mark partners and other members of the group.

Habitat

Leadbeater's possum is an arboreal species restricted to moist, high-altitude eucalyptus forests of southeastern Australia. It apparently requires mature montane forest, with mountain ash trees over 150 years old, and containing hollows that are used for the construction of nests.

Distribution

Leadbeater's possum was first discovered in 1867 in the Bass River Valley, and only five specimens were collected prior to 1909 when it was last seen. By 1921 it was considered extinct but was rediscovered in 1961 in the wet mountains 68 miles from Melbourne. Surveys conducted since then have confirmed Leadbeater's possum at more than 180 locations in the Central Highlands. The population reached its highest level of an estimated 7,500 individuals during the early 1980s, but that number is expected to decline by as much as 90 percent (see below).

Threats

Victoria's central highland forests were dominated by the mountain ash, the world's tallest hardwood tree. In 1939 a fire destroyed two-thirds of the forests, and the remaining forest has been degraded by excessive logging and inadequate forest management techniques. The fire and development have destroyed many of the tree hollows required by the possum for nesting. Tree hollows suitable for this possum require 120 to 200 years to develop, and the trees destroyed by the fire will not be replenished until the middle of the 21st century. The trees that were not destroyed in the fire have been felled on a rotation of 40 to 80 years, which is too short a time for hollows to form.

Conservation and Recovery

Leadbeater's possum is protected against taking by the laws of Victoria, but only some parts of its habitat are being managed with consideration of its welfare.

This species occurs in such small numbers that inbreeding and loss of genetic viability will be a problem if the population is reduced by 90 percent, as expected.

Western [=Rufous] Hare Wallaby

Lagorchestes hirsutus

M. Lochman, NPIAW

Status	Endangered
Listed	December 2, 1970
Family	Macropodidae (Wallabies)
Description	Long, soft fur, gray on the back and ruddy on the sides.
Habitat	Grasslands and woodlands, primarily in tropical areas.
Food	Grass and buds.
Reproduction	One young per pregnancy.
Threats	Loss of habitat, human hunters, and birds of prey.
Range	Western Australia

Description

An adult western hare wallaby, *Lagorchestes hirsutus,* stands about 12 inches high; it is between 12.5 and 19 inches in length, not counting the tail; and its tail is between 9.5 and 20 inches long. They weigh from 2.5 to 10 pounds. It is long haired with soft fur, yet it is adapted to a hot, arid climate. It is possible for it to survive without drinking water, getting all of its moisture from the plants it eats.

Other common names include western hare-wallaby, rufous hare wallaby, and mala.

Behavior

These are nocturnal animals that spend their days resting in hollows in the ground that they have often dug themselves. They seem to prefer open country with tall grass, but they will live in woodlands that have much ground cover. They blend in well to their surroundings and may freeze in place in an effort not to be seen by predators. When it flees it can generate great force with its hind legs and has been reported to jump over the heads of humans. When browsing, it flops it legs out to the side and makes slow, loping hops.

It is apparently territorial, although not enough have been observed in the wild for this to be a certainty. Males are more territorial than females, tolerating the presence of other males only if no females are around. Introduce a female to the males, and they become intolerant of one another. They mark their territories by rubbing their scent glands on stones.

Reproduction may occur year round under favorable conditions. Females reach sexual maturity at 5 to 18 months; males at 14 months.

The western hare wallaby prefers forbs and grasses with a high water content, but it can tolerate the high fiber content of spinifex. It may also feed on seeds and insects during the dry season.

Habitat

The western hare wallaby seems to have been somewhat adaptable to different climates. Its ancient range consisted primarily of semi-arid grasslands and woodlands, but it included wet, tropical woodlands as well. The animal's primary requirements are warm temperatures, an abundance of ground cover, and grasses.

The Bernier and Dorre Island habitats are sand plains with low, woody shrubs accompanied by spinifex hummock grasslands.

Distribution

Once found in central and western Australia, the western hare wallaby is now found only on Dorre and Bernier islands near Shark Bay, Western Australia, and in areas where it has been reintroduced to the wild by Australia's Wildlife Service.

Historically, the population has varied considerably, reaching a high in 1906. The 1978 population on Dorre Island was abundant because of fires on the island five years earlier which replenished the vegetation necessary to sustain larger numbers of wallabies. The population on the islands in 1990 were estimated at 1,700 on Dorre and 2,600 on Bernier.

Threats

Before settlement of the islands by humans, the principal danger to the western hare wallaby would have been predatory birds. When the Aborigines came they hunted the western hare wallaby for food. They would burn a patch of grassland a few hundred yards wide and catch the wallabies that were uncovered. This form of hunting was not a significant threat to the western hare wallaby's survival as a species because much grassland surrounding the burned area was untouched, leaving the animal both food and places to hide. Besides, the burned area would often begin regrowing with sweet grasses and budding shrubs, offering western hare wallabies particularly nutritious food.

Europeans brought with them foxes and dogs, both of which hunt western hare wallabies; these predators had severely reduced the western hare wallaby population. Europeans also brought with them forms of agriculture that required large amounts of land. Grasslands were burned to make way for farms; this destruction of its habitat greatly reduced the numbers of western hare wallabies. Further, the western hare wallabies were seen as pests that raided crops, and they were therefore poisoned and shot. When it was very nearly extinct, a tiny population was found near Shark Bay, Western Australia. In one of the more poignant conservation efforts in Australian history, private citizens and the Wildlife Service made heroic efforts to protect and breed the western hare wallaby, and the Wildlife Service has been cooperating with local Aborigines to reintroduce the wallaby into some of its old range in Western Australia. Even so, it still clings on the edge of survival, just above extinction.

Conservation and Recovery

The Aborigines used fire to hunt wallabies, and their skilled use of controlled fires positively contributed to the regeneration of vegetation that supported this species. The western hare wallaby is being reintroduced into the Tanami Desert where a mosaic burning program is designed to establish vegetative diversity.

Banded Hare Wallaby

Lagostrophus fasciatus

Status	Endangered
Listed	December 2, 1970
Family	Macropodidae (Wallabies)
Description	Dark gray or brown fur with light underparts.
Habitat	Dense brush in woodlands and grasslands in a temperate climate.
Food	Grasses and legumes.
Reproduction	Single young remains in the pouch for about 6 months.
Threats	Loss of habitat.
Range	Western Australia

Babs and Bert Wells/Nature Focus

Description

Likely the only surviving species of the *Macropodidae* subfamily *Stherinae* (snout-nosed kangaroos), the banded hare wallaby, *Lagostrophus fasciatus*, is small, with adults reaching between 16 and 18 inches in body length and having tails about 14 to 16 inches long. Its ancient *Stherinae* relatives from the Pliocene and Pleistocene epochs were much larger, with one possibly weighing 220 pounds (*Troposodon*) and another reaching over 9 feet in length (*Procoptodon*). It is probable that these ancient species came into conflict with the banded hare wallaby for forage lands, with the small banded hare wallaby eventually winning.

Its general shape is reminiscent of a mouse, with large eyes set forward on the head, and small (proportionately, much smaller than on most other wallabies), oval ears that turn forward, outward, and backward. Its hair is short and thick, with its coat a dark gray or brown on its head and back. gradually lightening down the sides and legs to very pale, even white, on the underbody. The dark upper body hair is flecked with pale hairs, and the light lower body is flecked with dark hairs. Its name "banded" derives from stripes of hair slightly darker than the base color that rise from the edge of the underside, up sideways across the back, and down to the opposite edge of the underside. It uses its forepaws for digging roots. A very agile, quick animal, it can bound and race off like a rabbit and is capable of sudden shifts of direction — probably an adaptation to help it evade airborne predators.

Behavior

The banded hare wallaby lives in dense brush, through which it creates paths that it regularly uses, with the tops of grasses often covering the path, creating a tunnel and shielding the banded hare wallaby from birds of prey. It does not drink water, instead getting sufficient moisture from dew and the plants it eats. It is nocturnal; during the day it rests in hollows in the ground or in thickets, protecting itself from the sun and predators. It is somewhat territorial, with males often being solitary and rejecting the company of others of its species. Females and their young sometimes form loose groups of perhaps ten and share thickets with one another, especially when sheltering during the day. Their breeding habits are still obscure, although it seems as though females will mate frequently and with many different males. Births in October and November are rare, although the banded hare wallaby may breed any other time of the year. After 6 months, they emerge from the pouch; after 9 months, they are weaned; and after 12 months, they reach sexual maturity.

Habitat

The banded hare favors a range with much dense brush, in both grasslands and woodlands. The climate tends to be temperate, with cool nights and warm days.

Distribution

In the nineteenth century, the banded hare wallaby lived in most of southern and western Australia, but it disappeared from its southern territory in mid-century. Drought and agriculturalization have pressed it into a small coastal territory in Western Australia, where it primarily populates a few islands in or near Shark Bay: Bernier Island, Dirk Hartog Island, and Dorre Island. Preservation of those islands' habitat seems to be its best hope for survival.

Threats

Australia's terrible droughts of the past two decades have been very hard on wildlife, including the banded hare wallaby, drying up much of its preferred habitat. Agriculturalization has also shrunk the animal's territory. Sometimes considered a pest, it has been subject to poisoning and shooting.

Conservation and Recovery

Its now small population lives not only on the Australian mainland, but on Western Australian islands, as well. If these islands are protected from encroachment by humans and predators such as foxes, dogs, and cats, and if the droughts do not parch them, the banded hare wallaby has a good chance of surviving on them.

Hairy-nosed Wombat

Lasiorhinus krefftii

C. Andrew Henley, NPIAW

Status	Endangered
Listed	December 2, 1970; June 4, 1973
Family	Vombatidae (Wombats)
Description	Short, gray fur, broad muzzle, and bearlike build.
Habitat	Semiarid woodland.
Food	Primarily grass, along with herbs, roots, leaves, and fungi.
Reproduction	Females do not ovulate during droughts; single birth after gestation of 22 days.
Threats	Loss of habitat and predation by dingoes.
Range	Australia: Queensland

Description

Hairy-nosed wombats, *Lasiorhinus krefftii*, look like a cross between a pig and a rat; they are stout, with broad muzzles and thick limbs. Their heads are squarish, with low-set eyes and high, pointed ears. Their coloration is gray to dark gray. Probably because it is very rare, measurements of the northern hairy-nosed wombat are hard to come by. In general, adults are 39 inches in length from tip-of-nose to base-of-tail, with a tail of 1 inch in length. They stand about 14 inches at the shoulder, and they weigh 70 pounds. They are very strong animals, and although sedentary in most of their habits, they can run very

fast. Like rodents, they are gnawers, and they have continuously growing teeth that are perpetually worn down by the fibrous foods they gnaw on.

The climate of the northern hairy-nosed wombat's habitat is arid, with long dry spells and frequent droughts. The northern hairy-nosed wombat's metabolism has adapted to this unforgiving climate by slowing down and conserving water. Nearly all water is absorbed from its feces, and its urine is very concentrated. During droughts, its females will not ovulate, conserving biological resources for better times.

The northern hairy-nosed wombat is also known as Barnard's wombat, Queensland hairy-nosed wombat, and the soft-furred wombat. Taxonomists have also treated the species as *Lasiorhinus barnardi* and *Lasiorhinus gillespiei*.

Behavior

Northern hairy-nosed wombats breed in the spring. Their young are cared for by their mothers in burrows until they are eleven months old. They reach sexual maturity at two years of age. They scent-mark territorial boundaries, but do not seem as determined to drive off intruders as common wombats (*Vombatus ursinus*) are. They are powerful burrowing animals, creating elaborate tunnel systems that are remade and expanded from one generation to the next. The resulting burrows are not the exclusive property of those who dig them, and they are loosely shared with whatever northern hairy-nosed wombats want to use them at any given time. Further, northern hairy-nosed wombats will link burrows together, forming communities called "warrens."

The northern hairy-nosed wombat ventures out only at night during the hottest periods of the year, and their tunnels feature an indentation that is a rest area near a burrow entrance where they may lie still and check the amount of light and temperature outside. During cool periods, they may venture out during the day. When outside, they forage for the grasses and other fibrous plants that compose their diet. When frightened, they run for the nearest burrow. If the northern hairy-nosed wombats inside are strangers, then they will tolerate one another. The northern hairy-nosed wombats normally rest most of the day and move slowly, conserving energy because of their energy-poor diet, and they may appear sluggish and unthreatening

to humans; their lack of fear of humans may make them additionally appealing. These appearances are misleading; they may tolerate being touched by people, but when held or otherwise antagonized they can do considerable harm to a person with their powerful legs and strong digging claws, and they are known to bite ferociously.

Habitat

The northern hairy-nosed wombat occurs in semiarid woodlands where dry spells and droughts are common.

Distribution

Once found in scattered communities in Queensland, the northern hairy-nosed wombat is down to its last community in central Queensland.

Threats

Loss of habitat to human activities has limited the northern hairy-nosed wombat to its present tiny community. It has been killed by people because its burrowing disturbed rabbit-proof fences. Dingoes are its foremost natural predator, and given the chance, could wipe out the remaining populations in minutes.

Conservation and Recovery

The few remaining northern hairy-nosed wombats live in an enclosure amid a cattle run in Queensland. Their short-term survival depends on the protection of the enclosed area. Their long-term survival probably requires that they be given a much larger reserve in which to propagate.

Eastern Gray Kangaroo

Macropus giganteus

Status	Recovered
Listed	December 1974
Delisted	January 1993
Family	Macropodidae (Kangaroo)
Description	Silver grey pelage.
Habitat	Semi-arid mallee, scrub, woodland and forest.
Food	Grasses and bushes.
Reproduction	One young annually.
Threats	Urbanization and agriculture.
Range	Australia: New South Wales, Queensland, Tasmania

M. Jones, NPIAW

Description

The eastern gray kangaroo, *Macropus giganteus*, is one of the larger macropods (kangaroos and wallaroos) with a comparably large cranium and a large body. Males are larger than the females, with the males measuring from 1.8 to 4 feet in length and females measuring from 1.7 to 3.4 feet long. The overall fur color is silvery gray with lighter coloring on the paws. The muzzle and surface of the nose are covered with fine hair between the nostrils and upper lip.

This species is a member of the *Macropodidae* family. Formerly, the eastern gray kangaroo and the western gray kangaroo, *M. giganteus*, were considered the same species. Since then they have been divided into two distinct subspecies with *M. giganteus* containing three subspecies. Common names for the eastern gray kangaroo include forester kangaroo, scrub kangaroo, and scrubber.

Behavior

The eastern gray kangaroo may be one of the most social of all macropods as it congregates in "mobs" (groups) of more than 10 animals consisting mostly of adult females and young. Adult males only join the groups when females are in estrus. The larger males prefer to accompany females who will soon be receptive, and they chase weaker males away. The highest-ranking male ranges over the largest area in order to investigate the most receptive females. In general, this species stays within a limited home range even when food and water become scarce.

suckling with a second born.

Behavior

The eastern gray kangaroo feeds predominantly on grasses, although they will also browse on bushes. A study comparing the food habits of red kangaroos and gray kangaroos found that gray kangaroos ate larger quantities of grasses and bushes than red kangaroos.

In another study comparing the food habits of Red kangaroos, gray kangaroos and sheep, it was found that gray kangaroos ate many more grasses and browsed more bushes than red kangaroos. Even during times of drought when grasses and forbs are less plentiful, the eastern gray kangaroo will spend more time foraging for this preferred food source rather than feeding on more plentiful plants.

In general, kangaroos are nocturnal, feeding from late afternoon to early morning and resting during the day. Eastern gray kangaroos find shaded shelter during the day.

Breeding occurs year round but peaks during the summer. The courtship includes the male sniffing the female, pawing her head, and clutching her tail with his forepaws. Successful copulation may require mating attempts for several days. One, seldom two, young are reproduced after a gestation period of 36 days. The newborn climbs to the pouch a few minutes after birth and attaches itself to one of the four nipples. Although the female gray kangaroo comes into estrus 11 days after the young is born and she may mate as soon as four months afterward, she will not give birth again until the first born leaves the pouch at about 9 months. The first born, however, may continue nursing until it is 18 months old, and may share the mother's

Habitat

The eastern gray kangaroo can be found in forests and woodlands over a wide range of eastern Australia including Tasmania. It occupies areas comprised of semi-arid mallee, scrub, woodland and forest. Dense cover seems to be required for this species. The densities of this species are very low in more arid regions of its range, where they may be confined to narrow belts of woodland bordering watercourses. However, this species is considered abundant and widespread over large areas of eastern Australia where rainfall exceeds 9.8 inches but has little seasonal trend or where summer rains exceed winter rains.

Distribution

The eastern gray kangaroo occurs over a wide range of eastern and central Queensland, New South Wales, Victoria, extreme southeastern South Australia, and Tasmania. The subspecies *M. g. tasmaniensis* is only found on the island of Tasmania. The population increases or decreases with drought conditions. Regional dry periods occur about every ten years, and between droughts the number of kangaroos increases. The most recent estimate of eastern gray kangaroos is 20,000 animals.

Threats

Kangaroo habitat has been lost or degraded due to urbanization and agricultural development. The eastern gray kangaroo has lost habitat to development and agricultural practices in eastern Queensland, New South

Wales and throughout Victoria. The eastern gray kangaroo has for many years been considered a pest and competitor to livestock, and bounties were paid for its scalp. Its skin is also valuable for leather and its meat is edible.

Conservation and Recovery

In 1989, Greenpeace petitioned that a ban on the commercial importation of products from *M. giganteus*, *M. fuliginous*, and *M. rufus* be reimposed. The U.S. Fish and Wildlife Service responded that the ban was unnecessary because even though about 70 percent of the population has been harvested for commercial use, hunting does not appear to threaten these species. In the decision by the U.S. Fish and Wildlife Service to pursue the investigation to delist this species, several comments were received by citizens of more than 40 countries. Many felt that the commercial harvest system is driven by commercial greed rather than conservation interests; therefore, the species should not be delisted. Some concerned entities felt that the quota system was insensitive to environmental or stochastic events that may adversely affect the kangaroo populations. In response, the U.S. Fish and Wildlife Service said that the harvest quota system has the capability to be sensitive to changes affecting the kangaroo population. With proper research the harvest can be modified to respond to these changes.

Another preservation concern is that many believe that the Commonwealth, State and Territorial Governments have not implemented to the fullest extent the 27 recommendations of the Australian Senate Select Committee. Additionally it is believed by some that Queensland has not fully implemented the terms of the 1990 Settlement Agreement between Greenpeace Australia, Queensland and the Commonwealth of Australia. In response, the Commonwealth of Australia has sought additional funding to implement relevant recommendations. The Queensland National Parks and Wildlife Service has initiated changes in its kangaroo management system to respond to some of the commitments in the settlement agreement.

Due to the population estimates for this species (4.7 million in 1987) and the fact that there are individual conservation programs, in November 1990, the Wildlife Legislative fund petitioned that *M. giganteus*, *M. fuliginous*, and *M. rufus* be delisted from the list of endangered and threatened wildlife and plants. The petition was assessed as possibly warranted and representatives from the U.S. Fish and Wildlife Service directly assessed the conservation efforts in Australia. The Service found that programs in New South Wales, Queensland, South Australia, and Western Australia were well developed and adequate.

The eastern gray kangaroo is protected by appropriate legislation, populations are regularly monitored, and are managed by a complex licensing system to regulate the extent of legal harvest. This species is protected on National Parks and Reserves which total about 5 percent of the continental land area. In January of 1993, the U.S. Fish and Wildlife Service found that the petition to delist the three species of kangaroo was warranted because kangaroo populations are large and management is adequate so it would be unlikely that these kangaroos will become endangered in the foreseeable future. When the kangaroos were delisted, the 1989 petition by Greenpeace to reinstate a ban on the commercial importation of kangaroo products was automatically dropped.

In the past Queensland has been criticized because of its harvest management system. In defense the system has been modified greatly during the past two years. Queensland now establishes its kangaroo harvest quota in the following manner. First, an extensive survey is conducted in mid-winter (June-August). Then, a conservative possible harvest quota is formulated from this information. The potential quota is then reviewed by the area Director, Regional Director, and Manager-Wildlife Management, Queensland then to the Macropod Management Committee to receive public input from the various interested parties. The final submitted quota is determined by the Queensland Minister who submits it to the Commonwealth for approval.

Tasmanian Forester Kangaroo

Macropus giganteus tasmaniensis

Zoological Society of San Diego

Status	Endangered
Listed	June 4, 1973
Family	Macropodidae (Kangaroo)
Description	Kangaroo with a large head and body, coarse, long-haired coat is silvery gray in color with lighter coloring on the paws; the muzzle and surface of the nose are covered with hair.
Habitat	Temperate rain forests.
Food	Grasses and shrubs.
Reproduction	Usually 1 young annually.
Threats	Urbanization and agricultural development.
Range	Australia: Tasmania

Description

The Tasmanian forester kangaroo, *Macropus giganteus tasmaniensis*, is heavier built and more powerful than the other closely related subspecies of the eastern gray kangaroo, *M. giganteus*. It is the heaviest and most powerfully built of all kangaroos, with a comparably large cranium and a large body. The very coarse, long-haired coat is silvery gray in color with lighter coloring on the paws. The muzzle and surface of the nose are covered with hair.

This subspecies is a member of the *Macropodidae* family. Formerly, the eastern gray kangaroo and the western gray kangaroo, *M. giganteus*, were considered the same species. Since then they have been divided into two distinct species. *M. giganteus* contains three subspecies, including *M. g. tasmaniensis*.

In Tasmania, this kangaroo is generally referred to as the forester because of its preference for woodlands.

Behavior

Females have an estrous cycle of 46 days. Although many kangaroos have a baby in the pouch and an embryo developing in the uterus at the same time (embryonic diapause), The Tasmanian forester kangaroo rarely exhibits this condition. In females, conception exhibits this condition. In females, conception does not generally occur until after the first young has vacated the pouch, at an average age of about 320 days. Usually, the interval between successive births is approximately one year. However, if the pouch young dies, the female returns to estrus within approximately 11 days. The Tasmanian forester kangaroo takes a relatively long time to reach sexual maturity with captive males first mating at 42.5 months and females at 21 months. In captivity, this kangaroo has lived to 24 years of age.

The Tasmanian forester kangaroo has been known to feed predominantly on grasses, although it will also browse on bushes. In general, kangaroos are nocturnal, feeding from late afternoon to early morning and resting during the day. However, they sometimes have been observed active during the day.

Habitat

The Tasmanian forester kangaroo can be found in forests and open woodlands on the island of Tasmania, especially in the northeastern area. Usually, this subspecies dwells in forests and grazes in natural clearings. It does not normally graze in fields and unfenced pastures like some of the other kangaroos.

Distribution

Historically, the Tasmanian forester kangaroo ranged throughout the woodlands of the south Australian island of Tasmania. It is currently restricted to the northeastern portion of the island.

Threats

Hunting had greatly reduced the numbers and distribution of the Tasmanian forester kangaroo by the early 1900s. Additionally, kangaroo habitat has been lost or degraded due to urbanization and agricultural development.

Conservation and Recovery

Australia has long been involved in conservation measures and participated in World Wilderness Congresses and Inverness, UNEP, IUCN, CITES, South Pacific Regional Environmental Program, and Findhorn. Australia was one of the first countries to adopt the World Conservation Strategy and to develop a National Conservation Strategy.

Parma Wallaby

Macropus parma

K. Atkinson

Status	Endangered
Listed	December 2, 1970
Family	Macropodidae (Kangaroo)
Description	Brown with white chest, throat and cheek stripe.
Habitat	Forests; prefers thick understory with grass patches.
Food	Grasses and other herbs.
Reproduction	1 young after gestation of 35 days
Threats	Alteration of habitat due to agricultural and commercial use; hunting.
Range	Australia, New Zealand

Description

The Parma wallaby, *Macropus parma*, has a grayish-brown back and shoulders, a white throat and chest, a dark spinal stripe, and white cheek stripes. Males weigh 9 to 13 pounds and stand about 16 inches at the shoulders; females are the same height but weight less, 7 to 10 pounds. The long tails may be tipped with white.

M. parma is also known as *Ptionoyrmnus parma*, and as the white-throated wallaby.

Behavior

The breeding season for the Kawau Island population is from March to July, and is associated with seasons when food sources are more abundant. Females reach sexual maturity at one year on the mainland and two years on Kawau Island. Gestation of the parma wallaby is about 35 days, after which one 0.03 ounce young is born. The young remains in the pouch for about 7 to 8 months, after which the mother may reproduce again. Weaning is completed by one year.

The parma wallaby feeds on grasses and other herbaceous vegetation. The parma wallaby is nocturnal, leaving the forest at dusk to feed. Normally, this wallaby forms feeding associations of 2 or 3 individuals.

Habitat

The parma wallaby inhabits wet and dry forests of Australia, but can be found in rainforests as well. It prefers a thick understory interspersed with grass patches.

Distribution

The parma wallaby was thought to have become extinct during the nineteenth century until a population was discovered on Kawau Island, New Zealand in 1965. Historically, it was abundant throughout Wollongong, New South Wales, Australia, and after the Kawau Island population was discovered, other individuals were found near Gosford, New South Wales. The parma wallaby is rare and the colonies are scattered, making breeding more difficult. Although small, the Kawau Island population is dense and competition for food sources has resulted in evolutionary pressures causing the females to be smaller.

Threats

When Europeans invaded and colonized Australia, they also brought Western plants, rabbits, and foxes. These new species proved catastrophic to the well-balanced ecosystem of Australia. Competition between pouched mammals and more advanced placental mammals was disastrous to Australia's native fauna and no doubt contributed to this species' decline during the nineteenth century.

During the 1960s pine plantations on Kawau Island were being seriously damaged by Tammar wallabies and foresters attempted to eliminate the population. When the parma wallaby was discovered in 1965 intermingled with the Tammar wallabies, the eradication program was halted.

Conservation and Recovery

After the rediscovery of the parma wallaby, breeding colonies were established in an effort by Australian zoos and world organizations to stabilize the population. The colonies in the Watagan Mountains in New South Wales appear to be increasing in numbers.

Greater Rabbit Bandicoot

Macrotis lagotis

ANCA

Status	Endangered
Listed	December 2, 1970
Family	Peramelidae (Bandicoots)
Description	Rat-like marsupial with long silky gray fur above and is colored fawn, blue or red laterally.
Habitat	Woodland, savannah, shrubby grassland and other arid areas.
Food	Insects, small animals and some herbaceous material.
Reproduction	Litter of 1 to 3.
Threats	Habitat loss.
Range	Australia: southern Queensland, Western Australia and the Northern Territory

Description

The greater rabbit bandicoot, *Macrotis lagotis*, has long silky bluish gray fur above and is colored fawn, blue or red laterally. Its tail is black from the rump to mid-tail, where it becomes white to the end. These bandicoots have large rabbit-like ears and a long pointed snout. The rabbit bandicoots were once considered the most attractive of the bandicoots and were often kept for aesthetic purposes. This species is unusual in that it will sit on its tail when it sleeps. The body of the greater rabbit bandicoot is 8 to 22 inches in length with a weight of eleven ounces to 5 pounds.

The greater rabbit bandicoot is also known as a bilby or rabbit-eared bandicoot.

Behavior

The greater rabbit bandicoot has strong forearms which it uses for foraging and digging spiral tunnels that can extend up to nine feet in length and go down to almost six feet in depth. Unlike the lesser rabbit bandicoot, it leaves the entrance to the burrow open throughout the day while it is resting.

The greater rabbit bandicoot's reproduction characteristics include a 14 to 75 day gestation period and pouch time. This species has 1 to 3 young that weigh less than 0.02

ounces at birth. The weaning period of the greater rabbit bandicoot is approximately eighty days. For about two weeks after weaning, the young are deposited in the nest and suckled periodically throughout the night. In captivity the life span of the greater rabbit bandicoot has been documented at about five years.

One of the most noticeable features of the greater rabbit bandicoot is that it hops like a rabbit.

The greater rabbit bandicoot feeds on insects such as ants, termites and beetles, larvae, seeds and fruits and sometimes on mushrooms and some herbaceous material. The greater rabbit bandicoot is known to be nocturnally active.

Habitat

This species dens in many spiral branched clay or loam tunnels that can spread out approximately twenty-five to thirty-five acres. The greater rabbit bandicoot is only known to survive in remote colonies located in temperate and arid regions of the Northern territory of Australia, although there have been sightings from the coast of Australia to mid-west New South Wales and Victoria, and south-east Queensland. Scrub grasslands, open scrub, woodland country are the territorial range of the greater rabbit bandicoot.

Distribution

The greater rabbit bandicoot is known from Southern Queensland, Western Australia and the Northern Territory. Today this species is only known to survive in remote colonies. In the late 1800s and early 1900s the populations occurred over most of the southern half of the continent of Australia. The numbers available today are considered scarce and threatened with extinction. Since the 1900s the populations have decreased in numbers especially in the more temperate regional zones. There was a documented specimen collected in 1907, and documentation of reports of sightings in 1926 near the Musgrave Range. New York Zoological Park kept a total of eleven species, none survived for more than a few months. Better results have been documented in the Zoological Gardens of London of five years and seven years in Frankfurt.

Threats

The bandicoot populations have been severely affected by habitat destruction and introduction of predators including domestic cats, dogs and foxes. *Macrotis* spp. are valued for their fur and were senselessly slaughtered for this lucrative market. Livestock ranching and farming as well as introduction of rabbits have affected the survival of the greater rabbit bandicoot.

Conservation and Recovery

Australia has designated the greater rabbit bandicoot as a legally protected species. Protected as a listed species in Appendix I of the 1973 Convention on International Trade in Endangered Species of Wild Fauna and Flora, there may not be any trade associated with the greater rabbit bandicoot without being subject to strict regulations. All trade for primarily commercial purposes is banned. Additional research is needed on the greater rabbit bandicoot concerning its distribution and habits. All precautions should be taken to avoid wiping out populations of the greater rabbit bandicoot wherever possible and those populations should be effectively protected.

Before this species' fur became a marketable commodity, the early colonists protected this gentle marsupial and allowed them to stay in or near their homes. This was probably due in part to their effectiveness in keeping mice and insect populations down.

Lesser Rabbit Bandicoot

Macrotis leucura

Thomas illustration, NPIAW

Status	Endangered (Probably extinct)
Listed	December 2, 1970
Family	Peramelidae (Bandicoot)
Description	Long ears and long silky hair.
Habitat	Arid habitats, including woodland, savannah, and grassland.
Food	Insects, vegetables, mammals.
Reproduction	Short gestation and development.
Threats	Habitat destruction; predation.
Range	Australia

Description

The lesser rabbit bandicoot, *Macrotis leucura*, also known as the lesser bilby, is a marsupial mammal and one of only two bandicoots in this genus. *M. leucura* has not been sighted since 1931. The lesser rabbit bandicoot is smaller than the common bilby, *Macrotis lagotis*, that ranges in body length from 8 to 22 inches; tail length from 4.8 to 11.6 inches; and weighs 11 ounces to 5.5 pounds. The muzzle is long and pointed with its hind legs being longer than its forelegs. The fur is long, silky with a blue-grey color and their ears are long and rabbit-like. It is distinguished from *M. lagotis* by its size and by the white fur along the upper surface of the tail.

The rabbit bandicoot is commonly referred to as the bilby.

Behavior

The lesser rabbit bandicoot is omnivorous with a natural diet of larvae, worms, mice, small mammals, seeds, fruits and fungi. It burrows and digs pits with its long nose and well adapted legs to find food. It is a solitary, nocturnal mammal.

The pouch, which opens at the rear, contains eight teats. The usual litter size is two young.

The lesser rabbit bandicoot digs burrows between dunes for resting, and closes the entrance to the burrow while in residence. It does not construct nests or pop holes in this burrow, unlike the bilby.

When threatened, the lesser rabbit bandicoot fights ferociously by snapping and biting while emitting harsh hissing sounds.

Habitat

The lesser rabbit bandicoot lives in areas of low vegetation and is documented as being located in the sandhills of Simpson Desert region, Central Australia. Associated vegetation includes spinifex, mulga and tussock grass.

Distribution

The lesser rabbit bandicoot has been recorded from the deserts in northeastern South Australia and in the Northern Territory. It was considered to be fairly common but has not been reported since 1931.

Threats

Reasons for the decline of this species are unknown. Because it was fairly common until 1930, it may be assumed that predators such as domestic cats, dogs, and foxes were introduced into the habitat after that time. *Macrotis* species are valued for their fur and were slaughtered for this lucrative market. The aborigines eat the rabbit bandicoot as a delicacy. In addition to demise of the population by predators, the infant mortality rate is high due to the aggressive, territorial nature of adults.

Conservation and Recovery

Although thought to be extinct, the lesser rabbit bandicoot is nonetheless protected under the conservation laws of Australia.

Numbat

Myrmecobius fasciatus

Taronga Zoo

Status	Endangered
Listed	December 2, 1970; June 4, 1973
Family	Myrmecobiidae (Pouched mice)
Description	Dark cheek stripe passing through its eye; ears are covered with long, coarse hairs; mouth is small, with a long thin tongue.
Habitat	Hollow log shelters in Eucalyptus/ acacia/conifer ecosystems.
Food	Termites
Reproduction	Average litter size is 2 to 4 young.
Threats	Conversion of forest habitat for agriculture; brush fires, predation by foxes, dogs, and cats.
Range	Western Australia

Description

The numbat is a small marsupial. There are two subspecies of *Myrmecobius fasciatus*, *M. f. fasciatus* and *M. f. rufus*. *M. f. fasciatus'* pelage is gray and its size is documented as "variable". The better studied rusty numbat, *M. f. rufus*, has a ground color which is deep red with speckles of white interspersed throughout. *M. f. rufus'* under parts are a tawny ochre and are never white as are the nominal race. Its head-body length is 9.5 inches, and its tail is just slightly shorter, measuring 7 inches. Across the dorsal region down along the hindquarters are six or seven inconspicuous transverse bars. These bars are white or cream colored. A dark cheek stripe passes through its eye and a white stripe is located just superior to the eye. The exposed region of the ears are covered with long, coarse hairs. The mouth of the numbat is small, with a long, thin tongue. The numbat's jaw has six molars on either side; it has a total of 50 to 52 teeth, which is more than any other terrestrial mammal.

The numbat has a long snout; a long protrusible tongue; and small degenerate teeth. It also has long claws on its forefeet which are utilized to dig for termites.

Behavior

Generally speaking, the numbat is not gregarious. This solitary *Dasyuridid* only associates with others of its kind in the spring when young are present. The normal litter size of the numbat is 2 to 4. Atypical of most marsupials, females of this species have no pouch. The young attach themselves firmly to the teats, which swell in their mouths (as is the status quo of all marsupials). Mother/young interactions include nursing from time of birth (January to April or May) through the Australian winter. By late August and September they are detached from the teats and are transferred to a nest or hollow log. By late October and November the young are foraging for termites on their own, and by December they are ready for their independence.

Numbats are the only fully day-active marsupial. They spend most of their active hours searching for food, foraging carefully under pieces of wood as they sniff out termite galleries. Upon locating termites, the numbat squats on its hind legs and digs rapidly with its strong clawed forefeet. It extracts termites with its long narrow tongue that darts in and out of its mouth. It does not chew its prey but swallows everything it digs up, including the soil and ants that happen to be in the vicinity.

The diet of the numbat consists almost exclusively of termites. The termites are taken from shallow subterranean galleries. The species of termite eaten is in accordance to their natural abundance. Ants are known to comprise 15% of this species' diet; in fact, ants have been noted as a consistent food source. This phenomenon, however, seems to be a result of ants swarming the termites when the galleries are broken into. Numbats may eat up to 20,000 termites a day.

Numbats are primarily solitary animals that occupy territories as large as 370 acres.

They dig burrows for shelter during the colder months, and nest in logs which are constructed of leaves and grass. In winter they may pair with the opposite sex, but in summer become solitary.

Habitat

It seems that the dependence on the termite goes beyond consumptive. Numbats may exploit the termite's consumption of eucalyptus wood which, in turn, results in the provision of the hollow log shelters essential to the numbat. In fact, the numbat is quite resistant to venturing far from its log shelter.

The numbat is restricted to the Eucalyptus/acacia/shrub and conifer ecosystems. These areas are dominated by broadleaf evergreens or grasslands with patches of broadleaf evergreen trees.

Distribution

Historically, this species was abundant in parts of Southern Australia, but is now restricted to the southwest of Western Australia. The population of *M. f. rufus* is now believed to be extinct.

Threats

This species' decline has been attributed to conversion of its forest habitat for agriculture. There are now only a few eucalyptus forests and woodlands in the southwest of Western Australia. Introduced fox also preyed on the numbat population, and the destruction of habitat made the numbat an easier prey.

Conservation and Recovery

The numbat is fully protected by law. The rusty numbat was known to be distributed through the Woomera Rocket Range and certain aboriginal reserves. Entry into these areas is very strictly controlled either for security reasons or by the Aboriginal Welfare Departments.

Most of the numbat's habitat is now secure from further clearing and degradation, but the population is so small that the only hope for the species are breeding colonies that are being established which may repopulate the depleted numbers.

Bridled Nail-tailed Wallaby

Onychogalea fraenata

M. Evans

Status	Endangered
Listed	December 2, 1970
Family	Macropodidae (Wallabies)
Description	Coat is light brown or gray; a bridlelike stripe runs along its cheek and the side of its neck and flank, past its shoulder.
Habitat	Temperate to tropical areas with brush and grass, sometimes in woodlands.
Food	Grasses and roots.
Reproduction	One litter a year, usually in May.
Threats	Loss of habitat to human agriculture and to drought.
Range	Australia: northern Queensland

Description

The adult bridled nail-tailed wallaby stands between 16 and 20 inches tall, has a body length of 20 to 28 inches, has a tail length that may reach 17 inches, and weighs between 11 and 20 pounds. The species may be sexually dimorphic, with males being somewhat larger than females (but this has not been confirmed). Along with the other nail-tailed species, it is sometimes called an "organ grinder" because of how it rotates its arms down and forward when hopping. Its back feet face forward when hopping.

The coat is dark gray with two white fringes running from the neck to the elbows.

A black stripe on the head and neck run to the white stripes. The hips are also banded with white stripes that are often very faint. The underbelly is white or cream colored.

Its digestive system shows adaptations for feeding on grasses, including bacteria that help break down the not easily digestible fibrous blades of grass. It also has enzymes that speed up the digestion of fibrous plant matter. For nutritionally poor forage such as dry grass, it has a large rumen tube that allows it to hold and process large amounts of poor value food. Thus, much of the digestion is completed by the time the food reaches the stomach, which enhances the absorption of nutrients.

Behavior

Primarily a solitary animal, the bridled nail-tailed wallaby may be found in groups of five or fewer females with young. When threatened, it tries to hide by climbing into a tree hollow, climbing a tree, or flattening itself on the ground, its legs spread wide. It flees by flattening down and crawling in tall grass or by bounding away at great speed. It is a nocturnal feeder, resting in daytime in hollows it has scraped into the ground amid the cover of brush or grass or resting in the cover of leafy trees. Little is known of its breeding patterns, although since its rediscovery there have been efforts in Australia to breed it in captivity.

Habitat

It once ranged in temperate and tropical regions of central and northern Queensland, Australia, favoring grassy and brushy locales. It now is found in the wild only in 27,500 acres in northern Queensland that is subject to monsoons.

Distribution

Once common, the bridled nail-tailed wallaby populated much of Queensland, Australia, particularly its central and northern areas. Its range has been reduced to a 27,500 acre area of wildland in northern Queensland.

Threats

The bridled nail-tailed wallaby had been thought to be extinct for decades before a small number was rediscovered in Queensland in 1973. Once numerous, it was valued as food by Aborigines and European settlers; the precipitous decline in numbers of this species occurred because of loss of habitat and human persecution. It does not adapt to the presence of humans or to agricultural lands. As its traditional territory was converted to farming or ranching, it either moved or died. Considered a pest because some other species of wallaby adapted to human incursions by feeding on crops, it was poisoned and shot along with the offending wallaby species, sometimes for a bounty.

Conservation and Recovery

Presently, human persecution is no longer a significant problem because the remaining tiny population lives in a remote wild area that humans have tried to protect by establishing the Taunton Scientific Reserve, where grazing and predators are controlled. Should the area become subject to human expansion, in the forms of communities, farms, or ranches, the bridled nail-tailed wallaby would likely become extinct in the wild. Naturalists are trying to breed the animal in captivity in Townsville, in northeastern Queensland, but the degree of effectiveness has yet to be determined.

The bridled nail-tailed wallaby is listed in CITES, Appendix I: Trade Prohibited, although the animal does not seem to have been the subject of trade. It is also included in the *IUCN Red List* as endangered.

Crescent Nail-tailed Wallaby

Onychogalea lunata

ANCA

Status	Endangered (Probably extinct)
Listed	December 2, 1970
Family	Macropodidae (Wallabies)
Description	Small kangaroo with a brown coat; Tail has a bare, hard, conical tip.
Habitat	Grasslands
Food	Grasses
Reproduction	The pouch period lasts roughly 115 days.
Threats	Loss of habitat to agricultural development.
Range	Central and southwestern Australia

Description

Very little is known about this extremely rare (probably extinct) animal because there have been few observations of it. The body length of an adult crescent nail-tailed wallaby, *Onychogalea lunata*, is 20 to 28 inches; its tail adds another 16 to 26 inches; and it stands 16 to 20 inches high. Adult males weigh 10 to 20 pounds, with females weighing 10 to 15.5 pounds. The crescent nail-tailed wallaby's tail has a bare, horny tip, the function of which seems to be unknown. Its coat is ashy gray above and pale gray below with defined crescent white shoulder stripes from the chest to the scapular region.

Behavior

As with the other nailtail species, the bridled nail-tailed wallaby (*Onychogalea fraenata*) and the northern nailtail wallaby (*Onychogalea unguifera*), the crescent nail-tailed wallaby rotates its arms down and to the front, leading local people to call them "organ grinders." Its back feet face forward when hopping. It digs into the ground to create temporary resting places. When threatened, the crescent nail-tailed wallaby tries to hide; it will climb into a tree hollow, climb a tree, or crawl on the ground in tall grass. It congregates in groups of no more than five.

Aborigines report that the crescent nail-tailed wallaby ate grass. It took shelter under shady trees, shrubs, or in spinifex hummocks.

Habitat

The crescent nail-tail wallaby lives in semi-arid to temperate grasslands, although aborigines recall that it also inhabited stony hills.

Distribution

The crescent nail-tailed wallaby once inhabited central and southwestern Australia, but has not been seen in its range for many years. It disappeared from the Flinders Range in South Australia in the 1890s, and disappeared from the western desert in the 1940s. It was last seen in the Jervois Range, Northern Territory, in 1956.

Threats

The crescent nail-tailed wallaby has proven to be incapable of sharing land with humans. As agricultural development has encroached on its range, it has retreated or died off, depending on whether native grasslands were available. It has not been seen for many years and is thought by many authorities probably to be extinct. There is a faint hope for its survival, though, because its cousin, the bridled nail-tailed wallaby was also thought to be extinct but was rediscovered in a remote area in the 1970s.

Conservation and Recovery

Because the crescent nail-tailed wallaby is presumed extinct, no recovery efforts are underway. In order for it to have survived, the crescent nail-tailed wallaby would have required an area free of human habitation, one in which native grasses were abundant.

The crescent nail-tailed wallaby is listed in CITES, Appendix I: Trade Prohibited.

Dibbler

Parantechinus apicalis

Dick Whitford, NPIAW

Status	Endangered
Listed	December 2, 1970
Family	Dasyuridae (Marsupial carnivores)
Description	Brownish-gray above and grayish-white tinged with yellow below; long snout, a long tapering tail, and rings around the eyes.
Habitat	Dense heath with thick leaf clutter.
Food	Insects and nectar.
Reproduction	After gestation of 44-53 days, the female produces up to 8 young.
Threats	Loss of habitat.
Range	Western Australia

Description

The southern dibbler, *Parantechinus apicalis*, is brownish-gray above and grayish-white tinged with yellow below. It has a long snout, a long tapering tail, and rings around the eyes. It weighs up to 3.5 ounces; males grow to 5.6 inches with a tail length of 4 inches.

Behavior

Mating occurs in March; the nest is often constructed at the end of a tunnel; after gestation of 44 to 53 days, the female produces up to 8 young which she carries in a shallow pouch. The young are dependent on the mother for 3 to 4 months, and reach sexual maturity at 10 to 11 months. Females may breed in successive seasons. It has been observed that in some wild populations males die after their first breeding season.

Dibblers eat pollen and nectar from the spikes of the Banksia flower, and from the insects that are attracted to the flower.

Habitat

Dibblers occur along beach shorelines and

inland in areas with dense heath and thick leaf clutter.

Distribution

Thought to be extinct, the southern dibbler was rediscovered in 1967 in the Mount Manypeaks Range after an 83 year disappearance. Since then, a few individuals have been captured in Fitzgerals River National Park, Cheyne Beach, and Torndirrup National Park along the south coast in Western Australia, and on Boullanger and Whitlock Islands, where there are thriving populations.

Threats

When Europeans settled Western Australia the dibbler was widespread, and declined as natural habitat was converted to farmland. Europeans also brought with them foxes and cats which were fierce predators of all *Dasyuridae*. Today, agricultural clearing is achieved by burning the brush, which kills animals as well as destroys the brush. Recreational activities may also disturb the habits and habitat.

Conservation and Recovery

Habitat protection is essential for the recovery of the dibbler. Cheyne Beach, where the dibbler was rediscovered in 1967, is part of a nature reserve.

Barred Bandicoot

Perameles bougainville

Babs and Bert Wells, NPIAW

Status	Endangered
Listed	December 2, 1970
Family	Peramelidae (Bandicoots)
Description	Long-nose; thin long ears; distinctive markings over its hindquarters;
Habitat	Woodland and open areas with thick vegetational cover.
Food	Primarily insects.
Reproduction	Litter size usually 2-3, but may be 1-5; females can breed when half-grown at about 3-4 months of age.
Threats	Habitat destruction; predation.
Range	Western Australia: Bernier and Dorre Islands

Description

The barred bandicoot, *Perameles bougainville* is the smallest of the long-nosed bandicoots, measuring 6.6 to 9.4 inches, weighing 6 to 8 ounces, with a tail length of 2.3 to 3.9 inches. The tail is dark above, short and brown with little hair. Its pelage is light gray to brownish gray above and white below. The hindquarters have dark bars. The ears are large (up to 1.6 inches long), thin, and pointed when upright; when laid forward, the ears may cover the eyes. The limbs are short and robust.

P. bougainville described by Quoy and Gaimard, 1824, consists of three subspecies: *P. b. myosura* (Western Australia), *P. b. notina* (South Australia and Western Australia), and *P b. bougainville* (Shark Bay). Despite much confusion within the *P. bougainville* species-group, there has been an agreement that a very similar species, *P. gunni*, the eastern barred bandicoot, is a valid species. Common names used other than the barred bandicoot are the little barred bandicoot, western barred bandicoot, marl and little marl.

Behavior

Little is known about the length of the breeding season. The barred bandicoot is very aggressive in captivity; however, pouch young have been known to breed in May and June and some year-round, with fewer young in late summer and autumn. The pouch contains 8 teats; litter size is usually 2 to 3, but may be 1 to 5; at birth young weigh 0.0009 ounce and are 0.5 inch long. The female can breed when half-grown at about 3 to 4 months of age; male matures at 4 to 5 months.

The barred bandicoot is nocturnal when it forages for insectivores and omnivores that include a diet of arthropods, worms, shellfish, small lizards, berries, and seeds and roots.

This bandicoot is solitary and nocturnal, typically found among the sand-hills. It constructs nests in a hollow beneath a shrub. It fills the nest with grass, and enters the nest through an opening that it restructures after entering. It normally uses the same nest for a week but may construct a different nest more often.

The barred bandicoot occupies home ranges. Young are produced from April to October, when two young are normally produced.

Habitat

The barred bandicoot nests in heaths, dune vegetation, hollows scooped out in sand, open areas in grasslands and scrub. Today, this endangered bandicoot appears to be mainly confined to Bernier and Dorre Islands at the entrance to Shark Bay on the west coast of Western Australia. Some range from arid South Australia south of the Tropic (in the southwest probably in the sand-plains only), southern Australia, northern Victoria, and western New South Wales to Liverpool Plains. A few may be possible in the western part of central Australia, southwest Northern territory, and northwest South Australia, where the terrain is open saltbrush and plains. It was also located on stony ridges along the Murray and Darling River systems. On Dorre Island it also occurs in dune scrub and on open steppes. The last specimen collected on the mainland of Shark Bay was in 1909. The barred bandicoot has been unrecorded on the Australian mainland since 1922.

Distribution

The barred bandicoot was originally found across South Australia from the islands of Shark Bay to the Liverpool Plains of New South Wales. By 1925 it was believed to be extinct in South Australia. Although the barred bandicoot has been recorded in recent times from small pockets in Victoria on mainland Australia, it is almost certainly extinct on the mainland, but still fairly abundant on Bernier and Dorre Islands.

Threats

The terrain of Southern Australia was drastically altered because of livestock farming, and the habitat of the barred bandicoot was disrupted beyond the species' ability to survive low population numbers and predation by foxes.

Conservation and Recovery

The Bernier and Dorre Islands where the barred bandicoot is mainly confined are now nature preserves.

Desert Bandicoot
Perameles eremiana

K. Wynn-Moylan illustration, NPIAW

Status	Endangered (Presumed Extinct)
Listed	June 4, 1973
Family	Peramelidae (Bandicoots)
Description	Pelage is brown to dull orange with white underparts. A darker stripe runs between the ears, and down the length of the back and tail.
Habitat	Arid, grassy regions.
Food	Insects, fruits; small mammals.
Reproduction	2, sometimes 3, young.
Threats	Habitat destruction; predation.
Range	Australia

Description

The desert bandicoot, *Perameles eremiana*, has a head and body length of 8 to 12 inches; the tail is about half the length of the body. The pelage is brown to dull orange with white underparts. A darker stripe runs between the ears, and down the length of the back and tail, and two rump bands run perpendicular to the back stripe. It has long ears and hairy feet.

P. eremiana is very similar to *P. bougainville* and they may be the same species. Because of its color variations, *P. eremiana* is also referred to as the orange-back bandicoot.

Behavior

The desert bandicoot feeds on insects, including termites, ants and beetle larvae, vegetables, seeds, and roots which it forages at night by digging or hunting.

It constructs grass nests in shallow, oval depressions. Two, sometimes three, young are produced.

Habitat

This species inhabits sand plains and sand-ridge desert with spinifex grassland and tussock flats. The preferred vegetation is spinifex growing in arid regions and having spiny leaves or seeds.

Distribution

The type specimen was collected from near Charlotte Waters in the Northern Territory. It may also have occurred in Western Australia near Canning Stock Route. It was apparently common in the Northern Territory as far north as the Tanami Desert. It has not been reported since 1943 and is assumed to be extinct.

Threats

The introduction of fox into the bandicoots' range would have contributed to the decline of some populations, but the most likely cause of decline is associated with the changes in habitat. When the Aborigines occupied the Tanami Desert, they cleared land with periodic fires, which helped the desert bandicoot. When the Aborigines left this habitat, the desert bandicoot declined over a twenty-year period from 1940 to 1960.

Conservation and Recovery

Should this species be located, conservation efforts would be focused on establishing a suitable habitat and protecting individuals from natural predators.

Yellow-footed Rock Wallaby

Petrogale xanthopus

C. Kentwell

Status	Endangered
Listed	June 4, 1973
Family	Macropodidae (Wallabies)
Description	Brownish-gray above, white below, with white cheek stripes that run from the corners of the mouth, below the eyes halfway to the ears, which are dark orange.
Habitat	Upper slopes and cliff-lines of woodland and shrubland.
Food	Herbaceous.
Reproduction	Breeds year round.
Threats	Loss of habitat; predation.
Range	South Australia: New South Wales and Queensland

Description

The yellow-footed rock wallaby, *Petrogale xanthopus*, resembles a kangaroo but is smaller. It is brownish-gray above, white below, and has white cheek stripes that run from the corners of the mouth, below the eyes halfway to the ears, which are dark orange. It has white side and hip stripes. Its forearms, hindlegs and feet are orange, and the tail is orange-brown with brown rings throughout the length. The tail may be tipped with dark brown or white. The subspecies, *P.x. xanthopus* is paler in coloration and the stripes are less pronounced.

P. xanthopus was first described in 1854 by Asa Gray. Another common name for this species is the ring-tailed rock wallaby.

Behavior

The yellow-footed rock wallaby is herbaceous, grazing on grass during the wet season and browsing on forbs during the dry season. It is strictly nocturnal during the summer when the temperature is above 40 degrees C. but may become active during winter days.

The yellow-footed rock-wallaby lives in colonies of up to 100 individuals in rocky areas where there is enough diversity of plant life. Under favorable conditions, it breeds year round. Its gestation period is about 32 days and the young remain in the pouch for about 195 days.

The yellow-footed rock wallaby occupies overlapping home ranges of up to 200 hectares.

Habitat

The yellow-footed rock-wallaby inhabits semi-arid terrain, particularly upper slopes, cliff-lines and flat tops of low tablelands and hills. The vegetation in these areas consists of *Acacia* woodland and shrubland. The primary rock surfaces associated with this species are silicified tertiary sandstones overlying cretaceous sediments.

Distribution

In the past, the yellow-footed rock wallaby occurred in the Gawler, Andamooka, and Fliders Ranges and the hills north of Olary in South Australia; and in northwestern New South Wales and southwestern Queensland.

Currently, it is uncommon in the Flinders Ranges north of Mambray Creek and in parts of the Gawler Ranges. An outlying colony exists on Carappee Hill near Darke Peak on Eyre's Peninsula. The species is rare in the Olary Hills. Specimens still exist in New South Wales north of Broken Hill. In the early 1990s the Queensland population estimates were raised from 5,000-6,000 to 20,000.

Threats

The beautiful skins of the yellow-footed rock-wallaby made it a prime target for fur traders, and by the 1880s the species was widely hunted for both its skin and for sport. The introduction of domestic dogs and cats, foxes and livestock placed much pressure on the weakened populations. Foxes are able to pursue wallabies into their sheltered areas, and feral goats compete for the wallaby's food sources, especially during dry seasons and drought, and for sheltering caves. Although the rock outcrops that comprise the rock-wallaby's habitat are not suitable for farming, the massive conversion of natural lands to grazing and farmlands has disturbed the ecological needs for this shy animal, and studies conducted in 1985-1987 concluded that a primary limiting factor to the yellow-footed rock wallaby is suitable habitat availability.

Conservation and Recovery

As early as 1912 it was obvious that the wallaby populations were being decimated throughout Australia, and the states adopted resolutions controlling the hunting of wallabies. It is protected today from hunters, but the most important recovery effort must be the control of feral goats. It has been observed that even after significant decline, this species can recover rapidly where there are no goats, but that it continues to decline if feral goats are abundant.

Little Planigale

Planigale ingrami subtilissima

P. Woolley and D. Walsh, NPIAW

Status	Endangered
Listed	December 2, 1970
Family	Dasyuridae (Marsupial mice)
Description	Smallest marsupial mouse about the size of a grasshopper with an extremely flat skull adapted for creeping into crevices.
Habitat	Savannah woodlands among grasses and cracks in the ground in Australia.
Food	Insects
Reproduction	Breeds year round. Produces 4-8 young per litter.
Threats	Habitat loss due to clearfelling of native hardwood forests; predation by feral animals.
Range	Western Australia: Kimberley

Description

The little planigale, *Planigale ingrami subtilissima*, is the smallest known marsupial with a body length of 1.8 inches and a tail length of 2 inches. It may be the smallest of all mammals.

P. i. subtilissima is a member of the *Planigale* genus, commonly called the flat-skulled marsupial mice because of their extremely flattened skulls. This is an unusual characteristic for a mammal but is a common trait for lizards. In fact, the little planigale behaves more like a lizard, scurrying between tough grass clumps and slipping through narrow cracks. The flattened head looks triangular from above. The short gray fur of this mouse-like marsupial has a salt and pepper appearance. The foot pads are smooth and soft.

P. i. subtilissima was originally described by Lonnberg in 1913 as *Phascogale subtilissima* from a specimen collected from a plain near Noonkambah, Western Australia. Formerly, this subspecies was considered a full species, *Planigale subtilissima*. Other common names for the little planigale are the Kimberley planigale and the long-tailed planigale.

Behavior

The little planigale feeds on insects and

their larvae, especially grasshoppers found by the thousands in its grassland home. It hunts at night and will attack prey as large as itself. It pounces on large insects, such as grasshoppers, and kills them by biting. It eats only the soft parts of the insect, discarding the head, thorax and wings.

Females have well developed pouches that contain 8 to 10 teats. Breeding may occur year round but appears to be most active from December to March. Four to eight young are born. After six weeks they become detached from the teats and are placed in a grassy nest, where the mother nourishes them until they become independent at three months.

Habitat

The terrestrial little planigale lives in the savannah woodlands and grasslands of the Kimberley Division of Western Australia. During the dry season it occupies grass tussocks and crevices in the moist soils of swamps and rivers. When the summer floods begin, it seeks refuge on higher ground.

Distribution

The little planigale has only been found in the Kimberley district in Western Australia. Because it is so small and secretive, no estimates of its population are known.

Threats

A dam on the Ord River destroyed some of the habitat of this little-seen subspecies. Otherwise, little is known about the reasons for its rarity.

Conservation and Recovery

Breeding in captivity has been attempted for the little planigale but without success. In general, Australia has been involved in World Wilderness Congresses and has participated in Inverness, UNEP, IUCN, CITES, South Pacific Regional Environmental Program, and Findhorn. Australia was one of the first countries to adopt the World Conservation Strategy and to develop a National Conservation Strategy.

Southern Planigale

Planigale tenuirostris

C. H. Tyndale-Biscoe

Status	Endangered
Listed	December 2, 1970
Family	Dasyuridae (Marsupial mice)
Description	Small marsupial mouse about the size of a grasshopper, with an extremely flat skull adapted for creeping into crevices.
Habitat	Grass and herbaceous plants with broadleaf evergreen trees.
Food	Insects
Reproduction	Young are born after a gestation period of 19 days.
Threats	Loss of habitat due to clearfelling of native hardwood forests; predation of feral animals.
Range	New South Wales, Queensland, Western and South Australia.

Description

The southern planigale, *Planigale tenuirostris*, is a tiny marsupial weighing no more than 0.31 ounces and measuring 3 inches and less in length. In the eastern specimens the tail length equals the head and body length, and the tail is longer than the head and body in western specimens. The coat is gray to cinnamon above, marked occasionally with white hairs. The underparts are paler and the underside of the chin is white. It has an extremely flat skull and narrow nose well suited for hunting insects. This is an unusual characteristic for a mammal but is a common trait for lizards. The southern planigale behaves more like a lizard, scurrying between tough grass clumps and slipping through narrow cracks. From above, this species appears more or less triangular with a rather narrow muzzle. Hence, one of this marsupial's common names is the narrow-nosed planigale.

The southern planigale is also known as the narrow-nosed planigale.

Behavior

The southern planigale is an agile climber that hunts beetles, grasshoppers, crickets, spiders and moths that hide in the soil cracks and vegetation. Its narrow skull allows it to wedge open insects' protective vegetation. Its soft fur and loose skin permit it to wriggle into very narrow crevices in search of prey. It is quick and fearless, and kills large prey by rapidly biting the body and head. It sits on its haunches while eating so that it can hold its prey with its front feet.

This species is essentially nocturnal but can become active during the day. In warm months it is active throughout the night but in winter confines its activity to just after dusk and before dawn. Much of the activity occurs below ground or in cracks.

The animals construct nests made from dried grass and insect parts. In colder months they huddle together to conserve energy. They also go into torpor during a portion of the 21 hour rest period each day, during which time their metabolism drops as much as 50 percent. During the cold months they will bask in the sun near the opening of a crack.

The southern planigale occupies a shifting home range, probably in response to food supplies. Population densities are very low, perhaps as few as one individual per hectare.

Breeding occurs from late July through January. After a gestation period of 19 days, an average of six young are born. The young remain attached to the teats for about 40 days, at which time the mother builds a nest for them. She continues to nourish them until they are weaned by 95 days.

Lifespan in the wild is probably 2 years, and a female might produce two litters per season. Populations of this species peak between August and January with low populations occurring in June.

Habitat

The southern planigale occurs in a variety of habitats that have cracking clay soils in the savannah woodlands and grasslands of New South Wales and Western Australia. In the savannah woodlands, the southern planigale is associated with grass and herbaceous plants underneath broadleaf evergreen trees growing singly or in groups.

Cracks in the soil are essential for this species' protection from summer heat and winter cold. The cracks that it occupies may be six feet deep, providing good thermal protection.

Distribution

The southern planigale has been found in New South Wales, Australia on the Darling between Bourke and Wilcannia, in the Moree District, and in Nyngan. It has also been reported from Cunnamulla, Queensland, Western Australia, and in South Australia.

Threats

The specific reasons for the rarity of this little seen species are unknown. Generally, species in this range were affected by loss of habitat due to clearfelling of native hardwood forests, and by predation of feral animals.

Conservation and Recovery

No conservation measures are known to have been taken for the southern planigale. However, in general, Australia has an excellent reputation for protecting rare and endangered species. Australia has been involved in World Wilderness Congresses and has participated in Inverness, UNEP, IUCN, CITES, South Pacific Regional Environmental Program, and Findhorn. Australia was one of the first countries to adopt the World Conservation Strategy and to develop a National Conservation Strategy.

Quokka

Setonix brachyurus

K. Griffiths, NPIAW

Status	Endangered
Listed	June 4, 1973
Family	Macropodidae (Wallabies)
Description	Cat-like marsupial with a short tail and ears and a brown coat.
Habitat	Shrubby coastal and swampy areas with eucalyptus forests.
Food	Strictly herbivorous.
Reproduction	After a gestation period of 28 days, females bear usually one young.
Threats	Habitat loss; predation by domestic dogs, cats, foxes, and livestock.
Range	Australia: Rottnest and Bald Islands

Description

The quokka, *Setonix brachyurus*, has long, thick, coarse brownish-gray hair. It measures 23 inches in length and weighs up to 8 pounds. The rounded ears are short as well as the tail.

The quokka was first discovered by Samuel Volchersen in 1658. This species is the only one of the genera *Setonix*. Species of the family *Macropodidae* are distinguished by their large hind feet, well-developed hind limbs, and large, sacculated stomachs (to efficiently utilize a diet composed of bulky foliage and herbs).

Behavior

This species may bond with the opposite sex for as long as three years. In ideal habitat conditions on the mainland, quokkas can breed year round, but on Rottnest breeding is restricted by water supplies. In cooler years breeding on Rottnest may begin in January, but may occur as late as March.

Females have a gestation period of 28 days. The litter size is usually only one. The young usually leave the pouch after about 175 to 195 days but will continue to nurse for an additional 3 to 4 months. Females have four mammae and well-developed pouches. Maturity of the quokka is approximately 12 months for males and 11 months for females. The life cycle of the quokka has been documented up to 10 years.

This species is terrestrial, like most macropodids but can climb to reach stems growing above the ground.

This species is herbivorous and feeds on a variety of plants. The quokka is a nocturnal species.

Habitat

The quokka is strictly terrestrial and is known to prefer shrubby coastal and swampy areas with eucalyptus forests. On the mainland of Australia habitat is restricted to dense vegetation in swamps amidst dry sclerophyll forest. This species makes tunnels through dense grass and undergrowth. During the wet season quokkas fight over possession of the best shelter sites. Sometimes 25 to 150 individual species will overlap territory. During the summer months most of the populations concentrate around available fresh water because the species needs shady locations and must be able to avoid heat.

The Rottnest Island habitat is much different from the quokka's preferred moist habitat. The island is seasonally arid, the vegetation is sparse and low to the ground, and potable water is scarce. The habitat becomes so depleted by the end of summer that the animals removed from sources of fresh water become anemic and die. During the dry season, the quokka changes its diet to succulent plants that provide moisture, and by selecting less nutritional plants deprives its body of important nutients.

Quokka populations disperse during the winter wet season but converge onto water-

ing holes, called soaks, beginning in November. Each soak is used exclusively by the same group of animals, who defend it. Quokkas form rigid social hierarchies, headed by adult males and based on age.

Distribution

The quokka was common in southwestern Western Australia at the time of European settlement. It seems to have always been restricted to the mainland range and to Rottnest and Bald Islands. The Rottnest population has remained stable but the mainland population declined severely during the 1960s.

Threats

Development of the islands for recreational purposes has been a major factor in the decline of this species. Livestock overgrazing also facilitates soil erosion. Soil erosion is a primary contributor to exotic vegetation invasion. Invasion by exotics choke-out or shade surrounding vegetation, deplete nutrient contents, and adversely affect endemic or otherwise dependent faunal species.

Conservation and Recovery

The flat, poorly vegetated Rottnest Island is ideally suited for studying the quokka's requirements for nutrition, temperature regulation, reproduction, immunology, ecology and social behavior, and this species is being widely monitored by mammologists.

Long-tailed Marsupial-mouse

Sminthopsis longicaudata

Babs and Bert Wells, NPIAW

Status	Endangered
Listed	December 2, 1970
Family	Dasyuridae (Marsupial mice)
Description	Gray above and tan to white below, with black marks around its eyes; long snout, flat head, long narrow feet, long claws and large ears.
Habitat	Rocky terrain supporting sparse spinifex.
Food	Beetles, ants, spiders, cockroaches, grasshoppers, flies and larvae.
Reproduction	May breed from August to December, producing up to six young.
Threats	Unknown
Range	Western and central Australia.

Description

The long-tailed marsupial-mouse, *Sminthopsis longicaudata*, is a bit larger than the common house mouse and has an extremely long tail. The head and body length is 3.1 to 3.9 inches in the males, with a tale length of over 7.8 inches. The tale has fine, long, brush-like hairs at the tip. The males weigh up to 0.7 ounces. The pelage is gray above and tan to white below. It has black marks around its eyes, a long snout and a flat head. This species has long narrow feet, long claws and large ears.

S. longicaudata was first described by Spencer in 1908. It is also known as the long-tailed dunnart and the long-tailed sminthopsis.

Behavior

The long-tailed marsupial-mouse is carnivorous and eats more than its weight in available insects. Its diet includes beetles, ants, spiders, cockroaches, grasshoppers, flies and larvae.

Little is known about the biology of this rarely seen species. It is nocturnal; it may breed from August to December, producing up to six young; in cold conditions it may become torpid; its tail is used for balance and is carried stiffly vertical when the animal is running, and it is an agile climber.

Habitat

The few specimens that have been collected came from different habitat types. One came from limestone caves; another from a spinifex hummock in the Gibson Desert; another from a plateau of sandy gravel soil with spinifex grassland; and another in a valley with low open *Acacia* woodland. A 1981 expedition found the long-tailed marsupial-mouse in a plateau composed of boulders, stones and sparse vegetation. Other specimens have been trapped in areas of rocky terrain supporting sparse spinifex, and among boulders in sandstone ranges.

Distribution

The long-tailed marsupial-mouse has been collected in the interior of Western Australia to Central Australia. A female with five young was collected in 1985 but prior to 1975 there were only a few known collected specimens. In 1975 a fourth whole specimen was found in the Gibson Desert. A few years later, eight animals were again located in the Gibson Desert, and subsequent expeditions have located animals in Murchison, Goldfields, Pilbara and Ashburton.

Threats

The reasons for the rarity of this little reported species are unknown. Only a couple of dozen specimens have ever been located, and these were in rugged terrain unaffected by human intervention.

Conservation and Recovery

The long-tailed marsupial-mouse is currently protected in the Gibson Desert Nature Reserve.

Large Desert Marsupial-mouse

Sminthopsis psammophila

Babs and Bert Wells, NPIAW

Status	Endangered
Listed	December 2, 1970
Family	Dasyuridae (Marsupial mice)
Description	Overall color is buff to gray; head is lighter gray spotted with short black stripes from the muzzle throughout the upperparts of the body; cheeks and flanks are buff and the underparts are white.
Habitat	Broadleaf evergreen trees and evergreen shrubforms of Australia.
Food	Carnivorous, feeding on insects.
Reproduction	Up to 6 young per litter.
Threats	Adverse habitat modifications.
Range	South Australia

Description

The large desert marsupial-mouse, *Sminthopsis psammophila*, is buff to gray. The head is lighter gray spotted with short black stripes from the muzzle throughout the upperparts of the body. The cheeks and flanks are buff and the underparts are white. The inside of the large ears are pink. Its tail has bristle-like hairs over the anterior portion; it is pale gray above and dark gray below.

S. psammophila is also commonly known as the long-tail dunnart. Dunnart is a native term for marsupial-mouse. This dunnart was discovered in 1894 and was not rediscovered until 1969. This species is also known as a sandhill dunnart.

Behavior

The large desert marsupial-mouse is carnivorous and eats larval insects and spiders. It is most active from late afternoon until dawn.

It digs burrows and constructs nests of grasses and leaves and may be found under rocks or logs when not looking for food. It may reproduce in the spring or summer, and females may produce up to six young per litter. There are eight teats.

Habitat

This marsupial-mouse is associated with broadleaf evergreen trees and evergreen shrubs. It lives in moist forest or savannah and sometimes occupies arid grassland and deserts. It has been located in sand dunes with hummock grass, in groves of desert oaks; in low, open eucalyptic woodlands, and in deserts.

Distribution

The large desert marsupial-mouse has been located near Lake Amadeus, at Mamblyn and Bonderoo on Lake Eyre Peninsula, South Australia and at Ayers Rock over the past century. A colony was discovered on the Eyre Peninsula of Southern Australia in 1969 but there have been no reported sightings since then. Currently, populations are known only from the Queen Victoria Spring Nature Reserve, the Yellabinna Regional Reserve, and the Maralinga Tjarutja Aboriginal Lands, all in South Australia.

Threats

Little is known about the large desert marsupial-mouse except that it has a very restricted range and may be subject to adverse habitat modifications.

Conservation and Recovery

The only population of the large desert marsupial-mouse is located near a wildlife reserve. The six states, two territories and the Commonwealth Government of Australia all have a high interest in preserving areas for protection for species' habitats. In all wildlife reserve areas protection is provided year-round.

Tasmanian Wolf [=Tasmanian Tiger]

Thylacinus cynocephalus

ANCA Illustration

Status	Endangered (Possibly extinct)
Listed	June 2, 1970; March 30, 1972
Family	Thylacinidae (Tasmanian wolf)
Description	Large body resembling a fox with striped markings over its entire body; tail resembles a kangaroo.
Habitat	Temperate rain forest.
Food	Feeds primarily on kangaroos, wallabies and ground birds.
Reproduction	Litter size is 1 to 4 cubs.
Threats	Hunting
Range	Australia: Tasmania

Description

The Tasmanian Wolf, *Thylacinus cynocephalus*, is a relatively large and slender fox-faced animal. It is yellowish-brown with 16 to 18 dark bars on the back and rump that have led to one common designation of "tiger," although it has the face of a dog. The head-body length is about 31.5 inches, the tail 15.8 to 19.7 inches, and the height at the shoulders is 24 inches. It weighs 33 to 77 pounds. The legs are short, and it is distinguished from dogs by the long, stiff tail that is thick at the base.

Not a tiger or a fox, this species is a marsupial and its marsupium is located anteriorly. This species' head is rather long; the zygomatic arch is somewhat robust and wide while the paroccipital process is small. The tail resembles a kangaroo's while the pouch is backward opening resembling that of an opossum.

T. cynocephalus is the only known species of *Thylacinidae*. It is also known as *Thylacine*, Tasmanian tiger, the kangaroo wolf, the zebra wolf and the hyaena opossum.

Behavior

The Tasmanian wolf is carnivorous. It appears to rest in dense forests during the day and hunt alone or in pairs at night, feeding primarily on kangaroos, wallabies, bandicoot, rodents and ground birds which it finds on grassland and woodland. This species hunts at dusk, night or dawn. Daylight hours are spent in the lair. It can sit on its tail like a kangaroo and leap 6 to 12 feet with great agility.

The female gives birth to up to four cubs and can carry two of them in her pouch at the same time. When not carrying her young, the mother leaves them in a nest-like structure, tent-shape in appearance, which she constructs of limbs, fronds and other surrounding vegetation. She will attend the young for up to three months.

Habitat

Adults make lairs in hollow trees, logs, in caves or around rock piles, perhaps in the rugged upland terrain of Tasmania, or perhaps in the west coast rain forest.

Distribution

The Tasmanian wolf once ranged over much of Australia and New Guinea but became extinct by 1,000 B.C., surviving only in Tasmania. At the time of European settlement, the species appears to have been widespread in Tasmania, especially in habitats adjacent to dense forests. The Tasmanian wolf is considered extinct by some authorities. There have been no valid reports of this species since the 1930s, although a 1961 expedition claimed to have found some tracks in a rain forest on the west coast of Tasmania.

Threats

The Tasmanian wolf has been persecuted because it became a sheep killer, hen yard raider, and was thought to attack humans. It was rare by 1914, and the last species was thought to have been shot in the 1930s, but there is evidence that a few individuals may survive in Tasmania's rocky uplands. The Tasmanian wolf was widely feared by hunters and by their hunting dogs. Even after the animal was dead, Europeans were known to "smash the animal to a pulp". There were actually only rare instances when this species would attack humans. Generally, these attacks surfaced from entrapment or if the animal felt in some way threatened.

In 1840 the Van Diemna's Land Company set a bounty for the Tasmanian wolf and in 1888 the Tasmanian Government set a bounty as well. Records indicate that over 2,270 animals were killed between 1888 and 1914.

Conservation and Recovery

In 1936 the Tasmanian wolf was granted legal protection in Tasmanian and take and killing became illegal. In 1966 a reserve extending from Low Rocky Cape to Kellista to South West Cape was designated for the protection of the Tasmanian wolf although at that time the species had not been seen for over 30 years.

Scaly-tailed Possum

Wyulda squamicaudata

Babs and Bert Wells, NPIAW

Status	Endangered
Listed	December 2, 1970
Family	Phalangeridae (Possums)
Description	Fine, dense, short fur generally pale gray, its black tips to its longer hairs give it a dark, mottled appearance.
Habitat	Rocky, wooded, spinifex regions.
Food	Fruit, leaves, and insects.
Reproduction	Gives birth during the dry season after gestation of 150 to 200 days.
Threats	Predation by cats, dogs and foxes.
Range	Western Australia: Kimberley

Description

The scaly-tailed possum, *Wyulda squamicaudata*, is a little-known *phalanger*. Its pelage is generally pale gray, the black tips of the longer hairs give it a dark and rather mottled appearance. A dark stripe runs from the shoulders to rump. Its fine, dense fur is short and soft, its head is short and wide; its claws are short and only somewhat curved. The scaly-tailed possum's tail is covered with thick non-overlapping scales; these scales probably assist in climbing. Its head and body length is 12 to 15.4 inches; its tail length is 11.7 inches; and its weight is 47 to 70 ounces.

Behavior

The scaly-tailed possum is a terrestrial herbivore/browser, and its principal food is the fruit of a sandalwood that grows among rocks. It also eats blossoms, nuts, leaves and insects. The scaly-tailed possum spends the day resting in cavities deep in rock piles and emerges at night to feed.

Females become sexually mature at two years of age. They give birth during the dry season (March-August). Young remain in the pouch for 150 to 200 days and are weaned after 8 months.

Habitat

This possum is recorded from rugged rocky terrain associated with wooded and spinifex regions. In fact, this is the only *phalanger* which does not exhibit an arboreal habit.

Distribution

The scaly-tailed possum is known from the Kimberley Division of Western Australia, the two farthest localities being some 300 miles apart. The type specimen, a female, was from Biolet Valley Station. The second specimen was collected at Kunmunya Mission. During an expedition from the end of 1965 through early 1966, Butler collected several specimens at Kaulumnuru Mission close to the most northerly boundary of Western Australia. It seems to be naturally rare. As its habitat is rather inaccessible to humans, it may in fact be more widespread than it is believed to be.

Threats

The scaly-tailed possum was probably adversely affected by the introduction of domestic animals such as cats and dogs, as well as foxes.

Conservation and Recovery

Intensive zoological exploration was undertaken in the Kimberley area of Western Australia's Northern Territory during the 1960s and the population biology of the scaly-tailed possum became much better known. Its habitat is now considered to be secure, and one population at the Prince Regent Nature Reserve is on protected land although all of Australia's endangered species are protected by national law.

Rabbits and Hares
Family: Leporidae

Volcano Rabbit (*Romerolagus diazi*)   Fernando A. Cervantes-Reza

General Characteristics of the *Leporidae*

Rabbits are highly adaptable animals whose speed (some can run 50 miles per hour), excellent hearing, and keen vision in both daylight and darkness provide natural defenses against their many predators. They are also capable of rapid reproduction, and in spite of a mortality rate of up to 90% of the young, they can quickly repopulate depleted numbers. Once thought to be rodents because of their incisor teeth, rabbits were reclassified in 1912 as a separate order (Lagomorphs) because they possess an additional pair of incisors. Unlike most rodents, the feet of rabbits are fully furred, their ears are larger, and their high set eyes give them a wider field of vision. Lagomorphs (which include pikas as well as rabbits and hares) occur throughout the world in almost every type of habitat. The oldest known fossils date to the late

Eocene (50 million years ago), but scientists think a more primitive form of rabbit precedes that date.

Leporidae are herbivores, and their diet includes a wide variety of grasses, leaves, bark and vegetables. Some species will eat snails and insects. Because they are such adaptable feeders, and because of their reproductive capability, *Leporidae* have historically caused great damage to both their habitat and to crops, and as such have come to be regarded as a pest. In Australia, where rabbits were introduced by European settlers as prey for their introduced foxes, rabbits were responsible for the widespread destruction of crops and natural vegetation, and are responsible for the decline of marsupials, with whom they compete for food sources. An eradication program undertaken in Australia in 1951-1952, which killed European rabbits with the myxomatosis virus but did not harm the forest rabbit, was successful in relieving the country of the rabbit infestation. However, it appears that European rabbits in Australia have developed some immunity to myxomatosis and are again gaining a prominence.

Female rabbits are able to reproduce rapidly because they reach sexual maturity in about 3 to 5 months, because of a short gestation period of about 40 days, and because they can conceive immediately after giving birth. Some species can conceive a second litter before the first litter is born. Rabbits give birth in nests that have been carefully constructed of hair and grass. Newborn rabbit "kittens" are naked and their eyes remain closed for several days. The mother suckles the young only once a day, for about 5 minutes; weaning occurs at 3 weeks. When the young are not being suckled, the nest is closed.

While rabbits and hares are generally prosperous worldwide, some relict species are near extinction. Those include the Sumatran hare (Sumatra), the Hispid hare (northern India and Bangladesh), the volcano rabbit (Mexico), the bushman hare (South Africa), and the Amami rabbit or Ryukyu rabbit (Amami Islands, Japan).

Hispid Hare [=Bristly Rabbit]

Caprolagus hispidus

Priscilla Barrett illustration

Status	Endangered
Listed	June 14, 1976
Family	Leporidae (Rabbits and hares)
Description	Short inner fur is covered by bristly guard hares; the overall color is dark brown on the upperparts and brownish-white below.
Habitat	Grass thickets and woodlands.
Food	Shoots, roots of grasses and cultivated crops.
Reproduction	Gestation of 6 weeks.
Threats	Loss of habitat.
Range	India

Description

The hispid hare, *Caprolagus hispidus*, has short, wide ears, small eyes, large teeth, straight claws, and stocky back legs. The short inner fur is covered by bristly guard hares; the overall color is dark brown on the upperparts and brownish-white below. The hispid hare weighs up to 5.5 pounds.

Behavior

The nocturnal hispid hare feeds on shoots, roots of grasses and cultivated crops. Both males and females, which live in pairs, have home ranges. Mating occurs in January and February, resulting in small litters in about 6 weeks.

The hispid hare is much slower than other hares and depends on the tall grass habitat for protection. When pursued by natural predators, including foxes, jackals, and even birds, this hare uses stealth and camouflage, rather than speed, to escape predation.

Habitat

Until farmers burned it, the hispid hare lived in thick groves of thatch grass, which provided protection from predators as well as food. With this habitat transformed into pastures, the hispid hare adapted its diet but became vulnerable to natural and human predators. It survives today in grass thickets and woodlands.

Distribution

Thought to have become extinct in the early twentieth century, the hispid hare was rediscovered in the 1950s in the Himalayan foothills of northern India and Assam.

Threats

Before it was thought to have become extinct, the hispid hare was forced onto cultivated lands, where farmers shot it for food and as a presumed pest, and where dogs were able to kill it. In more recent times, the hare's thatch grass habitat has been altered or transformed into agricultural land and by flood control management; or destroyed by logging and by burning.

Conservation and Recovery

Protection of the remaining tall grass habitats is essential to the survival of this species; some of these lie within lands protected as national parks and wildlife reserves. Outside the protected areas, land management practices, particularly controlled burning, need to be established.

Ryukyu [=Amami] Rabbit

Pentalagus furnessi

Amami Ornithologists' Club

Status	Endangered
Listed	June 25, 1979
Family	Leporidae (Rabbits and hares)
Description	Dense, dark brown coat.
Habitat	Dense forests with bamboo.
Food	Bamboo shoots, stems, and sweet potato leaves.
Reproduction	1 hairless kit after a gestation period of 180 to 210 days.
Threats	Logging of old growth forests.
Range	Japan: Ryukyu Islands

Description

The Ryukyu rabbit, *Pentalagus furnessi*, is an unusual rabbit in that it has a dark and woolly coat that is composed of a dark brown, soft undercoat and a long, bristly top coat. Darker hair runs the length of the ridge of the back. This rabbit is 17 to 20 inches long. The claws are 0.4 to 0.8 inches long. It has small eyes and ears (ear length is 1.7 inches), a long snout, and short legs.

Behavior

The Ryukyu rabbit digs dens in a tunnel 3 to 6 feet long which leads to one or several burrows. Each burrow has an additional tunnel that provides ventilation and an emergency exit. The entrances are covered with grass or dry leaves during the day. Individuals usually live in couples or in small groups.

Mating season is November through December. Recent research indicates that after a gestation period of 180 to 210 days the Ryukyu rabbit produces one hairless kit. The young emerges above ground in 4-5 months.

The most important food sources for the Ryukyu rabbit are Japanese pampas grass in summer, and probably acorns of the pasania tree (*Castanopsis sieboldii*) in winter. It also feeds on bamboo sprouts, runners of the cultivated Japanese sweet potato, and tree bark.

The Ryukyu rabbit is nocturnal, using runways through the underbrush to migrate to foraging areas.

Habitat

The Ryukyu rabbit inhabits mountain slopes near waterways in broadleaf and evergreen forests associated with pasania, evergreen oaks, and tree ferns. There is some bamboo but it is rather scarce. The Ryukyu rabbit prefers thinner vegetation with grassy underbrush. It is thought that this rabbit's dark fur served as camouflage when it inhabited dense primary forests before they were cut. The preferred habitat is near a waterway or near pools.

Distribution

The Ryukyu rabbit's physical characteristics associate it with fossils from the Miocene era. It is believed this species or species closely related have occupied the Ryukyu Archipelago for at least 26 million years.

The Ryukyu rabbit is known only from Amami-Oshima (meaning "big island") and Tokuno-Shima islands of the Ryukyu Archipelago, Japan.

In 1993 Sugimura estimated that, based on pellet count, the population had decreased about 90% since 1977. He estimated the population to be about 5,000 individuals but in 1994 revised that count to 2,000 to 3,000 individuals.

Threats

Like many areas supporting human occupancy, the Ryukyu Archipelago has been subject to the clear-cutting of broadleaved evergreen forests, including old-growth and secondary forest, and this destruction of habitat has caused the rabbit's dramatic decline. The construction of forest roads has also contributed to the degradation of habitat. Also, humans have introduced carnivores, particularly cats and dogs, to the islands, and they have become predators of the rabbit.

Conservation and Recovery

The Ryukyu rabbit has been designated as a natural monument by the Japanese government and is fully protected from hunting. However, the conservation and management of the habitat, and the control of predators will have to receive attention if the species is to survive.

Volcano Rabbit

Romerolagus diazi

Fernando A. Cervantes-Reza

Status	Endangered
Listed	June 2, 1970
Family	Leporidae (Rabbits and hares)
Description	Small, round ears high-pitched, penetrating voice; colored dark brown dorsally and dark brown-gray underneath.
Habitat	Pine forests lined with a dense undergrowth of zacaton grass.
Food	Herbivorous, feeding primarily on zacaton grass.
Reproduction	Litter size varies from one to four, averaging two.
Threats	Habitat loss due to agricultural development.
Range	Mexico: Sierra Nevada and Sierra Chichinautzin mountain ranges.

Description

The Volcano rabbit, *Romerolagus diazi,* has been compared to the northern pika in that both possess similar tails, short ears and have high-pitched, penetrating voices.

This species is colored dark brown dorsally and dark brown-gray underneath. The ventral area is highlighted with yellow. The volcano rabbit measures up to 12 inches long and weighs about a pound, making it one of the smallest of all rabbits. It has short legs, short feet, and small, round ears; the tail is rudimentary to almost completely absent.

The volcano rabbit is commonly known as teporingo. This species was first described in 1893.

Behavior

Communication has been observed in the volcano rabbit although reasons are not completely understood. The volcano rabbit is very vocal when compared to the typically silent *lagomorphs*. The voice of this species has been described as a high squeaking noise, "like a wet thumb rubbed over a balloon." The other observed voice has been a high-pitched bark. The volcano rabbit will also thump its hind legs on the ground.

This species is gregarious and is found in colonies of 150 to 200 individuals. During good weather many rabbits have been observed above ground playing, fighting, foraging or sleeping among the bunchgrass.

Breeding takes place between January and April. Litter size varies from one to four, usually two, after a gestation period of 38 to 40 days.

This species is herbivorous and feeds primarily on zacaton grass. It seems there is no particular preference between old and new grass. The volcano rabbit has also been reported to feed on *Cunila tritifolium*, an aromatic mint. This species is reported to be active during both day and nighttime hours. It seems to be most active in evening and early morning and rests during the middle of the day.

The volcano rabbit constructs elaborate burrows in sandy, loamy deep soils. Nest chambers are constructed within the burrow, in old tree stumps and hollow trees, or in shallows beneath grass.

Habitat

The volcano rabbit inhabits open pine forests lined with a dense undergrowth of zacaton grass at elevations of 9,000 to 14,000 feet. Zacaton grass grows up to three feet tall and appears in large tussocks. This grass requires soft, deep volcanic soil. The volcano rabbit lives in burrows beneath the ground or under piles of rock. The burrows are dug into the soft soil and consist of a number of complex tunnels to facilitate easy escape. This species maintains tunnel-like paths through the tall vegetation underneath the overhanging zacaton grass.

Distribution

The volcano rabbit is restricted to the slopes of the volcanoes Popocatepetl, Ixtacihuatl, Iztaccihuatl, and Ajusco of the southern Valley of Mexico, only 40 miles from Mexico City. These slopes are in the Sierra Nevada and Sierra Chichinautzin mountain ranges. Population numbers may be as few as 1,000 individuals.

Threats

The volcano rabbit is primarily threatened by ongoing agricultural development and habitat loss. As a result of this development the species' primary food source is being destroyed. The volcano rabbit is also vulnerable to recreational practices.

In 1970, this species was reported to inhabit the same range as was described in its original description in 1873. However, agricultural development and slash burning is destroying the volcano rabbit's already limited range. Cultivation practices are progressing and there is a great demand for more acreage. Not only is this species being encroached upon by man and what he introduces into the area, but pine-zacaton vegetation is being cleared to meet anthropogenic demands for more agricultural pastures and fields.

The volcano rabbit is considered a vermin by Mexicans. The area in which this species lives is also considered a popular recreational area for the inhabitants of Mexico City. The volcano rabbit has also been used for target practice, in anticipation of quail hunting and hunting of other game birds.

Conservation and Recovery

In 1968, several volcano rabbit specimens were established in the Jersey Zoo in an effort to initiate the first captive breeding program for this species. The population at Iztaccihuatl is in a national park, but even these lands are used for livestock grazing, potato farming, and logging.

Martens, Civets, Linsangs
Family: Mustelinae, Viverridae

Spotted Linsang (*Prionodon pardicolor*)

Sim Siang Huat, Singapore Zoological Gardens

General Characteristics of the *Mustelinae*

Martens are the most agile, graceful and arboreal of the weasel family. They are opportunistic carnivores; the staples of their diet are mice, squirrels, rabbits and ground birds. They will also eat fruits and nuts. They hunt by staking out retreats which their prey depend on for safety; they subdue their prey by biting it on the back of the neck. The fisher marten of North America is the only small animal that can successfully attack a porcupine.

Most marten species mate in the late summer and produce 1 to 5 young the following spring after gestation of 5 to 6 months. The kits are blind and deaf at birth but mature quickly and can kill prey at 3 to 4 months. They become sexually active at 1 to 2 years when they establish territories, which they mark with an anal scent and with urine.

Martens, like their mink cousins, have soft, rich fur, and they have been widely trapped and hunted, and their hardwood forests have been logged throughout much of their range, which includes central and northern Europe, North America, Japan, India, and Southeast Asia. Because of habitat loss, the yellow-throated marten is threatened.

General Characteristics of the *Viverridae*

Civets are members of the mongoose family, *Viverridae*, but they look more like cats than prairie dogs. The true civets, including the large-spotted civet and the linsang, are indigenous to Asia, Africa, Europe, and the Near and Middle East. Civets are threatened because of being hunted for their oil used in making perfumes, and because much of their forest range is being logged or converted to agricultural use.

Civets are skillful nocturnal ambush hunters whose prey includes an array of rodents, rabbits, ground birds, and reptiles. They also eat fruit. Civets mark feeding territories or particular trees with scent from their perineal gland.

Linsangs are small quick animals that feed on carrion, lizards, and insects. Although the endangered spotted linsang does not have civet glands and has not been hunted for its scent, its coat is beautiful, making it a target. However, it is the loss of habitat that causes this resourceful, adaptable animal to be pressured.

Formosan Yellow-throated Marten

Martes flavigula chrysospila

Frank W. Lane

Status	Endangered
Listed	June 2, 1970
Family	Mustelidae (Weasels)
Description	Overall light brown; head, upper body, and legs are black; head and back have a silvery sheen; neck and chest feature a bright yellow vest.
Habitat	Forests.
Food	Primarily rodents and musk deer.
Reproduction	2 or 3 young after gestation of 135 to 152 days
Threats	Loss of habitat; natural predation.
Range	Taiwan.

Description

The Formosan yellow-throated marten resembles a weasel in shape, and its dexterity is reminiscent of monkeys. The head-and-body length of an adult is 18 to 26 inches, with its tail adding another 15 to 18 inches. An adult's weight is 6.5 to 13 pounds. Their fur is short and dense, and it is colorful and shiny. Colors for the head, back, and legs vary from dark brown to black, with the head and back featuring a silvery sheen. Mixed into this coloration are shades of light brown, which cover most of the rest of the body. The Formosan yellow-throated marten gets its name from the large, bright splash of yellow that covers its throat and chest.

Behavior

It is possible that mature females and males mate for life, but this is not certain. Formosan yellow-throated martens hunt in pairs and family groups. When their prey is large, they wear it down by surrounding it and persistently biting it. Although they live in trees, they frequently hunt on the ground; they require large ranges and will travel 5 to 12 miles a day in search of food. They are agile and move through tree branches with ease, and they are clever animals that evade traps and poisons humans set for them. They are primarily active during the day, resting at night.

They may have two breeding seasons per year, coinciding with periods of rain, but their breeding has not been observed enough for this to be known for sure. Gestation lasts 135 to 152 days, usually resulting in 2 or 3 young, although as many as 5 are possible. They are weaned at 2 months of age. What role the male plays in caring for the young is unclear, but it plainly has an interest in them once they are weaned because the parents and their young coordinate their hunting in order to bring down large prey. At one year of age, a Formosan yellow-throated marten is indistinguishable from an adult, but it does not reach sexual maturity until it is 3 years of age.

Habitat

The Formosan yellow-throated marten lives in mixed and coniferous forests in mountainous regions.

Distribution

The Formosan yellow-throated marten lives in a few areas of Taiwan that are not populated by humans.

Threats

The loss of habitat is particularly serious for the Formosan yellow-throated marten because it needs a large range in which to search for food. The exploding human popu-lation in Taiwan has greatly reduced the marten's required habitat.

Conservation and Recovery

The Formosan yellow-throated marten needs a protected forest where it and its prey are protected from human intrusion.

Spotted Linsang
Prionodon pardicolor

Sim Siang Huat, Singapore Zoological Gardens

Status	Endangered
Listed	June 14, 1976
Family	Viverridae (Civets and genets)
Description	Small, catlike predator with a fox-like face and very large eyes and ears; tan at the top of the body to white on the lower body, with some yellowish brown on the legs; 8 to 10 black or dark gray tail rings.
Habitat	Tropical forests.
Food	Primarily rodents, but also insects, small reptiles, and birds.
Reproduction	Mates in February and August, producing litters of two.
Threats	Loss of habitat and human predation.
Range	India (Assam), Burma, Cambodia, Laos, Nepal, and Vietnam.

Description

The spotted linsang, *Prionodon pardicolor,* is very reclusive and little is known about it. Its shadings of light brown and yellow-brown fur combined with its spots enable it to blend in with its forest habitat, making it hard to see. Adults are 15 to 16 inches long from tip-of-nose to base-of-tail; the tail adds another 13 to 14 inches. It weighs about 21 ounces.

It is remarkable-looking creature, seemingly a cross between a cat and a fox. The head is foxlike but narrower and proportionally longer, with a long muzzle. Its eyes are very large and dark, probably adaptations for night vision. Its ears are tall, pointy, and mobile, suggesting keen hearing. The torso is slim; the legs are slim and wiry; the tail is long and fluffy. The spotted linsang's coat is soft and dense, with short hairs. The hair on the legs is especially short; the paws are well covered, well padded, and large, featuring retractile claws.

The complete covering of the legs by hair helps to distinguish linsangs from other members of its family, *Viverridae*. Two other important distinguishing features are the absence of the upper second molar and the absence of a perineal gland. Another possible distinguishing feature is the absence of body odor.

Behavior

The spotted linsang is known to science primarily from dead and captured specimens and has been little studied in the wild. It is primarily an arboreal animal, although it often comes to the ground to hunt. It is nocturnal, sleeping during the day in nests lined with dry leaves and perhaps twigs; the nests are in tree hollows or under tree roots.

The spotted linsang may have two breeding seasons, one in February and another in August. Litters have one or two young, with two seeming more common. The young are kept in tree or root cavities lined with dried vegetation, perhaps until they are to be weaned. Whether or not they are taught to hunt is uncertain.

Habitat

The spotted linsang prefers dense tropical forests, although it seems willing to adapt to drier climates.

Distribution

The spotted linsang was once distributed throughout most of the mainland of Southeast Asia. It has probably disappeared from Sikkim and Thailand and may have disappeared from other of its host nations.

Threats

Much of the spotted linsang's range has been denuded of the forests it and its prey require. The deforestation has been caused by clear-cut logging, expanding agriculture, expanding human settlements, and war. Hunting for its fur coat may also be a problem.

Conservation and Recovery

The spotted linsang has the misfortune to live in a part of the world that, with exceptions, is hostile to naturalists and their efforts. War, drug running, and hostile governments make its range very dangerous for naturalists and even forest rangers. Further, logging companies tend to be hostile toward the presence of anyone who might interfere with their business. Against these obstacles naturalists need to record the numbers and favored territories of spotted linsangs and wildlife preserves need to be established and protected. Vietnam has taken a step in this direction by creating the Vu Quang Nature Reserve, on the border with Laos. Whether spotted linsangs still survive in this reserve has yet to be recorded, and poaching and illegal logging remain significant problems yet to be controlled for the park. Thailand is taking steps to establish reserves that would be ideal for spotted linsangs and other wildlife, but the drug dealers of the north make the conservation work very dangerous; it is possible that the spotted linsang has disappeared from Thailand. At the far northwest of the spotted linsang's range is the Kosi Tappu Wildlife Reserve of Nepal; this reserve is rich in the prey upon which the spotted linsang depends and may be a place where the spotted linsang still survives. Unfortunately, the park is not well protected and is under pressure from a burgeoning population of immigrants from India and the building of a hydroelectric dam.

Malabar Large-spotted Civet

Viverra megaspila civettina

Viverra megaspila   WWF/Rom Whitaker

Status	Endangered
Listed	June 25, 1979
Family	Viverridae (Civets and linsangs)
Description	Long body, short legs, and gray to dark yellow fur with large black spots on the flanks.
Habitat	Evergreen rainforests.
Food	Small mammals and birds, reptiles, eggs, insects, frogs, and snakes.
Reproduction	Average litter size of two young.
Threats	Agricultural development, and perhaps hunting.
Range	India

Description

The large-spotted civet, *Viverra megaspila*, has a long body, short legs, and gray to dark yellow fur with large black spots on the flanks which may fuse into stripes; and a crest of erectile black hair running along the center of the back from shoulder to rump. A longitudinal row of spots borders either side of this crest. The 12 to 18 inch long tail has 5 to 7 white bands and a black tip. The claws are nonretractable. It weighs up to 24 pounds.

The Malabar civet, *V. m. civettina*, is a subspecies of the large-spotted civet.

Behavior

Civets have been captured and kept by humans because of the secretion they emit from their perineal gland. When sprayed by the civet, the secretion has a penetrating, nauseating odor that becomes quite pleasant when the secretion is diluted. The animals mark their territory by pressing the perineal gland against an object; they also mark territory with their feces. The odors from the secretion and feces persist for a long time, thus providing points of reference for the civets as well as announcing their presence to intruders. The odors may also facilitate at-tracting a mate.

Civets are solitary animals except during the breeding season. They are capable of breeding year round, and they produce an average litter size of two young. The young are raised in shelters built by other animals, or in dense vegetation and they remain with the mother for about a month when they are weaned.

The diet of civets includes small mammals and birds, reptiles, eggs, insects, frogs, and snakes. Captive civets will eat fruits. Civets hunt mainly on the ground, at night, and subdue prey with their teeth.

Habitat

The Malabar civet occurs in evergreen rainforests.

Distribution

Viverrine civets are endemic to most of southwest India but the Malabar civet seems to occur only in the Western Ghats. Its popula-tion is estimated at under 500 individuals. Thought to be extinct, three specimens were captured in 1987.

Threats

Civets have long played an important economic role in East African and Oriental countries because of their long-lasting aro-matic compounds and use of civet oil for medicinal purposes. Today, they are most threatened by the loss of habitat due to agri-cultural development, and perhaps hunting.

Conservation and Recovery

The Malabar civet probably occurs in several wildlife sanctuaries in the states of Kerela and Karnataka in southwest India, especially in the Parambikulam Wildlife Sanctuary and the Dandeli Wildlife Sanctu-ary, where they are protected from hunting and habitat encroachment.

Otters
Family: Mustelidae

Southern River Otter (*Lutra provocax*)　　　　　　　　　　　　　　　C. Allan Morgan

General Characteristics of the *Mustelidae*

Otters are members of the weasel family and are classified into four genuses: *Lutra*, the river otters; *Pteronura*, the giant otter; *Aonyx*, the clawless otters; and *Enhydra*, the sea otters. Except for *A. congica*, otters are equally at home in the water as on land. The webbed paws facilitate swimming and their face whiskers are sensitive to water turbulence and are used to locate prey. Otters eat frogs, crayfish, crabs and fish, eels, frogs and even birds. Some otter species catch prey with their claws, but most otters, including the endangered giant otter, snare prey with their jaws. Because they have a high rate of metabolism, otters digest their meals within a few hours and must feed several times a day. Agile hunters, they are usually able to quickly attain food, which includes fish, frogs, crabs, birds, rodents and rabbits.

The *Lutra* otters are generally solitary and pair for only several months during the breeding season, while the Giant otter lives in an extended family group with strong bonds between the breeding pair. All otters are very vocal; they use their calls as greetings, summons, threats and alarms. They also communicate through scent markings, which help identify sex and sexual receptivity. Otters, especially the giant otter, mark their territory with a strong combination of scent glands, urine and feces, so strong an odor as to be overpowering.

Lutra otters are excellent swimmers and generally occur near the shore. They dig permanent burrows beside the water whose main entrance slopes upward to a nest chamber above the water line. While away from their primary burrow, they take shelter in rocks or driftwood. They swim by moving their hind legs and tail, and they can remain underwater for up to 8 minutes. They are also very adept on land and are able to run at speeds of up to 20 miles per hour.

Otters are clever and resourceful, and are able to overcome many obstacles. However, pollution and trapping have caused the giant otter (*Pteronura brasiliensis*) and marine otter (*Lutra felina*) to become endangered, and the southern river otter (*Lutra provocax*) to a vulnerable condition.

Cameroon Clawless Otter

Aonyx [=Paraonyx] congica microdon

Cape Clawless Otter (*Aonyx capensis*)   USFWS

Status	Endangered
Listed	June 2, 1970
Family	Mustelidae (Otters)
Description	Brown with lighter underparts and white markings on the face, throat and chest; weighs up to 45 pounds.
Habitat	Small, torrential mountain streams with dense rainforest.
Food	Insects, small mammals, and frogs.
Reproduction	2 or 3 young after gestation of about 60 days.
Threats	Hunting; drowning in fish nets.
Range	Nigeria and Cameroon

Description

The Cameroon clawless otter, *Aonyx congica microdon,* is brown with lighter underparts and white markings on the face, throat and chest. It weighs up to 45 pounds. Its common name, "clawless," derives from the small, blunt claws that lack webbing. The claws, scanty hair, and teeth suggest that it is less adapted to water than other otters.

Behavior

This clawless otter feeds on soft prey such as insects, small mammals, and frogs. They forage with their claws in mud and under stones.

Little is known of this rare species, but it is thought that they reach sexual maturity at about 1 year and give birth to 2 or 3 young after gestation of about 60 days.

Habitat

The Cameroon clawless otter occurs only in small, torrential mountain streams with dense rainforest.

Distribution

The Cameroon clawless otter occurs in a narrow range along the Congo River in Nigeria and Cameroon.

Threats

Although the fur of *Aonyx* species is not as fine or desirable as *Lutra* otters, they have been hunted for their pelts. They are also accidentally killed in fish traps, although *A. c. microdon* is less susceptible to this type of death than *A. capensis* and *A. cinerea* because of its land orientation.

Conservation and Recovery

Educating indigenous people of the rarity of the Cameroon clawless otter may help to reduce kills, but better management of the rainforests is the only hope of sustaining this highly endangered animal.

Marine Otter

Lutra felina

Richard Ostfeld

Status	Endangered
Listed	June 14, 1976
Family	Mustelidae (Otters)
Description	Long body, rough, grayish coat, a short tail, small ears, broad muzzle, and webbed feet with nails.
Habitat	Exposed, rocky seashore with strong winds.
Food	Primarily on crustaceans and mollusks.
Reproduction	2 to 5 young after gestation of up to 120 days.
Threats	Hunting; killed as pests; pollution.
Range	Chile, Peru.

Description

The marine otter, *Lutra felina*, has a long body, rough, grayish coat, a short tail, small ears, broad muzzle, and webbed feet with nails. It weighs up to 10 pounds but much smaller individuals occur.

Local names for the marine otter include chungungo and nutria del mar.

Behavior

Unlike the long-tailed ottter, *Lutra longicaudis*, whose diet is principally fish, the marine otter feeds primarily on crustaceans and mollusks.

Mating occurs in December and January, and 2 to 5 young are produced after gestation of up to 120 days.

Habitat

The marine otter occurs along exposed, rocky seashore with strong winds. Although it will not inhabit rivers, it has been recorded hunting in rivers at an altitude of 2,000 feet. It prefers aquatic areas associated with seaweed.

Distribution

The marine otter occurs along the coast and offshore islands of Chile, and in the Paracas wildlife reserve in Peru, where 200 to 300 individuals survive. The largest population is off Chiloé Islands, south of Chile. It seems to have disappeared from the Cape Horn region and from Argentina where it was once abundant.

Threats

Fishermen kill marine otters because they prey on prawns, and the limited available suitable habitat prevents these otters from relocating to less vulnerable areas. Habitat alteration, including the harvesting of algae, and especially the removal of invertebrate prey by shell fishermen, has contributed significantly to the otter's decline. They are also hunted for their pelts, and heavy metal runoff from mines in Northern Chile has degraded their habitat.

Conservation and Recovery

The marine otter inhabits coastal areas which are used by fishermen, and the competition between animal and man for the prawn reserves must be mitigated in Peru. Pollution inland has made its way to the sea where it is affecting marine life, and the discharge of pollutants needs to be controlled.

Long-tailed Otter

Lutra longicaudis

Aníbal F. Parera

Status	Endangered
Listed	June 14, 1976
Family	Mustelidae (Otters)
Description	Dark brown with a paler grayish underside, light brown cheeks and throat, and yellow shading around the chin.
Habitat	Remote areas of large tropical rivers with slow currents.
Food	Mainly fish but also mollusks, crustaceans, and small vertebrates.
Reproduction	1 to 4 young.
Threats	Hunting and pollution.
Range	Brazil, Paraguay, Argentina, and Uruguay.

Description

The long-tailed otter, *Lutra longicaudis,* is dark brown with a paler grayish underside, light brown cheeks and throat, and yellow shading around the chin. Sometimes there are spots or patches. Its entire tail is flat, fringed with hair; its strong claws are webbed.

Behavior

The long-tailed otter's primary food source is fish but also includes mollusks, crustaceans, and small vertebrates.

The breeding season varies with locality; litter size ranges from 1 to 4 young but 2 to 3 is average. The length of gestation is unknown.

Habitat

The long-tailed otter occurs in remote areas of large tropical rivers with slow currents.

Distribution

The long-tailed otter occurs in Brazil, Paraguay, Argentina, and Uruguay. It is not known if it survives in any significant numbers in Argentina and Uruguay, but there are protected populations in Brazil and Paraguay.

Threats

The long-tailed otter has been ruthlessly hunted for its fur, which is in high demand. Pollution, which has caused a decline in the fish population, also affects the stability of the habitat.

Conservation and Recovery

Although there are protected populations in the Emas National Park in Brazil, and throughout Paraguay where the habitat is inaccessible to hunters, all the countries in which populations occur must control commercial hunting and improve rising pollution.

Southern [=Patagonian] River Otter

Lutra provocax

Claudio Chehébar

Status	Endangered
Listed	June 14, 1976
Family	Mustelidae (Weasels and otters)
Description	Very dark brown coat, with a cinnamon underbody.
Habitat	Fresh water streams and lakes.
Food	Crayfish, mussels, and fish.
Reproduction	1 to 5, usually 2 to 3 young.
Threats	Hunting for its fur and loss of habitat.
Range	Argentina and Chile.

Description

Southern river otters, *Lutra provocax*, are 22.5 to 27.5 inches long, not counting their tails, which add 13.5 to 18 inches. Their fur is notably soft and is laid sleekly back along the body. The coat is very dark brown overall, with the underbody being a somewhat lighter cinnamon. A good swimmer that can spend 2 minutes underwater, the southern river otter has heavily webbed feet for swimming. Its claws are strong. Adapted to living much of its life in water, the southern river otter is shaped like a cylinder, with a sleek head for slipping through the water. Its muzzle is broad and whiskered; naturalists use the shape of its muzzle to distinguish the southern river otter from other otter species. Its ears are small, rounded, and set back on the head, adding to the head's streamlined appearance.

Behavior

Almost nothing is recorded about the southern river otter's behavior. It is probably (based on few observations) a solitary animal that only socializes during periods of mating, when males and females can be seen frolicking together; play seems to be an important part of the mating process. Young are probably cared for by the mother alone, but it is possible that, instead, family units form with the father participating in the care of the young.

The southern river otter requires fresh water to survive and cannot tolerate polluted water. It is probably mostly nocturnal, but it has been seen moving about in daylight. When active, it hunts in water; its primary foods are aquatic: crayfish, mussels, and fish. When it captures its prey, it does so with its mouth rather than its paws. The forepaws are dexterous and good at holding and manipulating objects. When resting, the southern river otter apparently seeks refuge in heavy ground cover along the water's edge.

Habitat

The southern otter lives near fresh, unpolluted water with heavy ground cover along the shores. The climate varies from hot to cold.

Distribution

The southern river otter ranges from central through southern Chile and in southwestern Argentina. It survives in Argentina only in two widely separated areas; it has lost the northern part of it range in Chile, and in the south it is restricted primarily to Andean river basins.

Threats

The southern river otter's coat is valuable, and as a consequence it has been hunted into near extinction and has been eliminated from most of its range. It has lost much of its northern habitat to agriculture and to water pollution.

Conservation and Recovery

Illegal hunting is the greatest problem the southern river otter presently faces; law enforcement needs to be tightened to help it, and it needs reserves that can be protected from poachers. It is listed in CITES, Appendix I: Trade Prohibited, which by international treaty prohibits trade in the southern river otter or its parts, including its coat, but most of the poaching is done by domestic hunters.

Giant Otter

Pteronura brasiliensis

Marshall Jones, FWS

Status	Endangered
Listed	June 2, 1970
Family	Mustelidae (Weasels and otters)
Description	Bright cream colored spots on the throat, a hairy nasal speculum, with a flattened muscular tail.
Habitat	Rivers of tropical rain forests.
Food	Fish, crustaceans, and other aquatic animals.
Reproduction	Usually two or three cubs are born, weighing 6 to 8 ounces.
Threats	Used as pets by local Indians; hunting for the fur trade.
Range	Colombia, Guyana, and Argentina

Description

The Giant otter, *Pteronura brasiliensis*, as the name implies, is distinguished by its large size. This species displays typical otter characteristics, although it also displays bright spots on the throat, a hairy nasal speculum, and a flattened muscular tail. The feet of the giant otter are webbed. This otter has a body length of 3 to 4.6 feet; tail length is 12 to 22 inches; and weight for the giant otter is 48 to 70 pounds. The pelt is dark brown, with cream colored spots on the chin, throat, and chest. The tail is flat; the limbs are short, making walking on wet banks difficult; and the hairless feet have palmed fingers with long nails. Its head is flat and wide, and its small rounded ears are far back.

The giant otter is also known as the water dog. There are two subspecies, *P. b. brasiliensis*, in the northern section of Brazil, and *P. b. paranaensis*, in the south.

Behavior

The giant otter usually lives in groups of four to eight. This group consists of both family and non-family members. The family unit consists of a male, the dominant female, and offspring of 1 to 4 cubs. The group will hunt, groom, and rest together. Communication is achieved through a series of sounds and barks. Scent markings outline territories.

Mating occurs January through April. Gestation lasts for 65 to 70 days and usually two or three cubs are born at the beginning of the dry season, which may occur from June to October. Each cub weighs about 6 to 8 ounces at birth. Cubs remain in the den for about two months and stay with the parents for 2 to 3 years. When the cubs are young, one member of the group will remain in the den while the rest of the group fishes.

The giant otter is carnivorous, feeding on fish, small invertebrates, such as crustaceans, and other aquatic animals. It may dive for fish; diving depths have been measured to be a few inches to 9 feet and do not exceed 72 seconds. It eats as much as 8 pounds of fish a day. It will eat smaller fish in the water but takes large fish to shore. Adult otters fish together but do not share their prey. Even the young must beg, often loudly, for their share of the catch.

The giant otter is diurnal. Daytime hours are spent in the river with periodic resting on riverbanks free from dense vegetation.

The giant otter marks its territory and feeding grounds with a strong odor composed of scent glands, urine and feces. They will clear an area of vegetation by trampling, then use it as a latrine to ward off any curious intruders.

Habitat

The giant otter can be found in the rivers of tropical rainforests in South America and in lagoons and swamps near large rivers. It prefers fairly shallow, slow riverine currents with dense vegetation along the banks.

The giant otter constructs lodges (or dens) consisting of simple burrows with tunnels and chambers. The female will bear her cubs in the lodge.

Distribution

The giant otter is known from tropical riverine habitats of South America. This otter was once widely distributed throughout Colombia, Guyana, south to Argentina, and west to the foothills of South America. Today the giant otter occurs in isolated remnant populations over its historic distribution. One healthy population occurs in the Madre di Dios River in Peru. The population of the Giant otter is unknown, but its numbers were rapidly depleted during the 1960s when 20,000 skins were exported from Brazil alone.

Threats

The natives value this species' pelt. The natives also hunt the giant otter for its meat. Young otters are often raised as pets by these Indians.

The primary factor, however, for the giant otter's decline is hunting for the fur trade. It has been estimated that in a 15 year period between 1950 and 1965 at least 50,000 pelts were exported from Brazil and Peru. Astonishingly enough these numbers exclude any other hides that may have been exported from other countries. Giant otter skins brought $250 to native trappers in the 1980s.

Conservation and Recovery

In an effort to promote propagation of endangered otters such as *P. brasiliensis*, the Asian small-clawed otter, *Aonyx cinerea*, has been adopted into the Species Survival Plan by the American Association of Zoological Parks and Aquariums. As a result, *A. cinerea* will be paid particular attention and scrutiny as captive breeding programs are established.

The giant otter is protected by law in Brazil, Ecuador, and Peru but is not protected in Colombia, Guyana, Surinam and Venezuela, although it is protected from export by CITES. However, even in the countries where it is protected, poaching continues to be a problem.

Solenodons

Family: Solenodontidae

Haitian Solenodon *(Solenodon paradoxuus)*

General Characteristics of the *Solenodontidae*

Weighing over two pounds, solenodons are among the largest insectivores in the world, but they have not always been insectivores. Before Europeans arrived in Cuba and Hispaniola, they were carnivores, eating beetles, crickets, insect larvae, millipedes, worms, and termites. They may also have eaten amphibians, reptiles, and birds. Only occasionally preyed upon by large snakes and birds, the solenodons were dominant predators until Europeans introduced dogs, cats, and mongooses to the islands, which found solenodons easy prey. When they were dominant, solenodons had a long lifespan and low reproductive rate. The young are born in nesting burrows and remain with the mother for several months, learning to forage for themselves at about two months.

The Cuban solenodon, which is the rarer of the two species, is preyed upon by cats and mongooses; in Hispaniola dogs are the major threat. On the Haiti side of Hispaniola, the solenodon is probably extinct, but in the Dominican Republic and on Cuba populations survive in remote, dense forests.

Cuban Solenodon

Solenodon cubanus

Status	Endangered
Listed	June 2, 1970
Family	Solenodontidae (Solenodons)
Description	Very dark brown to black hair with white or brownish yellow highlights
Habitat	Tropical forest to brushlands.
Food	Mostly insects
Reproduction	Single young
Threats	Competition and predation.
Range	Cuba

Lydekker, *The Royal Natural History*

Description

There are only two species of solenodons remaining in existence, the Cuban solenodon, *Solenodon cubanus*, and the Haitian solenodon, *Solenodon paradoxus* (see separate entry). The two are easy to distinguish from one another: The Cuban solenodon has long, silky fur, whereas the Haitian solenodon has shorter, coarser fur. Its coloration is very dark brown to black, sometimes with white or buff highlights; the Haitian solenodon is yellow or buff, sometimes reddish, with black or dark brown streaks. The Cuban solenodon has a longer tail but is overall smaller than its Haitian relative. It also seems to lack the Haitian solenodon's ball-and-socket joint where the nose meets the skull, having a cartilaginous pad there instead. Strong muscles in the nose and the pad enable the nose to move about flexibly, especially up and down.

The Cuban solenodon is a thick, rounded animal. It is 10 to 12 inches in head-and-body length, with a tail of 10.5 to 12 inches in length, and it weighs 1.25 to 1.5 pounds. It hair is laid back over its rounded body but shaggy at it fringes. The Cuban solenodon digs in the ground, pulls over stones, and pries open logs in its search for food; for this, it has long, thick claws on its forepaws, as well as powerful forelegs. The hind feet are used for grooming. The animal's most prominent feature is probably its very long cartilaginous nose, with nostrils on the sides. It uses the nose to pin down its prey, then it darts forward, scooping up the prey with its lower jaw. The lower jaw has incisors with grooves on their insides (hence the name "solenodon," meaning "grooved teeth"). It is not yet known whether the Cuban solenodon is venomous and squirts its venom mixed with saliva into its victims the way the Haitian solenodon does. Like its Haitian relative, the Cuban solenodon has an unusually large cerebellum, which may mean that it has a good memory.

Behavior

Very little has been recorded of the Cuban solenodon's behavior. It probably lives in family burrows. In those burrows females give birth to a single young, sometimes very rarely two. The female has two teats near her anus; the newborns attach themselves to these and are dragged about when their mother moves.

The Cuban solenodons are nocturnal animals, using their sense of smell to seek out prey, mostly insects such as ants and beetles, but also larger prey such as rodents, lizards, and birds. When it is up and about, it walks only on its toes, and it zigzags; when startled, it bounds about almost randomly as it seeks shelter; it is very fast. When it finds prey, its digs it out of the ground, pries open its wooden hideaways, or overturns the rocks that protect it. If the prey is large, the Cuban solenodon uses its nose to hold its victim down, then darts forward and scoops it up with its lower jaw. It is possible that it eats some vegetable matter, although authorities disagree on the matter, with some asserting that in the wild the Cuban solenodon eats no vegetable matter at all. This is important in terms of the animal's conservation because farmers think it damages their crops and therefore kill it as a pest, but if it does not eat vegetation, then it may actually benefit crops because it eats harmful insects, and farmers may be convinced to aid in the species' preservation.

Habitat

The Cuban solenodon occupies a variety of habitats; it is most commonly found in temperate woodlands, but it also lives in tropical forests and temperate to semiarid shrublands. It seems to favor montane ranges, but this may be the result of humans pressing it out of most of the rest of its habitat.

Distribution

The Cuban solenodon probably once occupied nearly all of Cuba, where it competed with few other predators for prey and space. It is now found only in Oriente Province.

Threats

Loss of habitat and competition with imported predators brought the Cuban solenodon perilously close to extinction, and even with Cuba taking measures to protect the animal, it still is very endangered. Farmers think it spoils their crops and therefore kill it as a pest. Wild dogs, in particular of imported predators, prey on the Cuban solenodon and harass it wherever it is found.

Conservation and Recovery

The Cuban solenodon was long considered extinct, in spite of occasional sightings beginning in the 1950s. In the last decade or so, several small populations have been discovered in Cuba's Oriente Province. Cuba has established two reserves for the animal, and it is reportedly going to create a third reserve.

Haitian Solenodon

Solenodon paradoxus

USFWS

Status	Endangered
Listed	June 2, 1970
Family	Solenodontidae (Solenodons)
Description	Yellow or buff hair, long and flexible nose.
Habitat	Woodlands and areas with good ground cover.
Food	Insects, frogs, lizards, and birds.
Reproduction	Single young.
Threats	Predation; habitat destruction.
Range	Dominican Republic and Haiti

Description

There are only two species of solenodons remaining in existence, the Haitian solenodon, *Solenodon paradoxus*, and the Cuban solenodon, *Solenodon cubanus* (please see separate entry). The two are easy to distinguish from one another: The Haitian has shorter, coarser fur than the Cuban solenodon. Its coloration is overall yellow, sometimes reddish, with black or dark brown streaks, especially a black forehead, whereas the Cuban solenodon is very dark brown or black, with white highlights. The Haitian solenodon has the shorter tail. Further, the Haitian solenodon's nose is attached to its skull by a ball-and-socket joint that the Cuban solenodon lacks. This joint allows the long cartilage of the nose to move about with great flexibility.

The Haitian solenodon is not one of the world's beauties. It is shaped like an oversized shrew, 11 to 13 inches in head-and-body length, with a tail of 8.5 to 10.5 inches in length, and it weighs 1.25 to 2.25 pounds. It hair is laid back over its rounded body and is mixed with oily secretions that smell somewhat like a goat. The tail and hind legs are nearly hairless, and the forelegs are hairless except near the torso. The forepaws have long, thick claws that are used for digging, for prying open logs, and for moving stones out of the way. The hind feet are used for grooming. The animal has a very long cartilaginous nose that, because of its unusual ball-and-socket joint and strong muscles, can be poked into cracks, holes, and difficult-to-reach spots; its nostrils are on its sides. Its upper incisors extend forward out of the mouth and under the nose. The solenodon ("grooved teeth") gets its name from its lower incisors, which are grooved on the inside. The Haitian solenodon produces venom that mixes with saliva when it bites and is then squirted through the grooves and into the victim. This venom can be deadly to small animals and cause uncomfortable inflammation in humans; it probably immobilizes prey. The Haitian solenodon has an unusually large cerebellum, which may account for its good memory: It remembers others of its own kind even after long separations, and in captivity it remembers the name given it by its caretakers and will respond to hearing its name.

Behavior

The Haitian solenodon is poorly studied in the wild, and different authorities vary greatly in their accounts of its behavior. For example, some authorities declare the animal to be a solitary creature with its largest social unit being that formed by a mother and her immature young, but others declare the animal to be gregarious and fond of the company of its own kind. The latter view may result from confusing the Cuban solenodon, which has been seen living in groups with as many as eight members, with the Haitian solenodon, which is very likely solitary. In any case, the habitat for the Haitian solenodon is so very disrupted and the animal's numbers so very few that whether it really is gregarious in the wild may never be determined.

Young are born in an underground nest; they attach themselves to their mother's teats, which are near her anus, and are dragged about as she moves. The Haitian solenodon's

mating ritual consists of whistling like birds, rubbing together, and the male defecating and urinating in spots where the female has been. The period for gestation is not exactly known; but observations of captive animals suggest that it lasts over 64 days.

The Haitian solenodon is nocturnal, spending its day in a hole in a tree or root, a crack among stones, or a burrow in the ground. It leaves its hideaway for intervals of 45 to 60 minutes, usually to search for prey. It walks in a zigzag pattern, and when frightened, it will dodge about in an exaggerated zigzag; it can move very fast when it is motivated to do so. While walking, its nose is constantly searching for indications of food, primarily insects such as ants and beetles, although it will eat earthworms and seems fond of snails, whose opened shells will be scattered outside its burrow. Its larger prey includes snakes, small mammals, and small birds. Some authorities believe it eats a small amount of vegetable matter such as bitter oranges and bananas; others insist that it eats no vegetable matter at all.

Habitat

The Haitian solenodon would probably prefer to live in woodlands, which would be places where its prey were abundant and where it could take shelter from its principal predators, raptors and boas; woodlands are rare in Haiti. It requires a range in which it can find an abundant supply of insects, and where it can burrow into the soil.

Distribution

The Haitian solenodon once occupied all

of Haiti and the eastern edge of the Dominican Republic, but it is now mostly restricted to far western Haiti.

Threats

Human beings have nearly erased the natural habitat of Haiti, to which the Haitian solenodon has spent millions of years adapting. With this habitat destruction has come the loss of prey for the Haitian solenodon, as well as room in which it can live in its natural state. Old World immigrants brought with them animals that are much more capable predators than the Haitian solenodon; these feral dogs, cats, and mongooses have taken away much of the insect and small animal prey on which it depends.

Conservation and Recovery

The condition of the Haitian solenodon is considered very severe by every naturalist who has written about it in the last few decades, and at present it is expected to become extinct on any day. Naturalists have been calling, without much success, for immediate and strict government intervention on the Haitian solenodon's behalf; it needs a well-protected reserve, secure from human intrusion, in which to live. Establishing such a preserve may be impossible in a land where newly planted trees in reserves are stripped from the ground almost overnight for firewood, where soil erosion has become an ecological nightmare, and wild animals are often killed on sight.

It is possible that some Haitian solenodons survive in the mountainous border region between Haiti and the Dominican Republic. A preserve in that region might have a chance to successfully protect the Haitian solenodon, although cross-border poaching has stripped even the Dominican Republic side of much of its wildlife. The Dominican Republic has made a good effort to protect its population of the Haitian solenodon, including its illegal export to foreign zoos. Even so, the Dominican Republic needs to designate and protect some of its remaining wildlands as reserves if the Haitian solenodon is to survive for the long term. Some Haitian solenodons survive in zoos, where they breed adequately, and the animal may soon be wholly dependent on zoos for its continued existence.

Hutias, Beavers, Porcupines and Chinchillas
Families: Capromyidae, Castoridae, Erethizontidae, and *Chinchillidae*

Chinchilla   Rich Block

General Characteristics of the *Capromyidae*

The hutia family, *Capromyidae*, consists of 3 genera and 13 species, some of which are known only from skeletal remains. Originally, there were 8 genera and over 30 species of hutia in South American and the Caribbean. All species are found in the Lesser or Greater Antilles (West Indies).

All of the Cuban hutias are fairly large rodents with dense, short fur and long, coarse guard hairs. They have a broad head, small ears, short legs and broad feet. Variation in fur coloration is tan, yellow-red, brown and black.

Hutias live in pairs and breeding may occur year round, often in communal nests. One to 3 young are born after a gestation period of 17 to 18 weeks. The young are well developed at birth, having hair, eye sight, and mobility. After only 10 days of suckling, the young are capable of feeding themselves.

The Cuban hutias are active during the day when they forage for fruit, leaves, bark and lizards.

Hutias were hunted for food by early explorers and settlers and are still hunted for food during lean times. They are relatively easy to catch because they take refuge in water when threatened, and they are slow, clumsy swimmers. They have a limited ability to avoid predators and little fear of them. Although the Cuban hutias are protected by law, it is difficult to enforce protection against fishermen in the small cays where they occur.

General Characteristics of the *Castoridae*

There are two species of beavers, the North American beaver, *Castor canadensis,* and the European or Asian beaver, *Castor fiber.* Some taxonomists consider the European beaver to be a distinct species, *Castor albicus,* because of differences in the skull. Biologically, they are similar species, although the North American beaver is considered to be more advanced. Both were derived from giant animals weighing up to 700 pounds during the Pleistocene, 10,000 years ago. Today, beavers are the second largest rodent, weighing up to 70 pounds (the largest is the capybara, weighing up to 140 pounds).

Stream beavers, the *Castoridae,* have flat tails and webbed hind feet making it well adapted for its semi-aquatic life. It is a powerful swimmer, using its broad, strong tail for propulsion and steering. Because a translucent membrane covers the beaver's eyes, it can see underwater, and it can block water from entering its throat with its tongue, allowing beavers to carry sticks under water as they construct dams and shelters. With their large, rodent teeth that have a chiseled edge, beavers are adept at gnawing and can fell large trees. Beavers construct dams as increased protection for their lodges against predators, and to widen their water habitat to gain access to a wider supply of food. Slow and clumsy on land, beavers prefer to swim to their food sources. Dams also guard against any drop in water level due to weather conditions. Beaver dams have been recorded as long as 350 feet and 10 feet high.

Beavers have evolved an exceptionally stable family unit which includes a continuing relationship between male and female, low birthrate, and sustained parental care until the young are fully mature. Both parents attend the kits, helping to feed them solid food and teaching them how to construct dams and lodges.

General Characteristics of the *Erethizontidae*

New World porcupines, the *Erethizontidae,* are tree-dwelling rodents which, unlike Old World porcupines that are ground dwellers, have well developed claws and pads on their feet that assist in climbing. Tails vary among subspecies, but the South American species, of which the thinned-spined porcupine is one, have spineless tails that are also used for gripping limbs.

South American porcupines obtain much of their leaf diet from trees, but they will also forage on the ground for roots, tubers, insects, and reptiles. Poorly sighted, porcupines use hearing, smell and touch to locate food and navigate. Newborn porcupines are able to see and walk, and can climb after a few days, and seem to be able to escape predators by navigating through their arboreal habitat.

Because of their quills, porcupines have few natural predators, and only the fisher marten is able to regularly attack and kill porcupines as a food source. The destruction of the forests in South America is the reason the thinned-spine porcupine is endangered; otherwise, all species of porcupines are excellent survivors.

General Characteristics of the *Chinchillidae*

Chinchillas are small (weighing less than 2 pounds), rodents that occur in the mountains of Peru, Argentina, Chile, and Bolivia. Their dense, bluish-gray and yellowish fur has made them a prize for furriers, and all species are under pressure from trapping. The chinchilla's pelt, however, has limited durability which, when combined with the animal's small size, requires many animals to satisfy the demand for fur coats. Viscachas, which are members of the *Chinchillidae* family, are also prized for their fur as well as their meat; they are also considered pests to livestock ranching because their urine destroys pastureland and their burrows cause injury to men and cattle. There are two chinchilla species: the short-tailed chinchilla (*C. c. boliviana*), which is a subspecies of the now extinct king chinchilla (*Chinchilla chinchilla*), and the long-tailed chinchilla (*Chinchilla lanigera*).

Chinchillas are nocturnal and they have a keen sense of sight and hearing. They have typical rodent teeth — two teeth up and down — which grow continuously and are worn down with use. They feed on grasses and bushes by holding the food between their front paws while sitting on their longer, stronger rear feet.

Female chinchillas can breed once a month and may produce 2 or 3 litters a year. One to three, but usually two young are born after gestation of about 110 days. The young become sexually mature at 4 to 6 months. Life expectancy in captivity is up to 10 years.

Cabrera's Hutia

Capromys angelcabrerai

Raphael Borroto

Status	Endangered
Listed	May 16, 1986
Family	Capromyidae (Hutias)
Description	Rat-like rodent with stout body, coarse fur, small ears and eyes, and a broad head.
Habitat	Mangrove swamps off south-central Cuba.
Food	Fruit, green vegetation, bark, and possibly small animals.
Reproduction	1 to 3 young after gestation of 2 to 4 months
Threats	Hunting
Range	Cuba: Cayos de Ana Maria

Description

Cabrera's hutia, *Capromys angelcabrerai*, is a rodent similar to the dwarf hutia, but having a relatively shorter tail. It is found only on the Cayos de Ana Maria off south-central Cuba. Its body length is 8 to 10 inches and the tail is 6 to 7 inches. The back and sides are ochre to brown, the stomach a lighter shade of the same color, and the plantar sections are white.

C. angelcabrerai was first discovered in 1974 and was described by Varona in 1979.

Behavior

Cabrera's hutia is probably mostly herbivorous; it consumes fruit, green vegetation, bark, and possibly small animals (e.g., lizards). Little is known of Cabrera's hutia's habits, but it is probably diurnal for the most part.

Cabrera's hutia builds communal nests of tree branches and leaves in red mangroves above the high tide level. Females produce 1 to 3 offspring after a long gestation period of 2 to 4 months.

Habitat

Cabrera's hutia inhabits mangrove swamps above the high tide level.

Distribution

Cabrera's hutia is only found on a few small islands (Cayos de Ana Maria) off the south-central coast of Cuba. It was thought to be extinct shortly after discovery but was rediscovered in abundance in a few localized areas in the 1990s.

Threats

The main threat to Cabrera's hutia is its use as food by local fisherman, and other persons who visit its island habitat. When driven from its nest it takes refuge in water. This species is slow and clumsy, and easily captured.

Conservation and Recovery

The survival of Cabrera's hutia depends on the ability of the species to avoid human contact, and on the good will of the local people not to kill entire populations.

Large-eared Hutia

Capromys auritus

Status	Endangered
Listed	May 16, 1986
Family	Capromyidae (Hutias)
Description	Large rodent with brown fur, 12 inches in length and a 7 inch tail.
Habitat	Mangrove swamp on Cayo Fragoso Island.
Food	Fruit, green vegetation, bark.
Reproduction	Females produce 1 to 3 young; gestation lasts from 2-4 months.
Threats	Hunting
Range	Cuba: Cayo Fragoso Island

Description

The large-eared hutia, *Capromys auritus*, is the second smallest hutia, with a body length of about 12 inches and a 7-inch tail. Its rough coat is dark brown.

Behavior

The large-eared hutia is mostly herbivorous; it consumes fruit, green vegetation, bark, and possibly small animals (e.g., lizards).

Little is known of the large-eared hutia's habits, but it is probably diurnal for the most part.

Large-eared hutias construct large round communal nests situated in the roots of mangroves about one foot above water level. Constructed of small sticks, they contain several chambers and many entrances.

Habitat

The large-eared hutia is found only in a mangrove swamp on Cayo Fragoso, an island off north-central Cuba.

Distribution

The large-eared hutia was not discovered until 1970 and is known only from one area of mangrove swamp on Cayo Fragoso, an island off north-central Cuba. The population is thought to be very small and vulnerable.

Threats

Hutias are used for food by local fishermen and other persons who visit their island habitats. The large nests are easy to locate, and fishermen capture the animals by placing sacks over the exits. The animals that escape the nest are driven into the water, where they are slow and clumsy, and thus easily captured.

Conservation and Recovery

In 1980 a nature reserve was established on the island of Fregoso and on other nearby cays where hunting is completely forbidden.

Dwarf Hutia

Capromys nana

Priscilla Barrett

Status	Endangered
Listed	May 16, 1986
Family	Capromyidae (Hutias)
Description	Small rat-like rodent with short limbs, small eyes and ears, and a broad head.
Habitat	Swamps.
Food	Fruit, green vegetation, bark.
Reproduction	1- 3 young; 2 to 4 month gestation.
Threats	Agricultural development
Range	Cuba

Description

The dwarf hutia, *Capromys nana*, is the smallest of the hutias, measuring about 8 inches in head and body length, and 6 to 7 inches in tail length. It has an outer layer of coarse, rough fur and an under layer of softer, dense fur. The coat is not a solid color because individual hairs are colored differently, from gray and red to brown and black. The snout and tips of the ears are white. The tail has sparse hairs that are black above and yellow to brown below, tipped in black.

Behavior

The dwarf hutia is mostly herbivorous; it consumes fruit, green vegetation, bark, and possibly small animals (e.g., lizards). Little is known of the dwarf hutia's habits, but it is probably diurnal for the most part.

Habitat

The dwarf hutia is found only in the Zapata Swamp, located about 100 kilometers (62 miles) southeast of Havana, Cuba. It inhabits the restricted, dry brushy islands and mangrove thickets that border the swamp.

Distribution

The dwarf hutia is currently confined to the Zapata Swamp southeast of Havana. Fossil remains, however, indicate that it once occurred over a much larger part of Cuba. Discovered in 1917 from jawbones, there have been no verified sightings of the dwarf hutia since 1937, when several live specimens were captured, but it is believed to survive because of the discovery of tracks and fecal droppings.

Threats

Agricultural development is a potential threat to the small remaining habitat of this species. The dwarf hutia is taken for food by fishermen who visit its swamp habitat, and they have been known to kill hutias in large numbers. Predation on the young by introduced rats and mongooses have been a major contributing factor to the drastic reduction of hutias.

This species occurs in such low population numbers that inbreeding and loss of genetic viability could present major threats to its continued survival.

Conservation and Recovery

A nature reserve has been founded in the Zapata swamp, and although this helps protect against habitat incursion, it is difficult to enforce laws prohibiting the hunting of hutias.

Little Earth Hutia

Capromys sanfelipensis

Status	Endangered (Probably extinct)
Listed	May 15, 1986
Family	Capromyidae (Hutias)
Description	Stout-bodied, rat-like rodent with a reddish tail, small eyes and ears, and a broad head.
Habitat	Low and dense vegetation on Cayo Juan Garcia, off southwestern Cuba.
Food	Fruit, green vegetation, bark, and possibly small animals.
Reproduction	1 to 3 young after a gestation period of 2 to 4 months.
Threats	Hunting, low population.
Range	Cuba: Juan Garcia Cay

Description

The little earth hutia, *Capromys sanfelipensis*, is slightly larger than, and similar to, the large-eared hutia (*C. auritus*), but having a mostly reddish tail.

C. sanfelipensis was described by Varona in 1970.

Behavior

The little earth hutia is mostly herbivorous; it consumes fruit, green vegetation, bark, and possibly small animals such as lizards.

Little is known of the little earth hutia's habits, but it is probably nocturnal.

Habitat

The little earth hutia is found only in an area of low and dense vegetation of waist-high clumps bordering mangrove thickets on Cayo Juan Garcia off southwestern Cuba.

Distribution

The little earth hutia has been recorded

only from Juan Garcia Cay, a very small island off southwestern Cuba. It is thought to be uncommon, and was not located at all during an expedition to Juan Garcia Cay in 1980.

Threats

The little earth hutia was probably hunted by humans for food, but the most devastating reason for its decline was competition from and predation by introduced rats on an island habitat whose entire area is only 340 acres. Additionally, fires set in the 1980s to drive out mosquitoes burned critical habitat.

Conservation and Recovery

There is little hope that the little earth hutia still survives in the highly restricted habitat.

Mongolian Beaver

Castor fiber birulai

Castor fiber   USFWS

Status	Endangered
Listed	June 14, 1976
Family	Manidae (Beavers)
Description	Light brown to dark gray coat, often with a mixture of browns and grays; the fur is thick, the tail is dark and shaped like a paddle, and the hind feet are much larger than the forefeet.
Habitat	Temperate forests and marshes with surface water.
Food	Tree bark.
Reproduction	Gestation lasts 105 days and results in four or five kits.
Threats	Loss of habitat and human predation.
Range	Mongolia

Description

The beaver of Mongolia, *Castor fiber birulai*, is a subspecies of *Castor fiber*, the European (or Asiatic) beaver. It has older evolutionary traits than its North American relative (*Castor canadensis*). For instance, its fur is less dense and less water repellant.

When well fed, this beaver is a plump animal with a rounded torso. Its head is short and rounded — probably an adaptation for swimming underwater. Its tail is broad and flat, somewhat like a ping-pong paddle, and moves up and down to propel the beaver through water. On land, the tail serves as a brace, allowing the beaver to stand upright. The hind feet are large, with long toes, perhaps to provide a firm grip in the ground when the beaver is gnawing on a tree. The forefeet are small and dexterous, capable of holding and manipulating small objects. They can grasp small branches and hold them while the beaver swims and they can place branches, stone, and mud in dams and lodge walls. The head is sleek, with small, rounded ears set well back on the skull, and small eyes set deep. Its jaws feature the typical rodent's incisors, shaped like chisels. As with other rodents, the incisors of the beaver perpetually grow and must be constantly ground down.

This is ideal for *birulai*, which fells trees by gnawing through their trunks. Sometimes the felled tree is too large for the beaver to pull to its pond and is abandoned, but the beaver has tremendously powerful jaws and heavily muscled hindquarters that allow it to grip most felled trees with its teeth and haul them to the pond, where the bark may be stripped for food.

Behavior

Beavers in general seem to fascinate people because of their extraordinary behavior: They are builders who shape and remake their environment. They build dams across streams in order to create ponds in which they hide from predators and which will freeze over in winter, creating a good environment for their lodges. Their lodges are sturdy and thick walled, protecting them from both predators and the elements. Within their ponds and lodges they form extensive family-based communities. Members of these communities cooperate in the care of kits and in the maintenance of the lodge, the dam, as well as of food supplies. Sometimes observers believe that beavers must be rational problem solvers because of their ability to build and maintain dams, but in-the-field experiments have shown that beaver behavior is formed by elaborately evolved instincts. For instance, an experiment on North American beavers tested their responses to breaks in their dams. A small hole in a dam would bring beavers rushing to fill it with branches, stones, and mud — suggesting a rational process of problem solving. Yet, when there was no hole but experimenters played a recording of the sound of flowing water, the beavers continued to respond as if they were filling holes — they were bringing building materials where none

were needed because they were instinctively responding to the sound. If they were rational creatures, they would not have done so.

The absence of humanlike powers of reasoning does not make beavers any less interesting. Instead, they are engrossing examples of how nature can create an extraordinary builder without creating the intelligence of a human being. The beaver not only adapts to its environment but also reshapes its environment to suit its needs. The beaver of Mongolia is a very good example of this. It lives in inhospitable lands in which humans have much trouble surviving; cold, skin piercing winds, arid summers, and winter temperatures thirty or more degrees Fahrenheit below freezing are common. Some human communities in the region cope by migrating with the seasons; the beavers stay put. Their thick fur coats help them endure very low temperatures, although the lowest temperature of winter could kill them. By creating marshy ponds, they create a water surface that can freeze over, providing some insulation that allows the water below to be somewhat warmer. The entrances to the beavers' lodges are below the surface of the water, enabling them to take advantage of the relative warmth below the ice. The subsurface entrances also help them maintain endurable temperatures in their lodges. The lodges are built of stones and mud, with an outer layer of wood in the form of branches and twigs. This keeps the bitter wind out and enables the beavers to maintain a lodge temperature that would still be too cold for humans but is comfortable for beavers, just above freezing.

The beavers form monogamous pairs that become the focus of the family units that maintain their marshy environments. These pairs have one set of kits annually, probably four or five kits in the case of *birulai*. The twigs the parents gather in warm months serve to feed the kits once they are weaned but still living in their lodges. The adults apparently eat little during winter, living instead off of their reserves of fat. The kits generally remain with their parents for two years, although remaining with them longer seems common. As yearlings, they help maintain the lodge and dam and help feed the new set of kits. As two-year-olds, they continue to help their parents and become dominant in a pecking order, just below their parents but above the new yearlings that are above the new kits. How *birulai* find mates and move on to form their own new family group is not clear. They leave pungent scent markings on the edges of their territories that may tell neighboring beavers not only of their presence and claim to their pond but of their age and sexual receptivity. Eventually, a male and female over two years of age bond and leave their homes to create a new one in a marsh uninhabited or abandoned by other beavers or to build a dam of their own across a flowing stream.

Habitat

Surface water, flowing or still, is an essential requirement of the beaver's habitat. Also needed are temperate woodlands that provide the bark the beaver eats. *Birulai* lives in a region that has very harsh winters, so it needs an abundance of building materials such as tree branches, stones, and mud for building its lodges in which it can maintain an ambient temperature just above freezing.

Distribution

Although the subspecies of the European beaver (also known as the Asiatic beaver),

Castor fiber, once extended continuously from Scandinavia through central Europe and deep into central Asia, they no longer do so but, instead, survive in patches scattered throughout their once large range. The subspecies *birulai* now survives in isolation from its cousins.

Threats

The decline of the beaver is tied to the popularity of its fur for clothing. Subspecies of *Castor fiber* began their decline in the Middle Ages, when they were exterminated from some countries because their fur brought extraordinarily high prices in the marketplace. The boom in the market for fur coats in the nineteenth and twentieth centuries resulted in rapacious hunting that nearly exterminated the beaver in the Old World. As one consequence, a few European nations have gone to the extreme of transplanting North American beavers (*Castor canadensis*) to replace the European beavers they have lost and have little hope of regaining. For the Mongolian subspecies, the merciless hunting has resulted in its separation from the other subspecies because the lands between them have been swept clear of beavers, and the hunting has resulted in the animal's own near extinction.

Loss of habitat is also a problem. Mongolia's human population has been growing, and as it has grown, it has required more land for human habitation, as well as agriculture. Beaver wetlands have been taken over by humans, leaving less and less habitat that is suitable for the beaver's survival.

Conservation and Recovery

The exact status of the *birulai* subspecies

is unclear because it lives in a part of the world that is remote from scientists and difficult to travel to, not so much because its cold climate is inhospitable as because regional governments do not want outsiders mingling among the local peoples. Even so, it is clear that a conservation plan for the beaver is needed; the high value of its coat makes it too tempting a target for hunters. Some of its habitat needs to be reserved and protected. This is urgent not only for the subspecies of beaver but for waterfowl and other animals that are dependent on the watery environment the beavers provide.

Thin-spined Porcupine

Chaetomys subspinosus

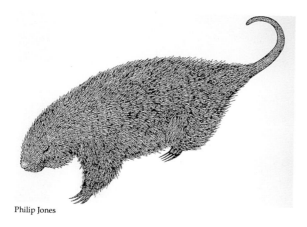

Philip Jones

Status	Endangered
Listed	June 2, 1970
Family	Erethizontidae (Porcupines)
Description	Long, barbed spines along its head and back, and its tail is scaled.
Habitat	Forests near brushlands and savannahs.
Food	Fruit
Threats	Loss of habitat.
Range	Brazil

Description

Very little has been recorded about the natural history of the thin-spined porcupine, *Chaetomys subspinosus*, and authorities disagree even about what it looks like. For instance, some authorities say that it has spines on its head and back, but others say that it has spines only on its head. It seems to be a dark brown animal with a robust body. The body of an adult is 18 inches in length, with the tail adding 10 to 11.25 inches. It is said to be heavy, but its weight is unrecorded. Its spines very likely cover the top and back of its head and cover its back to its tail. The spines lay flat, pointing backward, when the thin-spined porcupine is on the move but will be raised by muscles at their bases when the animal feels threatened. The spines are barbed in such a way that they will not only stick in a

victim but will continually work their way inward whenever the victim moves a muscle. Thus the spines can be life threatening, possibly working their way into a vital organ.

The tail is thick and scaled, which indicate that it is prehensile, although naturalists are uncertain of this. Other tree porcupines use their tails to grip branches in order to steady themselves among branches. The thin-spined porcupine has very strong feet with callused pads for gripping branches and trunks tightly. Although it has strong, pointed claws, they are not used to anchor the animal; instead it relies on its powerful grip. Its head looks somewhat like that of a mole, with a flattened snout and a rounded skull. Its eyes are set low on the skull, and its eyesight is poor — suitable only for close-up views. Its hearing is good, and its sense of smell is acute.

Behavior

The thin-spined porcupine eats fruits; it probably uses its keen sense of smell to find them. It climbs quickly through trees and is a good leaper. It is a noisy animal, making a wide variety of squeals, grunts, and huffs. Whether these noises serve as communication with others of its kind has yet to be discovered. It is nocturnal and lives almost its entire life in the middle to upper canopy of its forests; it may venture to the ground to feed.

Habitat

Forests are essential to the thin-spined porcupine's survival, but it is willing to live in thin forests near cultivated lands. Its forests are typically tropical, with high canopies.

Distribution

Occurrences of the thin-spined porcupine have been found in northern and eastern Brazil.

Threats

Natural predators of the thin-spined porcupine include raptors and cats. Humans are a threat primarily through their destruction of the thin-spined porcupine's forests for agriculture and expanding human settlements, as well as very heavy logging.

Conservation and Recovery

Some of the thin-spined porcupine's

range needs to be preserved in its natural state in order for it to have any chance of survival. Its range is home to endangered primates which would also benefit from the preservation of the range's natural habitat.

Chinchilla [=Short-tailed Chinchilla]

Chinchilla brevicaudata boliviana

Rich Block

Status	Endangered
Listed	June 14, 1976
Family	Chinchillidae (Rodents)
Description	Soft and silky gray and yellow fur with dark blue hairs on the back.
Habitat	Barren terrain with dense shrub cover, crevices, and rocks.
Food	Leaves, seeds, fruits, tender vegetation with a high fiber content.
Reproduction	Litters are produced twice, sometimes three times a year after a gestation period of 110 days.
Threats	Habitat destruction.
Range	Bolivia

Description

USFWS lists the Bolivian population of the short-tailed chinchilla, *Chinchilla brevicaudata boliviana*, as endangered; it is probable that both the short-tailed and the long-tailed (*C. b. lanigera*) are highly pressured throughout their entire range. Both subspecies have pelage that is gray above and yellowish underneath. The fur is soft and silky, with dark blue hairs on the back, which has made it a fur of choice among furriers worldwide. These rodents have large ears, very large eyes, and a bushy tail. Females weigh up to 28 ounces and the smaller males 18 ounces.

Behavior

The diet of chinchillas includes leaves, seeds, fruits, and other tender vegetation that has a high fiber content. Like many rodents, they perch on their large hind paws and hold food with their front paws while they eat.

Females may produce up to six young per litter, but the average is two. Litters are produced twice, sometimes three times a year after a gestation period of 110 days. The young are fully grown by ten months.

Habitat

Agile jumpers, chinchillas inhabit barren terrain with dense shrub cover, crevices, and rocks for protection. *C. b. lanigera* occurs at elevations of 2,500 to 5,000 feet; *C. b. boliviana* occurs at elevations over 6,500 feet.

Distribution

The whole range of the chinchilla species is Argentina, Bolivia, Chile, and Peru. The population for *C. b. lanigera* may be as many as 10,000 individuals; the population for *C. b. boliviana* is unknown but thought to be much less. USFWS considers the Bolivian population in danger of extinction.

Threats

Hunting for the fur industry around the turn of the twentieth century resulted in the severe depletion of chinchillas. Millions of skins were exported before chinchilla farms were begun in the 1920s. Chinchilla fur is vulnerable to deterioration by moisture and is not very durable, so that more skins were in demand for replacement coats. Since the capture of wild chinchillas was banned, habitat destruction because of the overgrazing of goats and by mining activities threatened *C. b. lanigera*. The more remote habitat of *C. b. boliviana* is not as vulnerable to human encroachment.

Conservation and Recovery

Because of the demand for chinchilla skins, the species has been farmed extensively. It has also been captively bred for reintroduction programs but inbreeding has reduced the viability of the stock. Although *C. b. lanigera* can be more easily captively bred than *C. b. boliviana,* the male offspring is often sterile.

Because of their value as economic resources, chinchillas are now being protected in reserves, and domestic animal grazing and hunting are being carefully managed.

Rats and Mice
Families: Muridae and Cricetidae

False Water-rat (*Xeromys myoides*)

C. Andrew Henley/Nature Focus

General Characteristics of the *Muridae*

There are over one thousand species of mouselike rodents, and they feature a vast variety of characteristics. Some authorities place all of these animals, from doormice to gerbils, in one vast family, *Muridae*. Others break them into two families, *Muridae* and *Cricetidae*, roughly a division between Old World and New World mice. They point to slight variations in the cheek muscles between Old World species and New World species and to the overall more primitive (meaning more ancient) anatomy of New World species in order to separate the two groups. Authorities in evolution sometimes go further and divide the mouselike rodents into three families: the *Muridae* and *Cricetidae* plus *Microtidae*, the voles and lemmings. We follow, here, the taxonomy used by the United States Fish and Wildlife Service in its designations of endangered species, which is to divide mouselike rodents into two families, *Muridae* and *Cricetidae*.

All members of *Muridae* (called murids) are rodents, which means that they are gnawers. They have long, sharp upper and lower incisors, with the incisors slightly recessed from the upper ones. When viewed from the side, the incisors are triangular, wider at the bottom and narrower at the top. These teeth grow constantly, but they are worn down constantly by incessant gnawing; gnawing also helps hone the incisors, keeping them sharp. The incisors are typically separated by a gap in the jaw from the cheek teeth. Murids are further defined by the shape of the jaws: They have a deep extension of bone under their cheek teeth to which the deep masseter muscle attaches. Murids and cricetids have a configuration of jaw muscles that is unique to mouselike rodents and which is used by anatomists to distinguish mouselike rodents from all other mammals. First, the middle masseter muscle attaches itself far back and low on the lower jaw and extends itself to the bone behind the eye, giving the lower jaw great leverage. The deep masseter muscle attaches below the cheek teeth and curves back into the skull, behind then over the eye, and attaches to bone just forward of the eye. This unique adaptation allows a mouselike rodent to exert the maximum possible force when moving its jaw up and down, as when gnawing.

Murids are separated from cricetids by having a more extensive development of the adaptations of its jaw and masseter muscles; that is, as a broad generalization with possible exceptions in individual species, the bone beneath the cheek teeth is deeper and extends farther back than in cricetids, and the deep masseter muscle attaches farther forward in the infra-orbital foramen (farther in front of the eye). The teeth of cricetids are also thought to be more primitive than those of murids, with murids having fewer ridges on their teeth. When researching the murids, be prepared for sharp differences of opinion among anatomists about the significance of the jaw and muscle formations, especially over whether the minor difference between murid and cricetid anatomy justifies their being separate families.

Mouselike rodents evolved during the Miocene epoch, with the cricetids — New World mouselike rodents and the hamsters — appearing first near the end of the Miocene, over five million years ago. The cricetids separated into a multitude of species that spread over much of the world, from lowlands to high mountains, from frigid climates to blazing hot ones. After this wave of speciation and expansion came the murids, represented first by the voles. Their teeth are smoother with fewer ridges than their predecessors, with their tooth enamel having a zigzag pattern not found in cricetids. The voles speciated throughout the Pliocene epoch (five million to two-and-a-half million years ago), primarily in Arctic regions. The rest of the murids evolved from cricetids in southeast Asia, beginning about five million years ago. These animals spread throughout the world, except for Antarctica, with much of their expansion coming in recent times. The murids include most of the familiar mouselike rodents such as the brown rat (*Rattus norvegicus*), the roof rat (*Rattus rattus*), and the house mouse (*Mus musculus*). Many of these murids hitched a ride on humanity's expansion, following humans wherever they went. These are also the species responsible for carrying the fleas that carried the black plague that killed about three-fourths of the people living in Europe in the Middle Ages, as well as many people in other parts of the world.

In general, murids are small animals. They have slender bodies with their hindquarters larger than their front legs and shoulders. Their heads tend to be long, with long slender snouts. Their faces feature whiskers and usually large eyes. Their fur can vary from short and bristly to long and shaggy, but it is usually of moderate length and usually lays back over the head and body. Most have long, slender tails. Murids have adapted to most of the world's climates and can be found nearly everywhere except Antarctica. The common New World vs. Old World terminology for indicating their difference from cricetids is largely an academic one, because murids inhabit the Americas as well as the Old World continents.

Like other rodents, murids are gnawers, and the adaptations of their teeth are primarily for a gnawing existence. Indeed, people often discover the presence of mice in their homes not by seeing them or by finding their droppings, but by finding shavings of wood. Gnawing through obstacles to get where they want to go is typical of murids. Their persistent gnawing has made some species pests, because they gnaw objects such as ropes that humans want preserved. Although they primarily gnaw vegetation such as wood (and sometimes dirt among burrowers), murids cannot be classified as strictly herbivorous; insects especially make up significant parts of the diet of some species, and a few may be carrion feeders.

All in all, murids are a lesson in how little adaptations can have enormous consequences. The murids have taken the adaptation of their masseter muscles, which allows them to bite hard and yet be small, and turned it into the foundation of hundreds of species and to seize niches in very diverse territories such as deserts in Africa, rain forests in Asia, ice lands in Europe, as well as lowlands and mountainsides.

General Characteristics of the *Cricetidae*

The 350 species of the family *Cricetidae* are mouselike rodents. Authorities disagree on the number of species because they disagree on what actually distinguishes a member of *Cricetidae* (called a cricetid) from a member of *Muridae* (murids). Some authorities lump almost all mouselike rodents into *Muridae*, including those that could be placed in *Cricetidae*, and for them there is no family called *Cricetidae*. Other authorities divide most mouselike rodents between *Cricetidae* and *Muridae*, distinguishing them very roughly as New World and Old World mouselike rodents, even though murids are found in the New World and cricetids may be found in the Old World. Cricetids are held by these authorities to be more primitive (that is, to have evolved earlier) than murids. Authorities on evolution sometimes go a step further and divide the major mouselike rodents into three families: the *Cricetidae*, the *Muridae*, and the *Microtidae*, these last being the voles and lemmings. We here follow the taxonomy used by the United States Fish and Wildlife Service in its categorization of endangered species: two families, the *Cricetidae* and the *Muridae*, with voles and lemmings being part of *Muridae*.

Although the fossilized remains of mouselike rodents are numerous, scientists have yet to fully sort out their evolution, and the exact distinctions between different groups of mouselike rodents are often vague. More than five million years ago, during the Miocene epoch, the

Cricetidae evolved, perhaps in North America. Their lower jaw, the cusps on their teeth, and the configuration of their jaw muscles set them apart from other rodents. They rapidly divided into hundreds, perhaps thousands, of species and migrated and spread throughout most of the world, adapting to frigid, hot, and temperate climates, occupying open lands and heavily forested lands, and filling niches in lowlands and very high mountains. The murids appeared later, probably in southeast Asia just before the start of the Pliocene epoch. They were first represented by the voles, which occupied mostly cold, northern regions and spread out and speciated throughout the Pliocene epoch, from five million to two-and-a-half million years ago. The murids were probably descended from the cricetids (some evolutions believe that voles and lemmings did not, which is why they put them in a separate family), and after the coming of the voles came an evolutionary explosion that saw the murids speciate into hundreds of species and spread throughout the world, except for Antarctica.

The members of *Cricetidae* are distinguished from their near relatives by their teeth, jaws, cheek muscles, and other small variations in anatomy, all of which are said to be more primitive — or less evolved — than in their *Muridae* descendants. The cheek teeth have more ridges than in murids, and the teeth are more irregular, with murid teeth being smoother. All mouselike rodents have bone underneath their cheek teeth, and in cricetids the bone is generally not as deep and does not reach as far back as in murids. The adaptation that sets all mouselike rodents apart from all other mammals is in the masseter muscles attached to the jaws. The middle masseter muscle is attached to the deep bone below and in back of the cheek teeth and extends to bone just behind the eye; this adaptation gives the lower jaw great leverage when biting. This feature is not entirely unique to mouselike rodents: The *Sciuridae* (for instance, squirrels) have a somewhat similar pair of attachments for their middle masseter muscle. On the other hand, the configuration of the deep masseter muscle is unique to mouselike rodents. The deep masseter muscle is attached to the lower jaw on the bone underneath the cheek teeth, and it curves upwards and back, then up over the eye to attach just in front of the eye. This makes maximum use of the space provided by the skull, allowing for the biggest possible muscle and providing maximum biting power. Some authorities perceive a difference between the masseter muscles of the *Cricetidae* and the *Muridae*, with the *Cricetidae* having ones that do not extend as far back and as far forward as in the *Muridae*.

Like other rodents, cricetids are gnawers, and their powerful configuration of cheek muscles enables them to gnaw vigorously while remaining small. Their upper and lower incisors are separated from their cheek teeth by gaps in the upper and lower jaws. When viewed from the side, the incisors are triangular, broad at the base and pointed at the top. The incisors grow continuously but are constantly honed by persistent gnawing. These simple adaptations, the ability to gnaw tirelessly and to remain small, have had enormous consequences. Perhaps in less than a million years, the cricetids evolved into a wide variety of animals, some so very distinct from one another that gnawing and the masseter muscles are all that they have in common. They include Europe's hamsters, Africa's pouched rats, South America's gerbils, and North America's woodrats. Some burrow (for instance the burrowing mice of the genus *Oxymycterus*), others hop through hot deserts or live in wetlands. Most subsist mainly on vegetation, but some are predators (for instance, the grasshopper mice of the genus *Onychomys*).

Cricetids are small creatures, ranging in length from about two inches to one foot, depending on the species. They are mostly nocturnal, although some, like the leaf-eared mice of the genus *Phyllotis,* are active during the day. Their fur tends to be in shades of brown or gray, darker on the upper body than on the lower body. The fur can be thick and downy (in cold climates), but is usually light and short, laying backward on the body. Their eyes tend to look like beads, and their ears tend to be long and oval shaped, and they are usually very mobile, able to twist back and forth when listening. The lengths of their tails vary considerably, with tree-dwelling species tending to have longer tails than other species. Although the behavior of individual species can vary greatly according to climate and region, most cricetids are nesters — woodrats may gather sticks for their nests while desert species may gather pieces of cactus. This gathering activity seems to be a common trait among cricetids.

Although much of their evolutionary history is murky, the cricetids offer interesting lessons in how adaptations can enable a species to proliferate and how adaptations can relate to environmental influences. The first cricetids, over five million years ago, developed a gnawing advantage over other small animals and used this one persistent trait to proliferate over most of the world, seizing opportunities wherever a good gnaw could open a path to food or to a safe haven. Further, they evolved recently as geological time goes. They spawned hundreds of species of their own and were the ancestors of the murids, who spawned further hundreds of species. This offers an interesting comparison to hominids (including human beings). The hominids have gone from many species to only one subspecies, *homo sapiens sapiens,* while cricetids have gone the opposite direction radiating greatly and surviving through diversity.

Greater Stick-nest Rat

Leporillus conditor

Taronga Zoo

Status	Endangered
Listed	June 4, 1973
Family	Muridae (Rats and mice)
Description	Rabbit-sized rat with a fluffy coat that is yellowish-brown above and creamy white below, and white patches on the top of the hind feet.
Habitat	Semi-arid shrubland.
Food	Leaves and fruits of succulent plants.
Reproduction	Breeding occurs year round; females produce 1 to 3 young after gestation of 30 days.
Threats	Habitat alteration to agriculture and grazing; competition from rabbits and plants.
Range	Australia: Franklin Island

Description

The greater stick-nest rat, *Leporillus conditor,* is about the size of a rabbit, weighing up to 12 ounces and measuring 16 inches from nose to tail. It fluffy coat is yellowish-brown above and creamy white below, with white patches on the top of the hind feet. The rounded ears are fairly long; the eyes are large; the stocky tail is squared at the tip.

Common names include the house-building rat, Franklin Island stick-nest rat, wopili-kara, kulunda, and wiranja.

Behavior

The most distinguishing characteristic of this species is the elaborate communal nests that it constructs, which may be as large as 5 feet in diameter and 3 feet high. The nest is constructed around a bush, which gives the structure its strength and stability. The rats then cut branches to size by gnawing to create interior chambers that house 10 to 20 individuals. In the center of the structure is a pad of grass or other soft vegetation; from this central court are tunnels that provide egress. These nest houses are very strong and provide protection against predators, who are usually unable to penetrate the structure. The stick-nest rats continue to improve and strengthen their house over time, and succeeding generations of animals improve and expand the original structure.

The diet of the herbivorous stick-nest rat includes the leaves and fruits of succulent plants such as the pigface and nitre bush.

Breeding occurs year round but peaks in the autumn and winter. After gestation of about 30 days, females produce 1 to 3 young, which attach themselves to her teats where they are dragged around until they are weaned in a month.

Habitat

Franklin Island is a semi-arid shrubland whose perennial plants provide the succulents necessary to sustain the stick-nest rat's diet and water demands. Franklin Island is also home to other endangered species, including the short-tailed shearwater, a bird that digs burrows used by the stick-nest rat for cover against predator owls.

Distribution

The greater stick-nest rat was once widely distributed throughout south Western Australia and South Australia, but it is now extinct everywhere except Franklin Island, where 1,000 to 1,500 individuals survive, and a few other reserves where captive-bred animals were released.

Threats

The mainland habitat of the stick-nest rat was permanently altered by livestock grazing and by the introduction of rabbits, both of which destroyed the rat's food resources. Introduced foxes and cats greatly increased predation on the rat, and it was able to survive only in the absence of food competitors and predators on isolated Franklin Island. Some plants introduced to Franklin Island have suppressed the native vegetation that the rats feed upon, and this is a continuing problem.

Conservation and Recovery

Franklin Island is part of the Nuyts Archipelago Conservation Park and is protected by law. Efforts are being made by the South Australian National Parks and Wildlife Service to maintain favorable conditions on Franklin Island by controlling predation and competition.

A captive breeding program was begun in 1985, and beginning in 1990 captive-bred individuals have been released on Reevesby Island, Shark Bay Nature Reserve, and St. Peter Island. The small populations on these islands appear to be stable, and there are plans to introduce the greater stick-nest rat onto other islands and the mainland.

Australian Native Mouse

Notomys aquilo

P. German, NPIAW

Status	Endangered
Listed	June 14, 1976
Family	Muridae (Mice and Rats)
Description	Hopping mouse resembling a miniature kangaroo, brown or gray in color, with soft fur and a long tail.
Habitat	Sand dunes, dry woodlands and many other arid areas of Australia.
Food	Seeds, berries, leaves and other available vegetation.
Reproduction	1-5 young after a gestation period of about 7 weeks.
Threats	Predation by domestic dogs and cats, foxes and livestock; loss of habitat due to clearfelling of forests.
Range	Australia: Queensland

Description

The Australian native mouse, *Notomys aquilo*, is an Australian hopping mouse that resembles a miniature kangaroo. Its soft fur is sandy brown above with white underparts. The long hind legs and the nose are pinkish. The head and body length is 3.5 to 4.3 inches, and the long tail measures 2.3 to 2.9 inches. It weighs 1.3 to 1.5 ounces.

Most of the native rats and mice of Australia are difficult to classify and an extensive investigation of skulls and teeth by a taxonomist is needed to classify these species. This mouse is also commonly known as the northern hopping-mouse.

Behavior

The Australian native mouse feeds on seeds, berries, leaves and other available vegetation but will not eat insects. It appears to be an adaptable feeder.

The native mouse is very social and breeds rapidly. It makes a twittering sound just before emerging in the evening, and when alarmed, it makes a high-pitched squeal.

This burrowing animal constructs a soil mound about six feet from the opening to the vertical shaft that leads to the burrow. Between the entrance and the mound are pop holes that also lead to the main shaft of the burrow. Burrows can be quite extensive — as long as ten feet and as deep as three feet. The burrow can be easily detected by tracks around the soil mound. Nests are simple structures made by placing minimal vegetation in a scooped out portion of the tunnel.

Females have four teats and produce 1-5 young after a gestation period of about 7 weeks. Mortality among the young is high, partly because of cannibalism. The young are born hairless. The mother carries them in her mouth and tends them in the nest rather than in a pouch. The eyes of the young do not open for about 3 weeks after birth.

Habitat

This species is found in sand dunes, dry woodlands and many other arid areas. One burrow was located in a coastal fore dune backed by a dense vine thicket that grew within 15 feet of the high tide mark.

Distribution

This species was first collected in 1867 on Cape York but has never been reported there again. It is presently restricted to Groote Eylandt in the Gulf of Carpentria in northern Australia and along coastal Arnhem Land, where it is plentiful in both locations.

Threats

This species was poorly known until recently, and so the causes of its decline are also unknown. Like many small mammals in Australia, it has probably been adversely affected by the introduction of livestock.

Domestic dogs, cats, and red foxes prey on small animals. It has been noted that feral cats may kill as many as 400 million native mammals, birds and reptiles each year. Livestock (sheep and cattle) overgraze and facilitate soil erosion. This erosion in turn promotes exotic vegetation dispersion which hinders the surrounding native flora and endemic or dependent fauna.

Conservation and Recovery

The two known populations on Groote Eylandt and Arnhem Land are stable but must be protected from any infusion of predators or livestock.

Field's Mouse

Pseudomys fieldi

G. B. Baker, NPIAW

Status	Endangered (Possibly extinct)
Listed	December 2, 1970
Family	Muridae (Mice)
Description	White undersides, possibly a gray tail, and pale brown everywhere else.
Habitat	Arid, rocky, mountainous regions.
Food	Probably seeds and insects.
Reproduction	Unobserved; probably 28 to 40 days, resulting in a litter of three or four.
Threats	Loss of habitat, imported predators, and imported competitors for food.
Range	Australia: Northern Territory

Description

The Field's mouse, *Pseudomys fieldi*, is known to science through only a few specimens; its normal size is very uncertain. Adults may have a head-and-body length of about 5 inches, with a tail of similar length, and they may weigh about 2 ounces. The mouse's fur is pale brown everywhere except on its undersides, which are usually a yellow-tinged white. It is possible that the underside of the tail is white, too.

The taxonomy of this species is disputed. USFWS lists *Pseudomys fieldi* as a full species and the Shark Bay mouse (please see separate entry) as *Pseudomys praeconis*. Other authorities argue that because subfossils have been found all along the west coast of Western Australia, *P. praeconis* and *P. fieldi* were continuous and showed no significant morphological differences. Under this taxonomy, the Shark Bay mouse, *P. praeconis* is merged with Field's mouse under the scientific name *P. fieldi* and is not recognized as a separate species.

Field's mouse is known in Australia as Alice Springs mouse and as Alice Springs pseudo-rat.

Behavior

The Field's mouse is probably a burrower that spends its days underground and its nights foraging. If it is typical of Australian mice in its kind of habitat, it eats seeds, flowers, and insects. Litters probably consist of 3 or 4 young, which likely take about 30 days to become independent.

Habitat

The Field's mouse has been found in the rocky, heavily eroded mountains of southern Northern Territory. The region is arid, although prone to seasonal rainfall.

Distribution

The Field's mouse probably never had a large range. It is restricted to the arid southern region of the Northern Territory, Australia.

Threats

Imported competitors for food are likely the greatest threat to the Field's mouse, although imported predators are also very threatening.

Conservation and Recovery

The Field's mouse may already be extinct. Its range is outside national parks and reserves, and, at present, there is little effort to conserve it — possibly because conserving the mouse is thought to be a lost cause. It needs an area without imported competition, away from imported predators and human habitations.

Smoky Mouse

Pseudomys fumeus

Robert W. G. Jenkins/Nature Focus

Status	Endangered
Listed	December 2, 1970
Family	Muridae (Mice)
Description	Coat is mostly gray to black, with a gray to white underside; the tail is gray to black on top, with white stripes lengthwise along its sides.
Habitat	Mountain sides and ridges with abundant shrubs and grasses.
Food	Seeds, berries, fungi, and insects.
Reproduction	Breeding is seasonal, with a gestation period of about a month, resulting in 3 to 4 young; 1 to 2 litters per breeding season.
Threats	Loss of habitat to human encroachment; predators.
Range	Australia

Description

The smoky mouse, *Pseudomys fumeus*, is a handsome animal. Its fur is mostly gray to black, with a blue tinge; its underside is gray to white, and its gray to black tail has lengthwise white stripes. The fur is sleek and laid back against the skin. An adult smoky mouse is 3.3 to 4 inches long, from the tip of its nose to the base of its tail; the tail adds another 4.3 to 5.75 inches. It weighs 1.5 to 3.25 ounces. Its head is long and sleek, with a slightly concave forehead. The eyes are dark and beadlike; the nose is thick; the ears are round and set at the back of the head. The smoky mouse's hind feet are short and wide, with the toes typically splayed out; the forefeet are small and dexterous. Its hindquarters are thick and round and its shoulders are large and prominent.

Behavior

The smoky mouse is something of an explorer, ever searching for new habitat in which to propagate. Males range farther than females and pay a heavy price for it; when the food-poor season lasting from September to November comes, the mice that ranged into marginal habitat die off. After this die off, the breeding season begins, with females producing 1 or 2 litters with 3 or 4 young. The mice feed on seeds, berries, fungi, and the moths that are attracted to the highland flowers. As the flowering season passes, the mice become dependent on fungi found near the roots of plants, as well as late-season berries.

Habitat

Surveys of eastern Victoria and southeastern New South Wales indicate the preferred habitat of the smoky mouse is ridgetop sclerophyll forest with a diverse understory of heath dominated by legumes. This vegetation complex is generated by natural brush fire; thus the smoky mouse's survival is dependent upon post-fire succession.

Distribution

In historical times, the smoky mouse ranged through Victoria into southeastern New South Wales, Australia. It now survives primarily in the Grampians, the highlands northeast of Melbourne and the coastal woodlands of eastern Grippsland.

Threats

The smoky mouse has lost most of its habitat to human settlements and agriculture. Imported predators such as foxes threaten it through most of its remaining range.

Conservation and Recovery

The smoky mouse needs to have a terri-

tory that is protected by law and managed by wildlife experts because its habitat is subject to disruption by humans and introduced predators.

Gould's Mouse

Pseudomys gouldii

John Gould illustration/Nature Focus

Status	Endangered (Possibly extinct)
Listed	December 2, 1970
Family	Muridae (Mice)
Description	Yellowish brown with white under-sides.
Habitat	Arid, rocky, mountainous regions.
Food	Seeds and grasses.
Reproduction	Gestation lasts 28 to 40 days, resulting in three to five young.
Threats	Loss of habitat, imported predators such as foxes and cats; imported competitors such as rabbits, and grazers such as goats and sheep.
Range	Australia

Description

Adult Gould's mice, *Pseudomys gouldii*, have a head-and-body length of 4 to 5 inches; the length of its tail is 3.5 to 4 inches. They weigh about 1.75 ounces. The mouse's fur is pale brown everywhere except on its under-side, which is usually a yellow-tinged white. It is possible that the underside of the tail is white, too. The profile of the Gould's mouse's head is triangular, with a pointy nose, plump cheeks, with eyes that are set forward and low, just above the cheeks. Its ears are oval and held wide open.

Behavior

Although it was once widespread, the Gould's mouse was little studied and not much is known about its habits. It is a bur-rower, creating nests about 6 inches deep in the ground. Its forefeet seem poorly adapted to digging, which may account for the ani-mal's preference for areas with loose or sandy soil. Gould's mouse lives in small groups of 4 to 8, and it may be territorial; mice from outside a group seem to be driven away by group members. Groups may be composed of relatives-by-birth, but this is far from certain.

Breeding among the Gould's mice may be seasonal, as it is with some of its related species in the *Pseudomys* genus, governed by annual rainfall. Gestation within the *Pseudomys* genus is usually 28 to 40 days; the Gould's mouse will have 3 to 5 young. Having 5 young may be difficult because females have only four mammary glands. Young likely cling to their mother's nipples while she moves about, until they are weaned.

Nests of soft, dried grass were constructed in extensive burrows dug about 6 inches below the surface, housing families of 4 to 8 individuals.

Habitat

The Gould's mouse seems to prefer the loose soils and sands of the plains.

Distribution

The Gould's mouse once had a huge range across Western Australia, South Australia, and New South Wales. It may survive in patches in southern Western Australia or the interior on South Australia, although many authorities consider it extinct.

Threats

Expanding human settlements and agriculture have eliminated most of the Gould's mouse's habitat, especially in New South Wales. Imported European predators such as foxes and cats are grave threats to the mouse. Imported competitors such as rabbits and grazers such as goats and sheep threaten the mouse's food supply.

Conservation and Recovery

It may be too late to save Gould's mouse, which may have lost all of its habitat and which does not exist in captivity. If its does survive, it needs a range without imported predators and far from most human activity. A survey being undertaken by Western Australia's Department of Fisheries and Wildlife to locate Shark Bay mice that may still survive on the mainland (please see the separate entry on the Shark Bay mouse) may turn up some Gould's mice, because the Gould's mouse once and still may inhabit the southwestern coast of Western Australia.

New Holland Mouse

Pseudomys [=Gyomys] novaehollandiae

D. Whitford, NPIAW

Status	Endangered
Listed	December 2, 1970
Family	Muridae (Rats and mice)
Description	Box-shaped, with large oval ears and large, almond-shaped eyes; tan or sandy hair on top and sides.
Habitat	Sand or soft soil amid low shrubs.
Food	Seeds, fungi, insects, and spiders.
Reproduction	Females have 1 litter in their first year and 3 to 4 litters in their second year; 2 to 6 young after gestation of 32 days.
Threats	Loss of habitat and predation.
Range	Australia and Tasmania

Description

The New Holland mouse, *Pseudomys novaehollandiae,* was observed in the 1860s near Sydney, Australia. It was not recorded again until 1967, when some were found in Ku-ring-gai Chase National Park. Full-grown New Holland mice will top 3 inches in length from nose to tail. Their bodies are compact, with about one third taken up by the head. Their ears are large and oval and can swivel from pointing forward, to outward, to pointing backward. The eyes are large, probably an adaptation for seeing at night. The tail is long and slender, about the length of the mouse's body. The New Holland mouse's fur is me-dium length and colored brown, tan, or sandy brown, with pale underparts.

Behavior

The New Holland mouse's cycle of growth and decline may be the reason for its having been missing for over a hundred years. Its population follows fires to a great degree. The population in a given locality will remain small until there is a fire in the woodland or shrublands. During the year after a fire, small shrubs will grow in the areas that were burned down. These shrubs provide the New Holland mouse with its favorite foods, and after about a year its population booms. This boom lasts until the plants have grown sufficiently to support other, larger herbivores, which in turn support predators who may also eat the mice. This results in a depletion of the New Holland mouse's food supply and a loss in individual mice to predators, causing the mouse population to decline — almost to disappear. Yet, a new fire elsewhere may bring about another boom in population in a new area.

The New Holland mouse is nocturnal. When caught in the open by a predator or human being, it either freezes or scampers down a tunnel. New Holland mice make two different kinds of tunnels in sands or soft soils: short ones, for sleeping or, perhaps, hiding, and long ones up to 18 feet long with chambers for nesting. The mice breed seasonally, from late winter to early summer. A female will have but one litter in its first year of life, but may have as many as four in its second year. New Holland mice, both male and female, live only one-and-a-half to two years.

Habitat

The New Holland mouse occurs in coastal areas with seasonal dry and wet weather that are prone to wild fires. They prefer sand or soft soil for their tunnels.

Distribution

There is evidence that the mouse's distribution has always been erratic. It occurs on the coasts of Tasmania, New South Wales and Victoria. After there has been a forest fire near the mouse, it moves into the recovering ter-

rain to feed on the new growth, especially seeding plants. Its population then explodes; once the forest recovers enough to support other, larger animals, the New Holland mouse's population shrinks — even disappears. Thus the mouse's past distribution has probably depended in large measure on where forest fires occurred and on how often those fires were near mouse populations.

Threats

Humans have tried to reduce the number of fires because of the harm they do to property, domesticated animals, and wildlife other than the New Holland mouse. Success in reducing the number of fires in coastal areas could diminish the mouse's distribution, although in spite of much effort, the Australians still suffer from terrible fires.

Conservation and Recovery

The New Holland mouse had been lost to science for over a century when it was found in the 1960s. One of its present problems with survival is that it prefers areas along the vegetated coast which are being developed. Thus, its habitat is constantly shrinking as the human urban areas expand. It is also prey to domesticated cats and dogs. Its best hope for survival may be protection in national parks.

Western Mouse

Pseudomys occidentalis

Hans and Judy Beste, NPIAW

Status	Endangered
Listed	December 2, 1970
Family	Muridae (Mice)
Description	Creamy yellow and dark gray fur, with waves of black hair; paws are white; underside is grayish white.
Habitat	Brushlands and woodlands.
Food	Plant stems, grasses.
Reproduction	3-5 five young born in the spring.
Threats	Loss of habitat to agriculture.
Range	Western Australia

Description

The western mouse, *Pseudomys occidentalis,* is beautifully colored. Its fur combines creamy yellow and dark gray hair with black hair that ripples through it; its paws are white like gloves; its underside is grayish white. The face is somewhat blunt, with a rounded nose and mouth. Whiskers thrust upwards, downwards, forwards, backwards, and sideways from its nose above the mouth. Other such hairs arch up and forward from above the eyes. Its eyes are set forward on the head and are proportionally large. The western mouse's ears are oval and very mobile, able to flick back and forth independent of each other. An adult western mouse is 3.5 to 4.3 inches long, from the tip of its nose to the base of its tail; the tail adds another 4.75 to 5.5 inches. It weighs 1.25 to 1.75 ounces.

Behavior

The western mouse seems to prefer to eat leaves and stems of plants, although insects, including beetle and moth larvae, may be a small part of its overall diet. It is probably nocturnal, but where it spends its days is uncertain. Breeding is seasonal with a female having one litter with three to five young each spring, with a total of six litters during her life.

Habitat

The western mouse's habitat is variable, and it seems comfortable in a variety of disparate settings. It is found in the seasonally dry region of southwestern Western Australia, and inhabits sparse brushlands, very dense brushlands with tall growth, and woodlands. The soil is usually sandy, but may be a mix of dirt and rocks.

Distribution

The western mouse lives in southwestern Western Australia, well inland. It was once widespread, but agriculture has left it only patches in which to live.

Threats

Loss of habitat to agriculture is the primary threat to the western mouse. In reserves, imported predators are a threat.

Conservation and Recovery

The protected areas that have western mouse populations may be too small for a healthy breeding population. Thus, in the long run a larger reserve or national park needs to be established, perhaps by connecting two or more of the small reserves. In the short run, the reserves need to be protected from predators imported from Europe such as cats, further loss of habitat to agriculture needs to be controlled — not necessarily halted — so that the mouse has enough continuous territory in which to mix and breed.

Shark Bay Mouse

Pseudomys praeconis [=fieldi]

Babs and Bert Wells/Nature Focus

Status	Endangered
Listed	December 2, 1970
Family	Muridae (Mice)
Description	Dark brown back, white on the underside; fur is very shaggy.
Habitat	Temperate ocean coasts.
Food	Leaves, stems, and flowers.
Reproduction	Gestation lasts roughly a month, resulting in three to four young.
Threats	Long-term change in regional climate, loss of habitat, predators.
Range	Western Australia

Description

The head-and-body length of adult Shark Bay mice, *Pseudomys praeconis*, varies from 3.3 to 4.5 inches. The tail length varies from 4.5 to 5 inches. They weigh from 1 to 1.75 ounces. The mouse's head has a long, narrow profile, with eyes placed well forward on its head; the ears are oval and mobile. The nose is narrow at its tip, with long whiskers. The toes can bend sharply in toward the bottom of the feet, enabling the mouse to grasp grass blades and plant stems tightly while it climbs among them.

There may be some color variation among grays and browns from one individual mouse to another, but in general the mouse's back is dark brown, gradually paling along the sides to buff, and then paling to white on the underside. The tail features a plain demarcation between its gray upper area and its white under area, with no gradual change from one shade to the other. The hair on the tail is short, but it is shaggy on the neck, torso, and legs.

USFWS regards the Shark Bay mouse as *P. praeconis,* but other authorities have merged Field's mouse, *P. fieldi* (see separate entry), with the Shark Bay mouse under the name *P. fieldi.*

Behavior

Shark Bay mice make tunnels through the grasses piled by the ocean at the tops of beaches and climb among the stems of plants that live nearby. They eats stems, leaves, and flowers, and may eat grasses, too. They are probably nocturnal and may spend the day out-of-sight in burrows. They may be fertile all year long, although this is not established with certainty. In captivity, gestation lasts 18 to 30 days (more likely 30 days) and results in three or four young. The young cling to their mother's nipples and are dragged about as she moves. At 15 days of age their eyes open, and at 30 days of age they are weaned.

Habitat

The Shark Bay mouse lives among grasses that have washed onto shore and among the plants that grow along the coast.

Distribution

The Shark Bay mouse once ranged along the coasts of Western Australia, and it probably ranged many miles inland, too. Its decline in numbers began before the arrival of Europeans, and the decline probably had nothing to do with Aborigines. Instead, a change in climate, the gradual drying up of the region, may be responsible for the decrease in numbers. At present, the Shark Bay mouse is only found on Bernier Island.

Threats

Changes in climatic conditions could affect the remaining Shark Bay mice. An influx of humans to Bernier Island, perhaps destroying the island habitat, or free-ranging foxes, cats, or other imported predators could exterminate the species.

Conservation and Recovery

Bernier Island is a protected reserve under the laws of Western Australia, and it is well managed by Western Australia's Department of Fisheries and Wildlife. Some Shark Bay mice were transplanted to Doole Island in 1993, but it is as yet unclear whether the transplantation has been successful. The Department of Fisheries and Wildlife may transplant Shark Bay mice to more islands and perhaps even to coastal areas on the mainland where it once lived. The Shark Bay mouse seems to breed well in captivity.

Shortridge's Mouse

Pseudomys shortridgei

Status	Endangered
Listed	December 2, 1970
Family	Muridae (Mice)
Description	Short face with a blunt nose, large eyes, and rounded ears; its hair is mostly grayish brown, with flecks of black; its undersides are pale.
Habitat	Brushlands
Food	Seeds, berries, flowers and fungi.
Reproduction	2 litters of 3 young per season.
Threats	Loss of habitat.
Range	Australia: Victoria and Western Australia

Hans and Judy Beste/Nature Focus

Description

The adult Shortridge's mouse, *Pseudomys shortridgei*, is 3.5 to 4.75 inches long, from the tip of its nose to the base of its tail; the tail adds another 3 to 4.3 inches. It weighs 2 to 3.25 ounces. Its forehead is flattened and drops sharply in the base of its short, blunt nose, which is rounded at its tip. The ears are set at the back of the head; they are round and are furred on the back. Its eyes are notably large. The coat is mostly grayish brown, with a scattering of black hairs. When viewed from above by a natural predator such as an owl, the mouse blends in with the earth. Its undersides are pale brown, and its feet are almost as pale. The hind feet are long and flat; the forefeet are shorter.

This species is also known as the heath rat, blunt-faced mouse, Shortridge's native mouse, heath mouse, and blunt-faced rat.

Behavior

The Shortridge's mouse has evolved to take advantage of the opportunities the brushlands of southern Australia once provided. The preferred territories for the mouse were ones that would look unpromising to humans: frequently dry heath with few trees. Before human land management took over, these lands were subject to seasonal growth controlled by rainfall, and seasonal, scattered fires that would put plant nutrients — in the form of ash — back into the soil, allowing for explosions of rich brush growth in following rainy seasons. Where such growth occurred, the Shortridge's mouse population would boom, with ample food to ensure the survival to adulthood of many young. These young would be able to survive long enough to find new territories to colonize. Even without fires, the mice would be able survive, although in small numbers. In the spring and summer they would breed — gestation would take place in about 30 days — and be able to take advantage of the seeds, berries, and flowers that would appear. In autumn and winter, they would eat underground fungi — a food source even in spring and summer if the rainfall had been light and subsequent plant growth had been brief and small.

Presently, the Shortridge's mouse retains its evolved behavior, but the fires to which it had adapted are by and large controlled by humans, eliminating the mouse's ability to have population spurts that ensure its ability to hold on in a variety of disparate regions. It lives in burrows, sometimes in groups; its ability to burrow helps it to find the fungi that feeds it for much of the year. A primarily nocturnal creature, it is shy of humans and hides in its burrows during the daytime. Born in a season of plant growth, young mice are weaned on flowers and berries and then are pushed out of their homes. This results in a high rate of mortality for the young, since most of the available food has been eaten by the time they are independent.

Habitat

Although it is not as dependent on fires as the New Holland mouse (*Pseudomys novaehollandiae*; please see separate entry), the Shortridge's mouse is nonetheless a fire chaser. It thrives on the new growth in heath that has recently been burned; otherwise it is dependent on seasonal growth — which in Australia's brushlands is not as rich in seeds, berries, and flowers as is recently burned land that is renewing itself. Its habitat is mostly temperate, although when it inhabited its full ancient range, it lived in arid areas as well as temperate ones. There is seasonal rainfall, and before humans began managing fires, there were somewhat seasonal fires, occurring when the brush dried.

Distribution

The range of Shortridge's mouse once extended from southwestern Western Australia to southwestern Victoria, but it is now known only in patches of Victoria and in a recently located colony in the Fitzgerald River National Park in Western Australia.

Threats

Human encroachment has eliminated most of the Shortridge's mouse's habitat. Not only have human settlements and agriculture taken over much of the mouse's best habitat, but the remaining habitat has come under human fire management, eliminating the brushfires that at one time signalled a boom cycle for the mouse's population. These boom cycles were important for the mouse's expansion into the full extent of its possible range:

The mice force their young out of their homes and into new territories; the growth after fires provided them with ample new territories to colonize. This was important for their survival; while they were widespread no local event such as a drought, plague, or flood could exterminate the species.

Conservation and Recovery

Although an endangered species, the Shortridge's mouse seems to be regarded by local people as more a pest than a creature to be conserved. It needs a territory well separated from people and imported predators such as foxes and cats. Such a territory would need to have a landscape dominated by brush, with soil loose enough for burrowing. If ample seasonal growth of seeds, berries, and flowers can be provided for the Shortridge's mouse, it may be able to survive, even without the sporadic wildfires that enabled it to be widespread.

False Water-rat

Xeromys myoides

C. Andrew Henley/Nature Focus

Status	Endangered
Listed	December 2, 1970
Family	Muridae (Rats and mice)
Description	Short, silky fur that is gray to brown above and white below.
Habitat	Salt water mangrove forests, sedges, swamps, freshwater lagoons and lakes.
Food	Hard-shell aquatic animals.
Reproduction	Mates throughout the year, producing 1 to 4 young per litter.
Threats	Pollution; reclamation of mangrove swamps.
Range	Western Australia

Description

The false water-rat, *Xeromys myoides*, has short, silky fur that is gray to brown above and white below. The short, rounded ears are pink on the inside, as is the nose and nose ring. It weighs less than 1.75 ounces and is 8.5 inches long, including the tail. It exhibits a strong, musky odor.

Behavior

Although discovered in 1889, the false water-rat has proven to be very elusive, and only 14 specimens have been preserved. Its behavior is limited to a few chance discoveries in the wild. A good swimmer, the false water-rat lives along the edge of water reserves where it feeds on hard-shell aquatic animals, especially crabs, as well as lobsters, shell-fish, and flatworms. They seem dependent upon mangrove roots, hollow trunks, and logs for foraging.

This rat seems to build simple burrow systems in peat banks, or domed, sedge-covered mound nests whose complex structure houses family groups comprising one adult male, several adult females, juveniles, and subadults.

It is believed that this species mates throughout the year, producing 1 to 4 young per litter.

The false water-rat is nocturnal, and

establishes its foraging pattern with the recession of the tide. It is territorial, and within its territory follows established pathways among the mangrove roots. It may travel over a mile during a single night of foraging. If it is too far from its burrow to return home before the tide rises, the false water-rat will take shelter in any suitable hollow.

Habitat

The false water-rat inhabits salt water mangrove forests, sedges, swamps, freshwater lagoons and lakes. It prefers shallow water near the coastline with prevailing tides.

Distribution

The false water-rat occurs along the northern coast of Western Australia and on and around Melville Island in the Northern Territory. In 1991 ten active nests were found in sedgelands of the Myora mangrove community on North Stradbroke Island. These nests varied from complex, domed, sedge-covered mounds to single burrow systems.

Threats

The false water-rat is threatened by the degradation of its habitat caused by pollution, the disturbance of water tables caused by adjacent agricultural development, and by the reclamation of mangrove swamps.

Conservation and Recovery

So little is known about the false water-rat that, except for preservation of coastal land along its known range, no conservation efforts can be undertaken. Some Australian conservationists are engaging in limited studies of the species, but its rarity makes it difficult to study. Radio-tracking of the population discovered at Myora in 1991 has provided the greatest source of data.

Central Rock-rat [=Australian Native-mouse]

Zyzomys [=Laomys] pedunculatus

Library/Anne Bowman/Nature Focus

Status	Endangered (Presumed extinct)
Listed	June 14, 1976
Family	Muridae (Rats and mice)
Description	Bristly brown or gray hair; white underparts; fragile tail, small round ears, and a narrow, sleek profile.
Habitat	Arid, rocky, mountainous regions.
Food	Seeds, roots, small insects.
Reproduction	May have multiple births of two or more young.
Threats	Predators and competitors.
Range	Central Australia.

Description

Based on only six specimens, the central rock-rat's, *Zyzomys pedunculatus*, dimensions seem to be about 3.5 inches for head-and-body length, 4 inches for tail length, two ounces for weight — these statistics are very much approximations. Its hair is bristly, stiff, and sharp. The hair varies from light yellowish brown to light gray on different specimens, with the undersides white. The ears are small and round, and the eyes are dark, round, and beadlike. The central rock-rat's skin is very fragile and can be torn easily. Its tail is thickened by folds of skin (not by fat), and the folds grow thicker as the animal ages. Its tail is very fragile and can be broken off by very little pressure. Central-rock rats that have lost their tails will bite off what remains, leaving a thick stump.

This species is also commonly known as the thick-tailed rat, and MacDonnell Ranges rock-rat. USFWS refers to this species as the Australian native mouse.

Behavior

Only six specimens have been taken by scientists since the central rock-rat's discovery in 1896, and their behavior has been little observed. They are probably nocturnal; they probably feed on plants and insects; they probably hide under rocks when threatened.

Habitat

The central rock-rat probably lives(lived) in areas with varied geology, from granite boulder fields to eroded sandstone cliffs. These sites provided diverse vegetation, from sparse hummock grasses to shrublands.

Distribution

By the time an explorer first recorded the central rock-rat, in 1896, it was probably already rare, although this is far from certain. It soon disappeared from the area where it was first discovered, probably driven out by cats and foxes. Since then it has been found in the western MacDonnell Ranges (near Mount Leibig about 180 miles west of Alice Springs) and the associated Reynolds Range and Davenport Range of Central Australia.

Threats

The central rock-rat is threatened by predators imported from Europe and herbivorous competitors such as rabbits, also imported from Europe.

Conservation and Recovery

The outlook for the central rock-rat is very poor. An extensive survey conducted in 1990 failed to located any evidence of its survival.

It is possible but improbable that some central rock-rats live in Uluru National Park in southwestern Northern Territory, but nearly all of its range is outside protected areas.

Sloths
Family: Bradypodidae

Three-toed Brazilian Sloth (*Bradypus torquatus*)

Laurenz Pinder

General Characteristics of the *Bradypodidae*

Two-toed sloths of the family *Megalonychidae* and the three-toed sloths of the family *Bradypodidae* are similar in appearance. They have rounded heads and flattened faces, small ears, and specialized hands that have two or three 3 to 4 inch claws. The underfur is short with fine hair, covered with long hair that is often infused with algae, which gives sloths a greenish hue that improves their camouflage. Sloths are highly specialized leaf-eaters, with compartmental stomachs that digest food for up to a month. Although exceedingly slow, sloths maintain fairly large home ranges of up to 16 acres. Three-toed sloths are nocturnal; two-toes sloths are diurnal. Two-toed sloths are distributed from Nicaragua to Colombia, and from Venezuela to northern Brazil and northern Peru. Three-toed sloths occur in Honduras through Colombia, Venezuela, the Guianas, Bolivia, Paraguay, northern Argentina, eastern Brazil, and Ecuador. Exceedingly successful species, sloths are threatened only by the loss of the coastal rain-forest habitat.

Three-Toed Brazilian [=Maned] Sloth

Bradypus torquatus

Laurenz Pinder

Status	Endangered
Listed	June 2, 1970
Family	Bradypodidae (Sloth)
Description	Sloth with long coarse fur gray-brown in color; its forelimbs are somewhat longer than the hind limbs and the forefeet have three very long claws.
Habitat	Forests of eastern Brazil.
Food	Leaves of trees.
Reproduction	Females produce a single young each year after a gestation period of about 6 months.
Threats	Loss of habitat due to deforestation.
Range	Eastern Brazil

Description

The three-toed Brazilian sloth, *Bradypus torquatus*, is an odd-looking *edentatid*. It has long coarse fur which is known to support algal growth. This pelage is long, stiff, and gray-brown in color, but the algae gives it a greenish-blue hue. *Bradypus* species range in size from 20 to 24 inches long and weigh about 8 to 11 pounds. *B. torquatus*, as well as all *Bradypus* species, has a vestigial, blunt tail about 3 inches long. It has long limbs, small eyes and ears, and a round, flat head.

The teeth are cylindrical and grow throughout life. This species has eight or nine cervical vertebrae. The forelimbs are somewhat longer than the hind limbs and the forefeet have three very long claws.

Linnaeus recognized the three-toed sloth as a unique species and systematically described these species and placed them in the genera *Bradypus* in 1758. This species is also commonly known as the maned sloth.

Behavior

The three-toed Brazilian sloth is a selective, nocturnal browser and feeds on leaves of trees, birds and flowers. With poorly developed sight and hearing, they depend upon smell and touch to identify food resources. The three-toed Brazilian sloth's stomach consists of compartments, and fermentative reduction occurs in both the stomach and in the intestines. This species has a low metabolic rate and a low core body temperature. This physiology is attributed to its diet of leaves which are high in abundance but low in nutrient value. *Bradypus* are active both during the night and day.

Three-toed sloths are highly arboreal and slowly move through the trees while suspended beneath by all four limbs. They usually hang by their hind paws; when not hanging they rest in the fork of trees. They occasionally descend to the ground where they crawl slowly on the soles of their feet.

The three-toed Brazilian sloth produces a single young, usually every other year, after a gestation period of 120 to 180 days. The mother nurses for a month and tends the young for another 6 to 9 months.

Habitat

The three-toed Brazilian sloth is restricted to the Atlantic coastal forests of eastern Brazil.

Distribution

Formerly indigenous to Honduras, northern Argentina, Paraguay, and Brazil, the known populations are restricted to eastern Brazil.

Threats

In the past, the three-toed sloth was hunted for its meat, but the decline of the three-toed Brazilian sloth is attributed to deforestation. The Atlantic coastal forests were cleared for coffee, sugar cane, coca and eucalyptus plantations, and for livestock grazing. Industrialization, including lumber and charcoal production, have further degraded the habitat.

Conservation and Recovery

Brazil has developed a system of parks and conservation areas which encompass about 15 million hectares. These areas include many of the major biomes of Brazil. The Brazilian government is planning to establish other areas to complete the representation of all of the Brazilian biomes, and international development assistance is also helping to build and maintain the system. Brazilian rubber tappers are also attempting to protect large areas in the Amazon Basin as extractive reserves. In this plan, the government can work with the rubber tappers in an effort to conserve major areas of tropical forest while continuing to maintain their livelihood.

Reserves with known populations of three-toed sloths include the Monte Pascoal National Park; Biological Reserves of Corrego de Veado, Sooretama, and Noa Lombardia.

The specialized diet of this species has not made it a good candidate for captive breeding or protection in zoos.

Armadillos and Pangolins

Families: Dasypodidae and Manidae

Pangolin (*Manis temmincki*)   Dick George, Phoenix Zoo

General Characteristics of the *Dasypodidae*

The armadillo's armor is composed of bony plates, called scutes, overlaid by horn. Most of the top surface of the body is protected with the armor, but the underbelly is soft skin. Their heads are flat with small, upright ears. Most species have 28 to 36 teeth in each jaw, but the endangered giant armadillo has 80 to 100 teeth. They have powerful front limbs which they use to forage for food and create burrow systems. The common long-nosed armadillo, which is the only species of armadillo to have become successful in the U.S., can excavate deep burrows in compacted soils, which protects it from the cold and from predators. It is also the only armadillo species that can swim. Of the five genuses of armadillos — long-nosed, naked-tailed, hairy, three-banded, and fairy — only the fairy armadillos are endangered, because of loss of habitat.

General Characteristics of the *Manidae*

The pangolin are the Old World cousin of the South American armadillo. Its upper parts, including the head and tail, are covered with overlapping horny scales. This heavy armor provides the pangolin with an impenetrable shield once it has curved itself into a ball. Of natural predators, only the large cats and hyenas are able to get to the tender underbelly. Humans, who hunt pangolins for their meat, medicinal, and aphrodisiac uses, comprise the greatest threat to the species.

Pangolins are ant and termite eaters, using their long, narrow tongues to ferret out these insects from their nests. They do not have teeth and do not chew their food, which is, instead, ground up and digested in the stomach. Their eyelids protect the eyes from insect bites and stings, and their nostrils are closed when foraging.

There are four species of African pangolins and three Asian species. Two of the African species are arboreal; the other two and the Asian species are terrestrial, but all pangolins are excellent climbers.

Pink Fairy Armadillo

Chlamyphorus truncatus

Vogt and Specht, *The Mammalia*

Status	Endangered
Listed	June 2, 1970
Family	Dasypodidae (Armadillos)
Description	The pink colored armor extends across the top of the body and is covered with soft white hairs.
Habitat	Dry, stony plains.
Food	Insects and insect larvae, snails, worms, reptiles, eggs, and the stems and tubers of plants.
Threats	Predation by domestic dogs
Range	Argentina

Description

The pink fairy armadillo, *Chlamyphorus truncatus*, is the smallest armadillo, weighing only 3 to 3.5 ounces and measuring 8 inches long, including the tail. The pink colored armor extends across the top of the body and is covered with soft white hairs. It has a broad plate over its rear.

Behavior

The pink fairy armadillo lives in burrows during the day and forages at night on insects and insect larvae, snails, worms, reptiles, eggs, and the stems and tubers of plants. Little else is known of this reclusive animal.

Habitat

The pink fairy armadillo is associated with grasslands, thornbush, or cactus in dry, stony plains.

Distribution

The pink fairy armadillo is restricted to

the desert of central and western Argentina.

Threats

Very little is known about this species, including reasons for its decline, but it is speculated that predation by domestic dogs as humans expand agricultural cultivation into the habitat is a serious threat.

Conservation and Recovery

Captive breeding programs have been unsuccessful; there have been no other conservation efforts.

Cape [= Temminck's Ground] Pangolin

Manis temmincki

Dick George, Phoenix Zoo

Status	Endangered
Listed	June 14, 1976
Family	Manidae (Anteaters)
Description	Long-tailed, heavily scaled mammal; scales cover all of its upper body, sides and legs, with dark brown hair on its underside.
Habitat	Tropical forests and savannah.
Food	Termites and ants.
Reproduction	Single birth after gestation of 139 days.
Threats	Human predation.
Range	Central, East and South Africa.

Description

The cape pangolin, *Manis temmincki,* eats only termites and ants and features a number of physical adaptations designed to help it feed. Its skull is simple — narrow, pointy near the nose, widening gradually to the back. The head has few muscles, with none for chewing; its eyes are small, recessed, and see poorly; its ear holes are small and scarcely visible. The cape pangolin's tongue is anchored at the pelvis and extends through a sheath into the mouth. About two thirds of it stretches out of the mouth when it is fully extended. The tongue is covered by sticky saliva that is produced by a large (about 22 cubic inches) salivary gland. Termites and ants stick to the tongue and when the tongue is withdrawn, they are deposited in a horny stomach that grinds them up. The forelegs have long, curved claws that can tear open termite nests. When the cape pangolin walks, the claws are curved back and up, protecting them from damage, while the edges of the forefeet bear the weight of the body. Small scales cover the head, beginning at the nose and gradually enlarge as they progress toward the back of the head; the scales become thick and large on the neck and over the rest of the body, all the way to the tip of the tail. Scales are continually shed and replaced by new ones. The cape pangolin is one of the two largest species of pangolin (the other is the giant pangolin, *Manis gigantea,* also a ground-dwelling species in Africa); it has a long tail of about 26 inches, and a head-and-body length of about 31 inches; adults weigh about 50 pounds.

Behavior

The cape pangolin moves slowly through its forest habitat, seeming to shuffle along. When it chooses to move fast, it rears back on its hind feet and charges forward at about 3 miles per hour, while using its tail as a counterweight and prop. Its thick, tough scales protect it from most predators; when threatened it curls into a ball, presenting nothing but scales to the outside world. The only natural predators that pose a threat to a curled up cape pangolin are hyenas and leopards because they have powerful, bone-crunching jaws. Even for them, the cape pangolin presents a formidable defense that is hard to break through.

The cape pangolin is nocturnal and sleeps in dens about 20 feet underground. When it is up and about, it relies on its senses of smell, touch, and hearing to find its way around, to locate termite and ant nests, and to find other cape pangolins. It makes hissing and huffing noises, perhaps to warn off rivals or predators; the role that sound plays in its social communication is unclear, although most naturalists think it plays no role at all. Its acute faculty of smell is probably its most important social sense, allowing it to detect the passage of other cape pangolins and to detect potential mates.

Males tend to be heavier than females. Mating seems to be seasonal, with births occurring between November and March. Their mating results in a gestation period of 139 days and the birth of a single young in its mother's den. The youngster is born with soft scales that gradually harden for about two weeks, when its mother first takes it outside. The youngster rides on its mother's tail for about three months, when it is weaned. The cape pangolin reaches sexual maturity after two years of life.

The cape pangolin feeds by tearing open with its foreclaws and powerful forelegs ground nests of termites and ants. Its tongue darts out to sweep up its swarming prey. Meanwhile, specialized muscles at the tip of its nose close its nostrils so that termites and ants cannot enter them, and its heavily fortified eyelids close against the bites of its targets.

Habitat

Cape pangolins live in warm climates. They live both in heavily wooded areas and open lands, requiring an abundance of prey and probably the presence of fresh water.

Distribution

The cape pangolin's traditional range extends from Central and East Africa south to northeastern South Africa. It has disappeared from some of that range.

Threats

Humans hunt and eat cape pangolins and have done so relentlessly, putting the animals in immediate jeopardy of extinction.

Conservation and Recovery

At present, the cape pangolin is not well protected anywhere in its range. It is likely that human intervention is needed to capture and place it safe havens, such as Tanzania's Serengeti National Park, Kenya's Amboseli National Park, and South Africa's Kruger National Park.

Giant Armadillo

Priodontes maximus [=giganteus]

Tracy S. Carter

Status	Endangered
Listed	June 14, 1976
Family	Dasypodidae (Armadillo)
Description	Dark brown except on the head and a band around the lower edge of the shell, which is whitish.
Habitat	Tropical evergreen forests to savannas.
Food	Termites, ants, spiders, worms, larvae, snakes and carrion.
Reproduction	1 or 2 young after gestation of 4 months.
Threats	Hunting; loss of habitat.
Range	Guyana and Brazil

Description

The giant armadillo, *Priodontes maximus*, is the largest of the armadillos. It is easily distinguished from the other species of armadillo by its size; the next largest armadillo is only half as large as *P. maximus*. Head and body length is 29 to 39 inches and tail length is about 20 inches. Adults can weigh as much as 130 pounds. Despite its size, the giant armadillo is remarkably agile and graceful; it frequently balances itself on its hind legs and tail.

The skin on the upper surface of the back, head and tail, as well as on the sides and outer surface of the limbs is modified into a series of horn-like plates. These are very thick on the back and sides. Eleven to thirteen of the rows of plates on the back and three to four at the neck are separated by areas of flexible skin, which allows the animal to flex its body. Hair covering is scant; only a few hairs are scattered between the plates. Coloration is dark brown except on the head and a band around the lower edge of the shell, which is whitish.

On the sides, this armor forms a carapace, which hangs down, protecting the limbs and soft underparts. Thus, the armor shields the animal from predators while allowing it to move with relative ease. The armor can comprise up to 20 percent of the animal's total body weight.

The front limbs are short, but very powerful. They are equipped with thick, hook-like claws, with the third claw being very large (about 7.8 inches along the curve).

The giant armadillo can have small, unenameled, peg-like teeth; up to 100 of them, which are shed as the animal ages.

Behavior

Giant armadillos are solitary creatures, rarely observed together except when mating. One or occasionally two young are born after a gestation of approximately four months. The young weigh about 40 ounces at birth and are covered with a soft, leathery skin which hardens in a few days. They are weaned at approximately four to six weeks, and attain sexual maturity at nine to twelve months.

Life span is said to be twelve to fifteen years. The giant armadillo takes its common name from the Spanish word "armadillo," which means "little armored one."

The giant armadillo has powerful forelegs which serve it well in digging for its primary food, termites. It has also been known to eat ants, other insects, spiders, worms, larvae, snakes and carrion. The giant armadillo is often accused of eating garden vegetables, but it probably digs in gardens to find insects, not for the vegetables. The giant armadillo is strictly nocturnal.

Habitat

The giant armadillo tolerates a wide variety of habitats, from multistratal tropical evergreen forests to savannas. It prefers well-drained soils. Its range extends east of the Andes in Colombia, Venezuela, and Guyana, south to northern Argentina.

Distribution

The giant armadillo has a wide range and is found throughout South America east of the Andes, from northwestern Venezuela to northeastern Argentina. The species is still common in Guyana and southwestern Brazil, but has disappeared entirely from the vicinity of human settlements in Peru.

Threats

The giant armadillos, like many other mammals in South America, are increasingly becoming the victims of both agriculture and the timber industry. South American farmers are known to persecute and attack armadillos for the damage done to cultivated fields by their extensive network of dens.

The giant armadillo is also hunted for a variety of other reasons: its armor is used to make a variety of containers and other handcrafted objects; its flesh is regarded as a delicacy; and it has an undeserved reputation as a "graveyard demon" which digs up and consumes the contents of graveyards.

Conservation and Recovery

The giant armadillo is protected against hunting or capture in Argentina, Brazil, Colombia, Paraguay and Peru, although law enforcement is difficult and sporadically applied. Populations may exist in nature reserves in Brazil, Peru, Colombia and Surinam, where the habitat is relatively secure from degradation. It is possible to captive breed this species, or move populations to habitats that are not being destroyed by residential and agricultural development.

Bats

Family: Pteropodidae

Bulmer's Flying Fox Fruit Bat (*Apoteles bulmeri*)   Charles R. Belinky

General Characteristics of the *Pteropodidae*

Bats are the only mammals that can fly. Two delicate layers of skin stretch from the sides of a bat's body to the ends of its long finger bones. The wings are pulled downward by muscles on the chest and under the upper arm, and raised by other muscles and muscle groups on the back that act on the upper humerus and scapula (shoulder blade). Some bats can fly 40 miles an hour or more.

The bat wing is essentially a modified hand. The digits, except the thumb, are greatly elongated to support the flight membranes with the aid of a lengthened forearm. The thumb is usually largely free of the membrane and has a claw, although sometimes this is small; the second digit in most *Megachiroptera* also has a claw but otherwise claws or nails are lacking on the wings of modern bats. Feet are usually relatively small, with five toes, each with a strong claw.

The flight membranes, which in many bats also join the legs and tail, are extensions of the body integument or skin. The membranes are muscular and tough but very flexible, with a high concentration of blood vessels. The membranes have many transparent or translucent hairs, sometimes in bands or fringes, and the body fur may extend onto the inner part of the membrane.

Bats appear to be relatively long-lived, with a maximum recorded age of 32 years. Many species have been known to survive 10 to 20 years. The average life-span is, however, likely to be considerably less.

Reproduction in bats is generally seasonal, with birth and development coinciding with periods of maximum food abundance. Most bats have only one offspring a year, but twins occur regularly in some species and up to 4 or 5 young have been recorded for a few species. Pregnancy can last anywhere from 40 to 60 days in small species to as long as 8 months in larger species. At birth the young are helpless but have strong claws and hooked milk teeth with which they cling to the mothers or to the ceiling of the nursery. Most *microchiropterans* (small insect-eating bats) are relatively small and naked at birth, and their eyes are closed. Baby *megachiropterans* (Old World fruit bats) are relatively large and hairy, and have their eyes open. Within two to twelve weeks, the young bats will begin to fly.

Many bats of temperate, and some tropical, zones give birth in nurseries where large numbers of bats are found. A nursery may contain several million or less than a hundred females and their young. Usually the young are left behind while the mother forages and feeds. Nursing lasts from one to three months while the young learn to fly, hunt, and feed. Infant bats emit loud calls with patterns that permit their mothers to reunite and nurse only their own infants; at close range, odor is also a likely component of the reunion. In some species the mother and infant call back and forth to each other, and the infant increasingly matches its mother's frequencies and in this way possibly learns some aspects of adult echolocation calls. Female bats have one pair of thoracic teats but a pair of false teats occur in the groin region in a number of species; these may provide an additional hold for the young, which grow rapidly and attain sexual maturity late in their first or second year.

Fruit bats, in general, have several common characteristics. They are medium to large bats, with a head and body length of 2 to 16 inches, and a forearm of 1.5 to 9 inches. They lack a tragus and the tail is very short, rudimentary, or absent, except in long tailed fruit bats. Many species are brownish or blackish, sometimes with a brighter mantle or with a gray or silvery tinge; others have speckled ears and membranes or a facial pattern of white spots or stripes, perhaps to aid concealment in foliage. Most roost in trees or in dimly lit areas of caves. Those that eat fruit have relatively short strong jaws with grinding teeth; and those that eat nectar and pollen have long muzzles with lightly built jaws and teeth, and a long, extensible tongue with brush-like papillae.

Small bats are known to forage for insects near the ground or among foliage. Approximately

70 percent of bat species feed on insects and other small arthropods such as spiders or scorpions; the size of their aerial prey ranges from gnats to large moths. Insects are captured in flight using the mouth; the tail membrane may be curled into a scoop from which the insect may be retrieved, or the insect may be deflected toward the mouth with the wing. Some bats glean insects from foliage, take them from the ground, or even skim them from the surface of the water. Small insects can be consumed in flight, but larger items are carried to a nearby perch to be eaten. Large numbers of insects are consumed by bats, which thus play an important part in the control of insect populations. Most bats are nocturnal, being active at night and resting during the day.

Bulmer's Flying Fox Fruit Bat

Aproteles bulmeri

Charles R. Belinky

Status	Endangered
Listed	January 23, 1984
Family	Pteropodidae (Old World fruit bats)
Description	Bat with small ears and large eyes with two delicate layers of skin that stretch from the sides of its body to the ends of its long finger bones.
Habitat	Subtropical climate of Papua New Guinea.
Food	Fruits, flowers, nectar, and pollen.
Reproduction	Possibly one offspring a year.
Threats	Overhunting for food.
Range	Papua New Guinea

Description

Bulmer's Flying Fox Fruit Bat, *Aproteles bulmeri*, is associated with the group *megachiropterans*, or Old World fruit bats. They have small ears, large eyes, and in general do not use echolocation. This group includes one family with about 41 genera and 163 species, including Bulmer's flying fox fruit bat.

Bulmer's flying fox fruit bat has two delicate layers of skin that stretch from the sides of its body to the ends of its long finger bones. The wings are pulled downward by muscles on the chest and under the upper arm, and are raised by other muscles and muscle groups on the back that act on the upper humerus and scapula (shoulder blade).

Bulmer's flying fox fruit bat was first discovered among fossil remains dating back 9,000 to 12,000 years in central Papua New Guinea. Shortly thereafter, one living specimen was taken in 1975 in the Hindenberg Ranges of far western Papua New Guinea. It had been killed by a native hunter in a large cave at an altitude of 2,300 meters. In November 1977, an intensive effort was made to locate this species, but a local hunter had already killed or driven away nearly the entire colony from the cave in which it was originally found. *A. bulmeri* was described by Menzies in 1977. It is also known as a fossil fruit bat.

Behavior

Bulmer's flying fox fruit bat feeds almost entirely on fruit, sucking out the juice and ejecting the pulp, or it feeds on nectar, flowers, and pollen.

Habitat

Because what we know of this species comes mostly from fossil remains, we are not sure of any specific habitat requirements, other than it is from a subtropical climate. The specimen taken in 1975 was found in a large cave at an altitude of 2,300 meters.

Distribution

Bulmer's flying fox fruit bat has only been found in Papua New Guinea. Today, this species may exist in remote parts of Papua New Guinea, but what we know has come from the numerous fossil remains that have been found at sites of human habitation.

Threats

Fruit bats are an esteemed food source in the area of Papua New Guinea. It is probable that hunting it for food has wiped out this fruit bat except in the remotest and most sparsely inhabited areas in the western part of the island.

Conservation and Recovery

Because Bulmer's flying fox fruit bat has not been sighted in modern times, it is not known whether it survives, and no conservation efforts are planned except to continue looking for it.

Bumblebee Bat

Craseonycteris thonglongyai

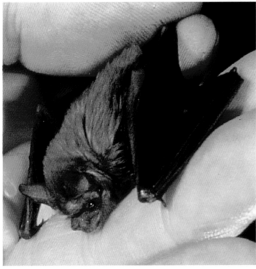

Merlin D. Tuttle

Status	Endangered
Listed	January 23, 1984
Family	Craseonycteridae (Bats)
Description	World's smallest bat; muzzle with a low transverse ridge above the nostrils, and relatively long and wide wings; brown to reddish gray with a paler underside; the ears are very large with a swollen tragus, and its face is pig-like.
Habitat	Roosts in the hot upper chambers of caves in limestone hills.
Food	Insects
Reproduction	Usually 1 offspring a year.
Threats	Deforestation; agricultural development.
Range	Western Thailand

Description

The bumblebee bat, *Craseonycteris thonglongyai,* is the world's smallest bat, and is among the smallest known mammals. It is the size of a bumblebee, weighing only 0.07 ounce. This species has an extensive tail membrane, but no external tail. It has a forearm length of .9 to 1 inch, and its head and body length is only 1 to 1.3 inches. This hog-nosed bat has a muzzle with a low transverse ridge above the nostrils but no noseleaf. The bumblebee bat is brown to reddish gray with a paler underside. The ears are very large with a swollen tragus; the eyes are small and

hidden by fur. Its face is rather pig-like, hence the name hog-nosed. It has relatively long and wide wings. *C. thonglongyai* was discovered in 1973, and named by Hall in 1974. This species is also known as Kitti's hog-nosed bat.

The bumblebee bat belongs to the small, insect-eating bats or *Microchiropterans.* They have large ears, small eyes, and they use echolocation. This group includes 17 families, about 146 genera and 814 species. The bumblebee bat is the single species of hog-nosed bats, and it belongs to its own family. The other group, *megachiropterans,* or Old World fruit bats, are usually larger. They have small ears, large eyes, and, in general, do not use echolocation. This group includes one family with about 41 genera and 163 species.

Behavior

The bumblebee bat feeds on insects around the tops of the dominant plants in its habitat. Like most bats, the bumblebee bat is nocturnal, being active at night and resting during the day. The bumblebee bat roosts deep inside caves and emerges at dusk to feed. It roosts in colonies of 10 to 15 bats.

Habitat

The bumblebee bat has distinct roosting and feeding areas. The roosting habitat of the bumblebee bat consists of the hot upper chambers of caves in limestone hills. This species' foraging habitat consists of teak-bamboo forest where the bats feed around the tops of the dominant plants. This habitat occurs in Western Thailand.

Distribution

The bumblebee bat has been found only at Sai Yoke, Kanchanaburi Province, in Western Thailand. The population is estimated at 200 individuals.

Threats

Humans are the main threat to the bumblebee bat. The teak-bamboo forest where this species survives has been highly affected by deforestation and teak logging above the sustainable rate. Vast areas of potential habi-tat have been lost, and loss of this habitat is probably a significant threat. These areas have been cleared for agriculture. Also, there have been Buddhist shrines located in some of the roosting caves of this species, which has not helped.

Conservation and Recovery

Preservation of roosting sites and identifying potential roosting sites are the immediate requirements to preserve this species. Because the bumblebee bat requires a specific habitat, locating protected alternative roosting sites is difficult.

Singapore Roundleaf Horseshoe Bat

Hipposideros ridleyi

Status	Endangered
Listed	January 23, 1984
Family	Rhinolophidae (Horseshoe bats)
Description	Dark grey nose, ears, and wing membranes; dark brown fur, with a horseshoe-shaped, noseleaf a strap-like flat structure above the nostrils.
Habitat	Lowland peat forests in small isolated patches, roosting in caves, mines, and hollow trees.
Food	Small arthropods, such as insects, spiders or scorpions.
Reproduction	Four offspring in April.
Threats	Medical research; logging.
Range	Malaysia

Description

The Singapore roundleaf horseshoe bat, *Hipposideros ridleyi*, has a dark grey nose, ears, and wing membranes. It has dark brown or black fur, and it weighs between 0.2 to 0.3 ounces. Bats are commonly distinguished by the length of their forearms, or wings. The Singapore roundleaf horseshoe bat has a forearm length of 1.8 to 1.9 inches. The tail length is 1 to 1.1 inches. The Singapore roundleaf horseshoe bat has a noseleaf, which is a fleshy structure of the skin surrounding and surmounting the nostrils. The noseleaf is distinctively horseshoe-shaped, with a strap-like sella (flat structure) above the nostrils and the central part of the noseleaf. It usually has an upright, triangular, cellular, and bluntly pointed posterior projection or lancet extending the noseleaf to the rear. The ears are relatively large and subtriangular in shape but have no tragus. The tail membrane encloses the tail. Males have a small sac behind the nasal layer that secretes a waxy substance.

H. ridleyi was discovered in 1910 in Singapore, and was described by Robinson and Kloss in 1911. It is also known as Ridley's leaf-nosed bat.

Behavior

Little is known about this rarely seen bat. The only population, found in 1975, occurred in a peat forest and took refuge during the day in a water pipe. It is believed that four offspring are produced in April.

Habitat

The Singapore roundleaf horseshoe bat inhabits lowland peat forests which occur in Peninsular Malaysia in small isolated patches.

Distribution

The Singapore roundleaf horseshoe bat has only been taken twice, once in Singapore in 1910, and once near Kuala Lumpur, the capital of Malaysia, in 1975, where 50 individuals were sighted. They have also been found in a very few localities in Sabah, Borneo. It is not known if the species still exists in Singapore.

Threats

This species occurs only in lowland peat forests near Malaysia. These forests have been heavily logged and have thus reduced the already limited range of the Singapore roundleaf horseshoe bat. The resulting patches of forest may not be enough continuous habitat for this species to survive. Deforestation is still occurring.

Conservation and Recovery

So very little is known about this bat that determining what it needs to survive is especially difficult. It appears to need a wide forested range in which to search for the insects it eats. It further seems to require holes in the ground or in trees in which it can breed and maintain the high humidity it requires when inactive. Most of its range has been logged, leaving it with patches of forest in which to forage; whether it needs continuous forest, in which case its situation may be nearly hopeless, or whether it can survive with patches of forest that are within its foraging range is unknown. As is the case with many endangered species in the Singapore roundleaf horseshoe bat's region, the burden for its preservation has fallen primarily on Malaysia, which has substantial wildlife reserves that its people by-and-large respect. These reserves may not adequately overlap the bat's natural range within Malaysia, and setting aside peat forests as reserves may be necessary if it is to survive.

Mariana Fruit Bat

Pteropus mariannus mariannus

Merlin D. Tuttle

Status	Endangered
Listed	August 27, 1984
Family	Pteropodidae (Fruit Bats)
Description	Medium-sized fruit bat with bright gold or light brown neck, males are slightly larger than females.
Habitat	Native limestone forests on Guam.
Food	Plants and fruits, including bread-fruit, papaya, figs, kapok, coconut; stems of leaves.
Reproduction	Single young are born.
Threats	Hunting and poaching, forest destruction.
Range	Guam

Description

The Mariana fruit bat, *Pteropus mariannus mariannus,* is a medium-sized bat. Ranges for body measurements of adults and subadults are: head-rump length of 7.6 to 9.4 inches; forearm length of 5.2 to 6 inches; wingspread 33.5 to 41.5 inches; and body weight 11.5 to 20 ounces. Males are slightly larger than females. The abdomen and wings are dark brown to black with individual gray hairs intermixed throughout the fur. The mantle and sides of the neck are bright gold or light brown. The color of the head varies from brown to dark brown. The teeth of the Mariana fruit bat are slightly heavier than those of other subspecies.

Other common names include Marianas flying fox, and Fanihi, the local name for fruit bats used by Chammorro residents throughout the Marianas.

Behavior

Reproductive characteristics are poorly understood for *P.m. mariannus*. These bats maintain a consistent social organization throughout the year. During the day, within larger colonies, about sixty-nine to eighty percent of all individuals roost in harems, which contain a single male and two to 15 females. Harem males are highly territorial and maintain exclusive breeding rights with these females. Harem males only rarely tolerate the presence of another male. Females appear to be loosely bound to a particular harem. Colonies may also contain one or two groups of bachelor males that roost in nearby trees. These groups may number from 10 to 120 animals. A few solitary males, comprising three to eight percent of the entire colony, roost on the periphery of colonies. Bachelor fruit bats have been observed occasionally to form separate smaller colonies with 10 to 125 animals.

Mating and presence of nursing young among the Mariana fruit bat has been observed throughout the year on Guam. There does not appear to be a seasonal peak in birth of young. Females give birth to a single young. The length of pregnancy and age of sexual maturity is not known. Other species of *Pteropus* have a gestation period of 4.5 to 6 months. Sexual maturity is probably reached by females at 6 to 18 months of age.

Little is known about the nightly movements and behavior of the Mariana fruit bat. Occasional sightings of bats at night indicate that animals in northern Guam may disperse throughout the forested areas of Anderson Air Force Base and Naval Communications Area Master Station to feed. When colonies are located on Pati Point, bats may travel as far as 6.2 to 7.5 miles to reach feeding sites on the island's northwest coast.

During the day, most of these bats are highly colonial and may roost in aggregations of up to 850 animals. A small portion of Guam's population roost solitarily or in small groups of 2 to 12 animals. Within larger colonies, some males form harems in which they defend females for breeding purposes. Harems usually encompass a single set of branches in the crown of a roost tree and may range in size up to 15 feet long and several yards wide and tall.

Habitat

Nine vegetative types have been described for Guam with four of these used regularly by the Mariana fruit bat. In northern Guam, where these animals are most common, bats forage and roost mainly in native limestone forest. Mature limestone forest is characterized by sparse undergrowth, a canopy 31 to 59 feet high and scattered taller emergent trees. Secondary growth limestone forest is shorter and has dense undergrowth.

At least six roosts are used by colonies of Mariana fruit bats on Guam. These sites occurred in limestone forest and were found along or within 328 feet of the large 260 to 590 foot cliffline that fringes northern Guam. Bats preferred to roost in mature fig trees at five colonies and in chopak at a six locations. Gagu and ficus are commonly used for roosting by solitary animals and small groups of two to 15 bats.

Coconut groves and strand vegetation are other plant communities used occasionally by bats for feeding and roosting. Coconut (*Cocos nucifera*) groves exist throughout the island with large stands present from Tarague Point to Uruno Point and on the Naval Magazine. This tree species commonly ranges from 40 to 80 feet in height. A thick understory is often present. Strand vegetation exists along rocky and sandy shorelines where halophytic conditions exist. Heights of vegetation range from short ground cover to trees up to 78 feet tall.

In southern Guam, a few fruit bats still inhabit ravine forests that grow on volcanic soils. It is lower in height and more brushy than limestone forest. Low-lying portions of this forest may flood seasonally. These areas are designated in the National Wetlands Inventory as palustrine, forested, broad-leaved evergreen.

Farms, savannas and mangroves are other habitats that receive little or no use at present but may have been used commonly in the past when bats were more abundant and widespread on the island. Residents often tell of fruit bats formerly entering farms to feed in cultivated fruit trees. Because known fruit bat foods occur throughout the island in a variety of habitats, it is likely that in the past, fruit bats also occurred islandwide.

Habitat use of Mariana fruit bats on the islands from Rota to Saipan is probably similar to that on Guam. However, there are no ravine forests on these islands. There does not appear to be any seasonal changes in habitat use.

Twenty-two species of plants are known to be used by fruit bats in the Marianas. This includes fruit of 17 species, flowers of 7 species and the leaf of one species. It appears that favored foods include the fruits of breadfruit, papaya, fadang (*Cycas circinalis*), figs, kafu (*Pandanus tectorius*), and talisai (*Terminalia catappa*) and the flowers of kapok (*Ceiba pentandra*), coconut and gaogao (*Erythrina variegata*). They also eat the stems of leaves and tips of small twigs of breadfrruits.

Most favored foods are available throughout the year and there appears to be little seasonality in their use. Exceptions are the fruits of breadfruits, which are ripe from April to December and the flowers of kapok and gaogao, which are present from January to March.

Animals in colonies sleep during much of the day but engage in other activities as well. These include: grooming; breeding; scent rubbing and marking; flying; climbing to other roost spots; and defending roosting territories (harem males only). Bats gradually depart colonies for several hours after sunset to forage.

Distribution

The Mariana fruit bat presently occurs on the southern Mariana Islands of Guam, Rota, Aguijan, Tinian and Saipan. Fruit bats also presently occur on all of the other Mariana Islands north of Saipan except Farallon de Pajaros and perhaps Farallon de Medinilla. This includes the islands of Anatahan, Sarigan, Guguan, Alamagan, Pagan, Agrihan, Asuncion and Maug. Populations of Mariana fruit bats are federally listed as endangered on Guam. The historic distribution of this species is identical to its present occurrence.

Federally-owned lands known to harbor Mariana fruit bats include Anderson Air Force Base, Naval Facility, Naval Communications Area Master Station and its Barrigada Annex, Naval Station, Naval Magazine and property held by the Federal Aviation Administration. Other lands owned by the U.S. government that possibly have fruit bats include Naval Air Station, Naval Hospital, Naval Station Nimitz Hill Annex and the War in the Pacific National Historical Park. The Territory of Guam owns a number of small parcels of land that are part of the known or possible distribution of Mariana fruit bats.

Threats

If the enthusiasm of the Chamorro people for cooked fruit bat is any indication of the animal's culinary value, then the Mariana fruit bats should be ranked among the great gourmet delicacies of the world. A major reduction in the population of these bats may have occurred between 1920 and 1945 when extensive hunting took place. Hunters report that fifty or more fruit bats can be easily killed in a single successful raid on a roost. Fruit bats are an important cultural food and served on special occasions such as fiestas, weddings, christenings and holidays. People are willing to pay high prices for the bats depending on special culinary qualities such as unique taste and size. The bats are cooked and eaten whole, including the fur. Bats are purchased on the black market and may bring 25 dollars per animal in Guam and Saipan.

Excessive hunting and poaching have been the most important causes in the decline of the Mariana fruit bats. A major reduction in the population of these bats may have occurred between 1920 and 1945 when extensive hunting took place. Although difficult to quantify, illegal hunting of fruit bats has continued since 1966, when bats were first granted partial legal protection. From 1981 to 1984, eight cases of hunting at colonies and seven cases of night hunting along flyways or at feeding sites are known. More unrecorded incidents undoubtedly occurred.

Colony hunting is the most destructive form of fruit bat hunting because animals in colonies typically roost close together in large numbers, and thus are highly vulnerable to shotgun fire. Hunters report that fifty or more fruit bats can be easily killed in a single successful raid on a roost.

Forest destruction has probably been a minor factor in the decline of bats on Guam. Large stands of native forest have been cleared for agriculture and housing in the central and north-central portions of the island. Sizeable tracts of forest were also destroyed during the invasion and bombardment of Guam in World War II and by subsequent construction activities on newly established American military bases. However, fruit bats were already considered uncommon by 1945. Sizable tracts of forest remained after the war and are still present today, yet few bats inhabit these forest lands. Food resources and potential roosting sites seem to be adequately available and not limiting the population of Mariana fruit bats.

The impact of predation by brown tree snakes on fruit bats is unknown but potentially serious. These snakes were first introduced to Guam after World War II. They seem capable of at least preying upon young bats. Stomach contents of large snakes routinely contain adult roof rats which are similar in size to juvenile Mariana fruit bats. One case of snake predation on bats has been reported by a local resident. Other evidence, although circumstantial, suggests that snakes may be preying on young bats at roosts. Large-sized juveniles may be vulnerable to predation because they are not yet able to fly and are too large to be carried by their mothers during night time foraging. Thus, they are left overnight at the roosting site where they may be susceptible to nocturnal predators.

Typhoons are a rare but potentially serious threat to Guam's small number of remaining Mariana fruit bats. Strong typhoons with sustained winds of more than 155 mph strike the island about every 10 to 15 years. Although there is no evidence that storms have ever greatly reduced fruit bat numbers on Guam in the past (probably due to the lack of serious observations), severe typhoons have been implicated in precipitous declines of bats on several islands in the western Indian Ocean. Gale-force winds on Guam are capable of denuding large forested areas of foliage and fruit and residents have reported finding dead bats under roosting trees after strong storms. Animals not killed directly by winds could face a period of up to several months of low food supplies.

Conservation and Recovery

The primary objective of this bat's recovery plan is to restore the island's population to threatened status. The population of the Mariana fruit bats should be increased to at least 2,500 animals with a minimum of two permanent colonies in northern Guam and one permanent colony in southern Guam.

Sources of mortality must be minimized to prevent further reductions in the present population and allow for expansion of new populations of Mariana fruit bats. It will be necessary for conservation officers, military security police, and federal wildlife law enforcement agents to work together in a combined effort to eliminate illegal fruit bat hunting. The Guam Aquatic and Wildlife Resources department with its staff of conservation officers is the primary agency entrusted with enforcing the island's conservation laws. Patrols by the officers for bat poaching should become a regular activity of high priority.

Studies of ecological requirements of fruit bats will provide information useful in further identification and management of essential habitats and bat colonies. Protection of forest habitat is needed for a long-term conservation program for fruit bats. Essential habitat areas were determined by studies conducted from 1978 to the present. These studies indicated that limestone and ravine forests, coconut groves, and beach strand vegetation are all preferred habitat of the fruit bats. Areas in northern Guam comprise a 27 mile-long strip of forest around the island's northern coastline. These areas will be valuable as habitat for bats and as a source from which bats will be able to recolonize the remainder of the islands in the future. Development on the islands should be allowed to continue, however, any forest clearing/alteration activities should be prevented as these would adversely affect the bats.

Information needed to efficiently and effectively manage essential habitat for fruit bats include the impact of introduced ungulates, plants, plant diseases and insects; needs for food trees; and criteria for buffer zones of vegetation.

The recovery potential of this bat appears to be high. A sex ratio skewed strongly toward females and the probable ability of females to produce young annually indicate that the Guam population of Mariana fruit bats is capable of doubling in size over two to three years.

Rodrigues Island Flying Fox Fruit Bat

Pteropus rodricensis

B. Hoffman, Philadelphia Zoo

Status	Endangered
Listed	January 23, 1984
Family	Pteropodidae (Fruit bats)
Description	Large bat weighing up to 2 pounds, with small ears, large eyes, and wingspan up to 5.6 feet.
Habitat	Lush, tropical vegetation with fruits in season year round.
Food	Soft fruit.
Reproduction	One young per year, with a gestation of 140 to 192 days.
Threats	Low numbers; natural disaster.
Range	Mauritius: Rodrigues Island

Description

The Rodriques Island flying fox fruit bat, *Pteropus rodricensis*, ranges in color from silver to dark brown and black. The mantle and head are brightly shaded with yellow, orange or red. The small ears are sharply pointed and the eyes are concealed by the long, silky fur.

Pteropus rodricensis is a member of the group *Megachiropterans*, or Old World fruit bats, which contains some of the larger bats, with wingspans of up to 5.6 feet and weight of up to 2 pounds. These bats have small ears, large eyes, and, in general, do not use echolocation.

Behavior

The Rodrigues flying fox fruit bat feeds during the day on the pods of tamarinds, rose apples, mangoes, and native palms.

Females have only one young per year, with a gestation of 140 to 192 days. The birth season is from September through December. Although the young may begin to fly at 3 months, they usually are not weaned until they are 4 to 6 months old, and may remain dependent on their mothers for a year. They do not reach sexual maturity until they are 1.5 to 2 years old. The maximum life expectancy of this bat is 32 years.

The Rodrigues flying fox fruit bat is a poor flyer, which makes it susceptible to destruction by high winds and capture by predators.

Habitat

The Rodrigues Island flying fox fruit bat occurs only in remnant forest patches, especially in tamarind trees. A large area of mixed natural vegetation, with fruits ripening at all times, is essential to supply this bat's food.

Distribution

The Rodrigues Island flying fox fruit bat occurs only on the tiny Rodrigues Island in the Indian Ocean, although it was probably once present on Mauritius and Round Islands. Until the early part of the twentieth century, it was considered abundant on Rodrigues, but by the 1950s the population had been reduced to 1,000. A cyclone desiccated this species in 1979, and as few as 60 individuals survived. A count of 650 individuals was confirmed in 1990 but a census the following year confirmed only 350 bats.

Threats

Deforestation remains the principal threat to this bat; less than 2% of its original habitat remains and much of the mixed vegetation has largely been destroyed. Between 1955 and 1968, a forest of old tamarinds was cleared, depriving the Rodrigues flying fox fruit bat of one of its most important roosting sites. In addition, cyclones periodically kill many of the animals, and the cyclones of 1968, 1972 and 1979 are known to have killed many individuals. The human population has hunted them for food, although they are fully protected by law.

Conservation and Recovery

The Rodrigues Island flying fox fruit bat has been captively bred successfully, and this population will be introduced to an Indian Ocean island outside the cyclone belt when a suitable, protected habitat can be identified. On Rodrigues Island, efforts are underway to banning deforestation, enforcing hunting bans, and monitoring the bat population.

Little Mariana Fruit Bat

Pteropus tokudae

Status	Endangered
Listed	August 27, 1984
Family	Pteropodidae (Fruit bats)
Description	Small fruit bats with brown to dark brown abdomens and wings and grayish to yellowish brown heads with dark brown throats and chins.
Habitat	Mature limestone forests.
Food	Probably fruits and flowers of trees.
Threats	Probably excessive hunting and poaching.
Range	Mariana Islands: Guam

Description

Adult little Mariana fruit bats, *Pteropus tokudae*, weigh about 5.3 ounces, are 5.5 inches long (head and body), and have a wingspan of 25 to 27 inches (forearm length 3.7 inches). The abdomen and wings are brown to dark brown with a few scattered whitish hairs. The mantle and sides of the neck vary from brown to light gold. The top of the head is grayish to yellowish brown while the throat and chin are dark brown.

Fanihi is the local Chamorro name for the fruit bat. Other common names include Guam flying fox, Tokuda's fruit bat, and Tokuda's flying fox.

Behavior

The only information on breeding was gathered from a single female shot by hunters on June 5, 1968. This animal was associating with or perhaps carrying a juvenile that was old enough to fly away. This may indicate that mothers care for their young for several months.

The diet probably consists of fruits and flowers of trees found in limestone forest.

Habitat

Only a single reference exists on the habitat used by the little Mariana fruit bat. Nine vegetative types have been described for Guam. An animal killed by hunters in 1968 was taken at Tarague Point in an area of mature limestone forest. This forest is characterized by sparse undergrowth, a canopy 31 to 58 feet high, and scattered taller emergent trees. Secondary growth limestone forest is shorter and has dense undergrowth.

Large stands of limestone forest occur in northern Guam, especially along clifflines. Soils in these areas tend to be thin and rocky. Limestone rock outcrops are a common feature.

When the little Mariana fruit bat was more abundant, it may have used a wider range of habitat types.

Distribution

The little Mariana fruit bat is known to occur only on Guam in the southern Mariana Islands. Its historic and present distributions are identical. A specimen of this bat was collected in 1968 at Tarague Point on Anderson Air Force Base in northern Guam. The location at which two individuals were collected in 1931 is unknown.

The possible present distribution of the little Mariana fruit bat includes the remainder of Guam. Federally-owned lands that could harbor the little Mariana fruit bat include Naval Facility, Naval Communications Area Master Station, Naval Air Station, Radio Barrigada, Naval Hospital, Nimitz Hill Navy Headquarters, Naval Magazine, Naval Station, the War in the Pacific National Historic Park and property held by the Federal Aviation Administration. The Territory of Guam owns a number of small land parcels possibly inhabited by the little Mariana fruit bat. Recently there have been several independent reports from hunters of a small fruit bat existing on the island of Anatahan in the Commonwealth of the Northern Mariana Islands. This bat may be the little Mariana fruit bat, and thus would extend the possible range.

Threats

Little is known about the causes of decline for the little Mariana fruit bat. This species has always been considered rare on Guam by hunters, elderly residents and scientific collectors. No documentation of its decline exists and, thus, discussion on the reasons for its disappearance is speculatory.

Excessive hunting and poaching have probably been the primary reasons for the decline of this species and *P. mariannus mariannus* (see separate entry), a second, larger species of fruit bat on Guam. Fruit bats are considered a delicacy in the Marianas. A major reduction in the numbers of both species of fruit bats probably occurred between 1920 and 1945 when extensive hunting took place. Post WWII habitat destruction (forest clearing, alteration, etc.) and predation by the introduced brown tree snakes (*Boiga irregularis*) are other potential factors leading to the decline of the little Mariana fruit bat. These factors, and future severe typhoons, threaten any little Mariana fruit bats presently remaining on the island.

Conservation and Recovery

The primary objective of this bat's recovery plan is to restore the islands' population to threatened status. Sources of mortality must be minimized to prevent further reductions in the present population and allow for expansion of new populations of little Mariana fruit bats. It will be necessary for conservation officers, military security police, and federal wildlife law enforcement agents to work together in a combined effort to eliminate illegal fruit bat hunting. The Guam Aquatic and Wildlife Resources department with its staff of conservation officers, is the primary agency entrusted with enforcing the island's conservation laws. Patrols by the officers for bat poaching should become a regular activity of high priority.

Studies of ecological requirements of fruit bats will provide information useful in further identification and management of essential habitats and bat colonies. Protection of forest habitat is needed for a long-term conservation program for fruit bats. Essential habitat areas were determined by studies conducted from 1978 to the present. These studies indicated that limestone and ravine forests, coconut groves, and beach strand vegetation are all preferred habitat of the fruit bats. Areas in northern Guam comprise a 25 mile-long strip of forest around the island's northern coastline. These areas will be valuable as habitat for bats and as a source from which bats will be able to recolonize the remainder of the islands in the future. Development on the islands should be allowed to continue, however, any forest clearing/alteration activities should be prevented as these would adversely affect the bats.

To efficiently and effectively manage essential habitat for fruit bats, data pertaining to the impact of introduced ungulates, plants, plant diseases and insects; needs for food trees; and criteria for buffer zones of vegetation are needed to provide protection of essential habitat of fruit bats.

Marine Mammals
Dolphins, Manatees, Seals

West Indian Manatee (*Trichechus manatus*)   Alan Maltz

General Characteristics of Dolphins

Dolphins (family *Delphinidae*), river dolphins (family *Platanistidae*), and porpoises (family *Phocoenidae)* are members of the order Cetacea, the whales. The great whales, the baleens (covered in the *World Wildlife Fund Guide to Endangered Species of North America*) do not have teeth but syphon plankton and other prey through a baleen apparatus. The dolphins and porpoises, which are toothed whales, are much smaller, although they grow as long as 15 feet. The river dolphins have long beaks, broad, short flippers, and very small eyes that produce poor eyesight. Two river dolphin species, the Indus and Ganges dolphins, are blind. All dolphins use echolocation to navigate and to identify and capture prey. The Indus and Ganges river dolphins weaned at 8 to 9 months, after which they lead a solitary life. These, the most primitive of marine mammals, have small brains and lack the sophisticated social behavior of the *Delphinidae*. The greatest threat to river dolphins is the alteration of their habitat due to dam construction. The Indus River dam system, begun in the 1900s and continuing throughout the century, has divided the dolphin habitat into 10 segments. This fragments breeding populations, and isolates individuals, making hunting easier for human predators. The water flows have also been severely restricted.

General Characteristics of Porpoises

Porpoises probably originated in the Northern Pacific Basin and radiated to warmer waters from Europe to Asia. There are five porpoise species within the family *Phocoena*, and one finless porpoise in the family *Neophocoena*. Two of the five *Phocoena* species are endangered or vulnerable, *P. sinus* (Vaquita) which occurs in the Gulf of California (Mexico) and *P. spinipinnis* which occurs in the coastal waters from Peru to Uruguay. Porpoises prefer shallow water, whereas many dolphins are deep sea swimmers.

Porpoises feed on fish and squid, which they swallow whole or tear into swallowable chunks. They feed in schools of 2 to 4 individuals; they detect prey through sight and sound, listening for noises generated by their prey. Like dolphins, they have good echolocation, but porpoises are not dependent on it for navigation and finding food resources.

Porpoises are not as gregarious as deep-sea dolphins, and they form large schools only when prey is abundant. Porpoises pair for mating during a 1 to 2 month span every 1 to 3 years. Mothers with calves are segregated from the school, although several mothers with their calves may school. Weaning occurs at 6 to 8 months, and a calf remains with its mother for several months after weaning. The lifespan of porpoises is from 12 to 24 years.

The major threat to porpoises is incidental capture by fishermen. Porpoises in pursuit of prey are not as aware of impending danger, and their echolocation sense cannot detect fish netting. Porpoises captured in nets usually drown.

General Characteristics of Seals

The "true" or "hair" seals of the family *Phocidae*, swim in sideways motions using their hindquarters for propulsion. They have powerful flippers that facilitate swimming and diving (to depths of 2,000 feet) but their weak forearms are used only for steering.

Seals feed on small or soft foods, which include fishes, squids, and krill. Usually solitary, most seal species aggregate because of concentrated food supplies or at resting places. Reproduction is determined by the female's perception of the optimal conditions in which to rear the young. Mating occurs just prior to or just after the young are weaned; weaning occurs from 1 to 12 weeks after birth; gestation is 10 to 11 months. Mating occurs in water among all seal species, except the elephant and gray seals.

Seals have long been hunted for their meat and skins, and over exploitation has resulted in the severe decline of some populations. The clubbing to death of baby seals brought world attention to commercial practices, but most seal populations are stable. The monk seals — Mediterranean, Caribbean, and Hawaiian — are seriously endangered, and a subspecies of the Saimaa seal, *Phoca hispida saimensis*, is vulnerable.

General Characteristics of Dugongs and Manatees

Unlike all other marine mammals, dugongs and manatees, of the order *Sirenia*, are vegetarians, and they inhabit warm, shallow waters where marine plants easily grow. They share feeding grounds only with marine turtles, but they do not compete for food because turtles feed on the blades of sea grass while dugongs and manatees forage the roots, which are a much denser resource for the huge mammals. The blubber in manatees provides thermal stability as well as nourishment during long periods of fasting (up to 6 months) when food supplies are scarce. Although large, these mammals have a low metabolic rate because little energy is required to regulate body temperature in tropical waters. And because they have no predators, they do not need to expend energy by moving quickly; dugongs and manatees are notoriously slow. Manatees have poor eyesight but good hearing; because they do not have echolocation capability, they often bump into underwater objects, another reason for them to move slowly.

Dugongs occur in the tropical coastlines along east Africa, Asia, Australia, and New Guinea. They differ primarily from manatees in their tail structure; manatees and dugongs have large, horizontal, paddle shaped tails that move up and down to propel the animal, but dugongs have a straight or concave trailing edge on their tails, whereas the manatees' is rounded. There is only one species of dugong; there are three species of manatees: the West African and West Indian manatees, which are similar, are tolerant of both salt and fresh waters; the Amazon manatee survives only in rivers.

Manatees are exceptionally docile and are very comfortable in the presence of humans (they will swim and play with people) and human developments, which has led to their decline. They are slow breeders, producing one calf every two years. Although calves begin feeding on plants within a few weeks after birth, they are not weaned for 12 to 18 months. Females do not become sexually mature until 5 to 8 years; males 6 to 8 years of age.

All three species of manatees and the dugong are endangered. They have been overhunted for their meat and skins, and where they occur near humans, they are susceptible to pollution, habitat destruction, and death by boats.

Dugong
Dugong dugon

Daryl Domning

Status	Endangered
Listed	December 2, 1970
Family	Dugongidae (Dugongs)
Description	Size and shape of a large dolphin, but with a less streamlined head and no dorsal fin.
Habitat	Seagrass beds of tropical marine waters.
Food	Seagrasses, marine algae, clams.
Reproduction	One calf per breeding season.
Threats	Hunting, net fishing.
Range	Southern Pacific and Indian Oceans.

Description

Dugong dugon, the dugong, is roughly the size and shape of a large dolphin, but with a less streamlined head and no dorsal fin. The muzzle is large and fleshy. The eyes are small. The external ears consist only of tiny openings and the nostrils lie close together at the anterodorsal tip of the snout. A pair of short upper incisor tusks are present, but these normally do not erupt except in adult males. The cheek teeth are simple and peglike. The neck is very short and the pectoral flippers are short and rounded, without nails. The two mammae are located in the axillae. The hind limbs are completely absent; and the tail fin is horizontally flattened and in the form of flukes like those of cetaceans. The body is gray to bronze in color, somewhat lighter ventrally, and sometimes with large unpigmented areas; the thick, smooth skin is often extensively scarred in older animals. This species can exceed 12 feet in total length and 900 pounds in weight, but most are smaller.

It is possible that untrained observers, or observers of animals at sea, might confuse *D. dugon* with small cetaceans such as *Orcaella* or, especially, *Neophocaena*, which lacks a dorsal fin; however, both these cetaceans are smaller than *D. dugon*, especially in length and girth.

D. dugon was divided into several species and subspecies in older literature, but today only a single taxon, *Dugong dugon*, is recognized.

Behavior

The dugong, in at least some areas, undertakes extensive long shore seasonal movements; some individuals may be migratory while others remain as residents in a given area. Distinct seasonal migrations can even occur within a single large bay. Local increases in the species' abundance are also reported during monsoons and rainy seasons, perhaps because this species takes shelter inshore from bad weather and is more conspicuous then. On a daily basis, individuals often travel several kilometers among various feeding and resting areas, sometimes following established and predictable routes. After feeding in one area for 1 to 4 weeks, they may move, individually or as a group, to a similar area several kilometers away.

Sexual maturity is reached at a minimum of 9 to 10 years in both sexes, but this is variable and in some animals may not occur for over 15 years. Gestation lasts one year or slightly more. Lactation can last at least 1.5 years. The usual litter size is one. Estimates of the calving intervals are from 3 to 7 years for various populations. Ovaries tend to be active (and calves tend to be born) in the latter half of the year, but there is no sharply defined breeding season. At a given time, both fertile and infertile adult males may be found in one population, and females also undergo sterile cycles. They do not seem to come into estrus soon after giving birth, but the conception can occur during lactation. Ovarian activity may be reduced in some old females, but one pregnant female 42 years old was observed. Sexual dimorphism in form and behavior is minimal. Simple courtship or display, possibly including agonistic behavior, seems to occur, and males may use their tusks to roll females onto their backs. Several males will pursue one female in attempts to mate, and mating seems to be promiscuous; but it is not known how often or for how long a female is in estrus.

Although precocial, newborn calves may require and receive some maternal assistance in learning to surface and breathe properly immediately after birth. Thereafter, the calf accompanies the mother closely for at least a year. This prolonged association may be important for communicating traditional knowledge of the habitat to the calf, as well as for socialization. The calf may begin to graze within 2 to 3 months after birth, but suckling probably continues throughout the period of cow-calf association. Parents of both sexes reportedly will try to protect calves from shark attacks and will continue to seek a calf in the area where it has been netted. Males tend to be on the outside of a herd; this may be an anti-predator tactic.

The diet of the dugong is composed of tropical seagrasses (families *Hydrocharitaceae* and *Potamogetonaceae*). It eats all species of seagrasses: younger plants are generally preferred to dense, older stands which are presumably less palatable, digestible, and/or nutritious. Both leaves and rhizomes are eaten (the rhizomes having a higher starch content and calorific value), except that in the case of *Enhalus* (which has the largest and most fibrous rhizomes) only the leaves seem to be eaten. Likewise, in the case of *Amphibolis* growing on hard sand, only the leaves and not the tough stalks or deeply buried roots are eaten. Even newborn animals may eat seagrasses, including rhizomes. The dugong leaves feeding tracks where it has stripped seagrasses from the bottom.

When seagrasses are unavailable, the dugong will resort to eating marine algae such as sargassum. This was observed following a cyclone which damaged seagrass beds in Australia. However, this species does not appear to chew algae adequately and may not be able to use it efficiently as a food source. Dugongs (possibly post-reproductive individuals) that have been observed feeding extensively on algae which is found around island margins and nearby reefs are lean, and offshore seagrass is probably more nutritious.

Various epiphytic algae has also been recorded in stomach contents of this species, probably ingested incidentally while feeding on seagrasses. Some marine invertebrates and fish have likewise been found in the stomachs. Some of these were also no doubt ingested accidentally, but the possibility cannot be excluded that they may eat some animals (such as clams and *holothurians*) deliberately, as they have been reported to do in captivity.

In subtropical areas such as Shark Bay, Australia, there are seasonal variations in seagrass availability which may have a significant impact on the energy budget of the dugong. The winter diet (mostly *Amphibolis*) is higher in fiber and lower in carbohydrate, and therefore furnishes less energy than the summer diet (mostly *Halodule*). In tropical areas, however, seasonal variations are presumably less important than variations in food availability due to locality, weather, tides, and other factors.

When not harassed or hunted, dugongs tend to alternate around the clock between feeding and resting and do not seem to have a regular day/night cycle. Where they forage intertidally, the tidal patterns impose rhythms on their activity. Where they are regularly hunted, as at Palau, they typically do not feed during the day but come inshore to feed at night. This restriction of inshore feeding to the hours of darkness as a result of human disturbance may greatly reduce the carrying capacity of an area.

Habitat

The dugong is characteristically associated with the seagrass ecosystems of the Indopacific region. It feeds on virtually all species of seagrasses, and is seldom found far from seagrass beds. Such beds may grow on either sandy or muddy bottoms. This species seems to prefer to feed in water 1 to 2 meters deep, and off points in preference to the coves between the points. The dugong inhabits tropical marine waters of normal salinity and pH, both clear and turbid. Individuals may also be found in brackish, and occasionally in hypersaline coastal waters. They prefer calm waters and will seek shelter behind reefs, headlands, or other features offering protection from rough water. This may be partly because protected waters favor growth of seagrasses, but also because surfacing and breathing are more energetically costly in rough water. Dugongs are usually found in water less than ten fathoms deep with temperatures between 18 and 33 degrees Celsius.

Parturition takes place in water 3 feet or less deep, or even entirely out of water. It may take place on sandbars or sandy flats; however, it is more likely to occur on a rising tide (to avoid stranding) and sometimes in hypersaline areas.

The dugong is a long-lived (50 to 60 years) mammal with low fecundity and a large investment in each offspring. The minimum pre-reproductive period is 9 to 10 years. The calving intervals are 3 to 7 years. The usual litter size is one. Human-caused mortality is doubtless the main limiting factor in most parts of its range, but mortality schedules are not known for any dugong population. Both juvenile and adult female mortality rates must be kept low for population survival. Judging from a simple population model, even the most optimistic schedule of reproduction and juvenile mortality requires an adult survivorship of about 90% per year for population stability.

Dugongs will take shelter in the lee of islands, reefs, or headlands when wind and seas are high, apparently because surfacing and breathing are more difficult and energetically costly in rough water. However, they avoid confined bays and narrow inlets. Ordinary resting areas generally lack seagrasses, give ready access to water 10 meters or more in depth, and have reference points such as reefs, reef embankments, or derelict ships. Disturbance by humans may force the dugong into unprotected waters where energy expenditure and danger from predators are high. Thermal refugia may be important in cooler areas at the margin of the geographical range.

Distribution

The dugong is a herbivorous, strictly marine mammal distributed widely in the tropical Indian Ocean and southwest Pacific. It may be encountered in shallow marine waters almost anywhere within this vast region, especially in the vicinity of seagrass beds on which it feeds. Occasionally this species is found crossing expanses of deep water between areas of suitable habitat, but normally the dugong prefers warm, shallow (less than 10 fathoms) waters, especially within bays or behind reefs where they can find shelter from surf and bad weather.

Threats

The dugong is hunted for food through-out its range, including Palau. This exploitation is believed to be the principal cause of its decline. There is a great deal of folklore concerning the dugong, and in the societies where it is traditionally hunted, it has great cultural significance and is often accompanied by elaborate rituals. Many parts of the dugong's body, including meat, fat, oil, bones, tusk, and "tears," are thought to have medicinal and aphrodisiac properties, and these (particularly the latter) very likely motivate some taking of the dugong in some areas. In Palau, the wearing of the atlas vertebra as a bracelet is an old custom that apparently continues today. The dugong has potential non-consumptive value as attractions to tourists in the Pacific Trust territories.

More localized causes of significant mortality have included entanglement in fishing nets (e.g., in Sri Lanka, India, Australia, Kenya, and Djibouti) and shark nets set to protect swimmers in Australia, and oil spills such as in the Arabian Gulf. In the late 19th and early 20th centuries there was an extensive commercial fishery in Queensland, Australia based chiefly on dugong oil, which was sold for medicinal purposes.

Current threats include continuation of traditional hunting (usually by harpoon), hunting with modern equipment such as outboard motors (which are used to chase dugongs to the point of exhaustion and easy capture), explosives (which have been used in Palau since World War II), fishing with large nets (especially synthetic-fiber nets), and protection of bathing beaches by shark nets.

Future threats include increased boat or amphibious aircraft traffic, petroleum exploration, more oil spills, vandalism or other harassment by sport divers, and destruction of seagrass beds by any means (e.g., dredging, sand mining, sewage or toxic waste disposal, silt runoff from agricultural or mining activities on land, changes in freshwater runoff, harvesting of seagrasses).

Conservation and Recovery

The endangered status of the dugong has been proposed to be extended in the Trust Territory of the Pacific Islands. Due to an oversight, individual dugongs that occur in this area of the Republic of Palau are not officially listed as endangered. The population consists of fewer than 200 individuals and is the most isolated population in the world. The Palauan population is seriously threatened by poaching.

The naturally low recruitment rate of the dugong renders populations highly vulnerable when exposed to increased rates of mortality. As a consequence of man's hunting, their populations throughout the range have diminished to relict numbers, and some have become extinct. The population at Palau has followed this pattern, and now fewer than 100 animals survive, a number too small to sustain an overall mortality rate of more than 10 animals per year, including those taken by hunters.

Gray Whale
Eschrichtius robustus

C. Allan Morgan

Status	Endangered
Listed	June 2, 1970
Family	Eschrichtiidae (Baleen whales)
Description	Blotched grayish black, slender body, broad, angular flippers and a series of humps.
Habitat	Cool northern waters in summer; warmer coastal waters in winter.
Food	Bottom feeder amphipods, isopods, mysids, tube worms.
Reproduction	One calf every 2 to 3 years.
Threats	Hunting
Range	Coasts off Siberia and Korea

Description

The gray whale, *Eschrichtius robustus*, is a moderate-sized baleen whale 36 to 46 feet in length. A slow swimmer, the animal is typically covered with many encrustations on its back. The body is blotched grayish black and slender, with up to five longitudinal throat folds and broad, angular flippers. Where other whales have a dorsal fin, the gray has a series of humps along the tail, called knuckles. Females are somewhat larger than males, weighing in at nearly 35 tons. The California gray whale is another common name for this species.

Behavior

The gray whale migrates farther than any other mammal, traveling as far as 10,000 miles round-trip from feeding grounds in the Bering and Chukchi seas to breeding grounds off the coast of Baja California and mainland Mexico. Gray whales typically travel in small pods of up to about 15 animals or in cow-calf pairs.

The gray whale is a bottom feeder, eating amphipods, isopods, mysids, tube worms, and other bottom-dwellers. While feeding, it scoops up large quantities of sand and rocks, often leaving a muddy trail that is visible from the surface.

The gestation period is 12 months, after which a single calf weighing 1,500 pounds is born. Calves are weaned after seven months, and growth is prodigious during the first year. The calf may gain as much as 27 pounds per day. Females calve every two or three years.

Emerging from the water, the gray whale spouts from its blow-hole at brief intervals and not more than 10 feet high. Its vocalization is in the form of a bubble blast that can be heard 1.5 miles away.

Habitat

The gray whale is a pelagic mammal that feeds in cool northern waters in summer and breeds in warmer coastal waters in winter.

Distribution

Historically, there were three major breeding populations of the gray whale. A population along the Atlantic coast was exterminated by whalers in the 17th century. A small Asian population off the coast of Siberia and Korea has been hunted to the verge of extinction. A third population migrates along the North American Pacific coast and is now protected from whaling.

The number of whales in the "summering" populations that migrate along the U.S. West Coast was estimated in the North Pacific at 25,000 animals in 1996. Recovery efforts have been so successful for the eastern North Pacific population (which breeds along the West Coast of North America), however, that it was delisted in June, 1994.

Threats

One of the easiest whales to hunt because of its slow speed and inshore habits, the gray whale was also one of the first to show the symptoms of species decline. Whalers eliminated the mammals from the Atlantic Ocean within the span of about 50 years. Japanese fishermen in the 18th century hunted in small boats, herding the whales toward the beach where they were taken with harpoons and nets. The last gray whale in Japanese waters was taken in 1933.

Nearly extinct in 1946, gray whale numbers have rebounded steadily to about 16,500, which is close to pre-whaling levels. Until a whaling moratorium went into effect in 1986, about 180 of these North American gray whales were taken every year off the coast of Siberia, primarily by Russian and Japanese vessels. Although in 1990, there were thought to be no more than 200-300 surviving whales in the Asian population, the 1986 moratorium on whale hunting has been so successful that numbers are thought to have increased above the endangered level, and the Japanese have been lobbying to gain rights to hunt for whale meat again.

Conservation and Recovery

The gray whale was first protected in 1937 by an international agreement and again in 1946 by an international treaty, although there were many violations of these agreements. The International Whaling Commission (IWC), which has regulated the whaling practices of 38 member countries since 1946, called for a total moratorium on whaling in 1986, which has been mostly successful. The Soviets, stinging under international criticism of their whaling practices, sought to repair their image in the fall of 1988, when their icebreakers made a heroic effort to free three gray whales trapped in Arctic ice. The U.S. Coast Guard had failed in an earlier attempt to free the whales.

The eastern North Pacific population is now thought to number between 25,000 and 30,000, and was delisted in 1994 because the Fish and Wildlife Service deemed the population had been successfully recovered. Since 1990, there have been no observed reports of incidental mortality related to commercial fishery operations in the eastern North Pacific. Based on logbook reports maintained by boat operators required by the MMPA interim exemption program during the 3-year period between 1990-1992, one injury and one mortality was recorded in the Bristol Bay salmon set and drift gillnet fishery in 1990. However, because research shows that logbook records are most likely negatively biased, these are considered to be minimum estimates.

The ban on whaling has been so successful that whale populations are thought to have recovered in other populations to levels above those that would be considered endangered; major whaling nations, including Japan, have been lobbying for the right to start whaling again.

Chinese River Dolphin

Lipotes vexillifer

Nigel Hicks

Status	Endangered
Listed	May 30, 1989
Family	*Piatanistoidea* (River dolphins)
Description	Long, forceps-like beak, broad flippers, triangular fin with a blunt peak and rectangular blowhole, bluish-grey and white.
Habitat	Wide, slow moving middle and lower portions of river waters.
Food	Fishes
Reproduction	Gestation is 10 to 12 months.
Threats	Habitat destruction, overfishing, pollution, heavy river traffic.
Range	China: Yangtze River

Description

Lipotes vexillifer, the Chinese river dolphin, is the most primitive of dolphins. It has a long, forceps-like beak with 30-35 conical teeth in both jaws. Broad flippers allow it tight turning and unfused neck vertebrae allow the head to move in relation to the body. It has a recognizable dorsal, triangular fin with a blunt peak. However, in other species, there is only a fibrous dorsal ridge. A rectangular blowhole is situated to the left of the mid-line just behind the forehead.

It has evolved small eyes (due to the fact that its vision is impeded in turbid rivers) located just above the angle of the gape. Because of the poor eyesight Chinese river dolphins use echolocation to find their food.

Their brains are small which relates to the early weaning and short learning period. Chinese river dolphins are solitary, lacking social behavior comparable to modern dolphins.

They can grow up to a length of 98 inches and weigh 300 to 510 pounds. The males appear to be smaller than the females, averaging 87 inches long and weighing 275 pounds.

Chinese river dolphins are pale, bluish-gray dorsally and white ventrally. The flukes and flippers are colored respectively. The lower jaw and the lower margin of the upper jaw are white with broad white stripes intruding from below onto the bluish-gray regions between the flipper and ear opening and in two areas on either side of the tail stock.

The common name given to this dolphin

by the fishermen in China is "baiji" and it is also the internationally agreed upon common name. In English, it is known as the Chinese river dolphin, Yangtze dolphin, or Yangtze River dolphin. It is also known as the White-fin dolphin, *pei c'hi*, Chinese lake dolphin, or white flag dolphin.

Behavior

When the dolphin approaches the surface of the water, its head region breaks the surface first, then is followed by the back and dorsal fin. The head then disappears and only the dorsal fin is exposed for some time before the animal becomes totally submerged. From a distance, sometimes only the dorsal fin can be seen from above.

Life history is a little known area. Calves are born at a body length of less than 3.7 inches and weigh less than 22 pounds. There is only one species in this genus.

In general, *odontocetes* prey on fish and cephalopods and usually swallow their food whole. Some of the fish prey includes large-scaled species, such as eel-like catfish.

Habitat

In the middle and lower portions of the habitat the river is wide, open and slow moving, with an average current speed of 3.3 to 6.5 feet per second. It has many sandbars and the downstream ends of well-developed sandbars tend to create zones of high fish productivity where this dolphin tends to be concentrated, especially during the rainy season.

Distribution

The Chinese river dolphin is endemic primarily to the lower and middle sections of the Changjiang (Yangtze) River in the eastern to central region of mainland China. It was formerly believed to be restricted to the Dongting Land and associated rivers. However, it is now found to be inhabiting a much larger area, virtually from the mouth of the Changjiang to Yichang. The population of the Chinese river dolphin numbers fewer than 100 individuals.

Threats

Habitat destruction is a primary factor in the endangerment of this dolphin. The banks of the Yangtze River have been extensively modified to prevent floods. Most of the lakes in the area have been isolated by sluice gates to retain the water for irrigation during the dry seasons and for fish cultures. Since the lakes are important areas for the breeding of many species, this isolation may have had adverse effects on the Chinese river dolphin by changing fish biomass and species composition in the river.

Some fish stocks in the river appear to be greatly reduced because of the loss of the nursery areas for the migratory species, overfishing, and pollution. The reduction in the prey fish availability may have had a direct role in the decline in population numbers of the dolphin.

The increased activity of boat traffic, industrial activity, and the exploitation of the fish resources have combined to present hazards to this dolphin. The most serious of the human induced threats seems to be accidental entanglement in bottom long lines, referred to as "rolling hooks," set to snag bottom-feeding fish such as sturgeon. The dolphins are also taken incidentally in fish traps and gillnets. Fishing gear may account for almost half of the known species' mortality.

In the lower regions of the river some dolphins are being killed by boat propellers. The river traffic is heavier in this region and it is expected to double within the next decade.

Fifteen to twenty percent of the known deaths are related to explosions usually associated with construction projects. Illegal fishing does occur with the use of explosives. It was recorded that six dolphins were killed in one construction blast.

Conservation and Recovery

A project to save the last population by captive breeding has so far failed, with only one animal successfully held in captivity.

Local superstition has had a positive effect on protecting the dolphin from human predation.

Mediterranean Monk Seal

Monachus monachus

USFWS

Status	Endangered
Listed	June 2, 1970
Family	Phocidae (Earless seals)
Description	Dark-gray or brown with a whitish or yellow spot on the belly.
Habitat	Prefers open beaches; because of hunting, lives in inaccessible rocky terrain on steep coasts.
Food	Octopus, cuttlefish, squid, and several species of fish.
Reproduction	One young after gestation of about 30 days.
Threats	Unsuitability of breeding habitat and predation by fishermen.
Range	Mediterranean Sea, Atlantic coast of northwest Africa, Madeira Islands (Portugal), Canary Islands (Spain)

Description

The Mediterranean monk seal, *Monachus monachus*, is a large marine mammal that weighs up to 900 pounds and grows to 10 feet in length. Named because its coloration resembles a monk's frock, this seal is dark-gray or brown with a whitish or yellow underparts. The fur often has a white ventral patch. The front flippers are well developed but the hind flippers are small.

Like all earless seals (having only ear openings but no outer ear structure), the Mediterranean monk seal has very well developed, strong hind flippers and weak forefront flippers that are used for steering but not for propulsion. Earless seals are clumsy on land, which makes them especially vulnerable when the female comes on land to give birth and to nurse the young until it can swim two weeks after birth.

Behavior

Recorded in the earliest known works of Ancient Greek literature, the Mediterranean seals once inhabited and bred on sandy beaches, but were banished to uninhabited rocky islands as the Mediterranean was colonized by humans. These seals are gregarious, forming groups whose size depends on the size of the habitat and number of animals in the area. The female mates every other year, in the summer, giving birth to one young after gestation of about 30 days. She crawls onto a beach where she delivers the pup, which is unable to swim for at least 14 days. Suckling continues for 2 months, and the young remains close to its mother for 2 years, until she mates again. Mediterranean monk seals reach sexual maturity at 3 to 4 years.

Mediterranean monk seals feed on octopus, cuttlefish, squid, and several species of fish. They fish twice a day, in the early morning and at sunset.

Habitat

Today, Mediterranean monk seals inhabit inaccessible rocky terrain on steep coasts. Before they were exposed to hunting by humans, they preferred open waters and open beaches, but today they prefer grottoes that can be reached only by underwater channels. They are seen openly only on the beaches of Mauritania.

Distribution

Once abundant throughout the Mediterranean Sea, the monk seal was widely hunted and driven to habitats unsuitable for breeding. Its numbers dramatically declined over the last 50 years, and today there are only 500 known individuals. The largest population of 200 individuals is in the Greek Islands; another large population is in Mauritania in the Atlantic Ocean; the remainder are scattered along the coasts of Tunisia, Morocco, Turkey, Bulgaria and Sardinia. Sightings have occurred on Madeira off the Portugese coast.

Threats

Today, the greatest threats to the few remaining seals are unsuitability of breeding habitat and predation by fishermen. Forced from beaches into sunless grottoes, pregnant females cannot produce enough vitamin D that is required for fetal development, and pregnancies will terminate before birth. Because the Mediterranean monk seal produces only one young every other year, the slow reproductive rate combined with low population numbers makes prenatal mortality a critical factor in the species' ability to repopulate itself. Moreover, the grottoes are subjected to rising water levels, and young seals that are inexperienced swimmers during storms, drown or suffocate in the grotto.

The fishing industry in the Mediterranean Sea threatens the monk seals because of the dwindling food supply and because monk seals are frequently caught in fishing nets where they drown or are killed by the fishermen, who consider them a competitor for fish and a destroyer of their nets. Fishermen also explore remote areas that the seals have inhabited, which may cause the seals to abandon the habitat or to abandon pups as they flee to safety.

Finally, all aquatic life in the Mediterranean Sea is threatened by heavy pollution as the countries bordering the sea are becoming industrialized. As large animals depend upon high quality water and an abundance of food sources, unbridled pollution has greatly diminished both.

Conservation and Recovery

Pollution and overfishing have resulted in such diminished numbers of fish in the Mediterranean that the European countries which border the sea have established emergency programs to improve the situation. Ecotourism in this part of the world whose economy depends on tourism, and whose famous movie-star tourists promote environmental causes, has generated an aura of respect for wildlife. The Greek government is the only one to take legal steps to protect the Mediterranean monk seal. It designated the Northern Sporades Islands as a national marine park, but rebellion by fishermen in this area makes enforcement difficult. The Hellenic Society for the Study and Preservation of the Mediterranean Monk Seal rescues orphaned pups and wounded adults, nursing them until they can be returned to the wild.

Saimaa Seal

Phoca hispida saimensis

USFWS

Status	Endangered
Listed	May 6, 1993
Family	Phocidae (Earless Seal)
Description	Dark gray to blackish-gray on the back with dark spots edged in white resulting in rings that cover most of the body.
Habitat	Large, deep, arctic, freshwater lake in southeastern Finland.
Food	Variety of bottom-dwelling crustaceans and fish.
Reproduction	Generally one young is born per reproductive period.
Threats	Predation by larger mammals; competition with local fishermen for food.
Range	Finland: Lake Saimaa

Description

The Saimaa seal, *Phoca hispida saimensis*, is a subspecies of the ringed seal, *Phoca hispida*, that has adapted to a freshwater environment. Body and skull measurements vary widely in the various subspecies of *P. hispida*. Males range in length (head to tail) from 49 to 59 inches and weigh from 143 to 209 pounds. Females are from 46 to 54 inches in length and weigh from 99 to 176 pounds. This seal has a short muzzle and the cuspids are fine. The fur is dark gray to blackish-gray on the back and a silvery to dark gray below. Dark spots are edged in white resulting in rings that cover most of the body. True seals (including this subspecies) have a difficult time moving on land or ice but are excellent swimmers.

P. h. saimensis is a member of the earless and true seals family, *Phocidae*. The ringed seal, *Phoca hispida*, has also been referred to as *Pusa hispida* and by the common name floe rat.

P. h. saimensis is a freshwater subspecies of *P. hispida*, the ringed seal. Another subspecies, *P. h. ladogensis*, has also adapted to a freshwater environment; it is only found in Lake Ladoga in northeastern Russia.

Behavior

The Saimaa seal molts during the middle

of the summer. Most of the moult period (up to 30 days) is spent sunbathing and fasting on ice floes.

Females first reproduce at the age of 5.8 to 8.3 years; males mature in about 7 to 7.5 years. Average longevity for males and females are 43 and 40 years, respectively. Males form harems of females; males emit an extremely strong odor during mating. Mating occurs soon after parturition (during lactation). Young (generally one per reproductive period) are born in March to April in snow caves or in the open on pack ice; pup fur is white. Lactation lasts for about 2.5 months if the ice flow is stable; since the Saimaa seal's breeding areas are more likely to be on land, this timeframe will vary.

The Saimaa seal is non-migratory. It eats a variety of bottom-dwelling crustaceans, fish, and planktonic crustaceans.

Information on the daily activity patterns of this subspecies are unknown. Every year during the middle of the summer, this seal molts. During this period they spend a large amount of time sunbathing and fasting. This period is followed by the seals' movement to deepwater habitats for the short arctic summer.

Habitat

The Saimaa seal inhabits a large, deep, arctic, freshwater lake.

Distribution

The Saimaa seal is endemic to Lake Saimaa, a land-locked freshwater lake in southeastern Finland (about 150-200 miles northeast of Helsinki). The 1958 population was estimated at 40 individuals; after adopting stringent measures to save the species, the population has risen to about 250 individuals.

Threats

Habitat alterations and impacts related to human activities have contributed to the decline of this subspecies. Heavy pollution has driven the seal from the southern part of the lake; elsewhere, pollution remains a problem.

Conservation and Recovery

In addition to two areas already protected, the Ministry of the Environment in Finland has developed a plan to protect two additional areas as natural parks in Lake Saimaa. When these parks are in place, the core parts of the four breeding areas will be protected. As it stands, only the terrestrial portions of the seal's habitat would be protected. The Government of Finland is considering a law making it possible to incorporate aquatic areas into the parks. To accomplish this, pertinent aquatic environments would have to be purchased from private landowners. These proposed actions are expected to reduce juvenile seal mortality and could make a significant contribution to the recovery of the subspecies.

Cochito [=Vaquita]

Phocoena sinus

Bob Brownell, USFWS

Status	Endangered
Listed	January 9, 1985
Family	Phocoenidae (Porpoise)
Description	Smallest living cetacean; weighing up to 12 pounds and measuring up to 5 feet long.
Habitat	Warm waters of the upper quarter of the Gulf of California (Mexico).
Food	Primarily fish and invertebrates.
Threats	Fishing nets; pesticides.
Range	Mexico

Description

The Cochito, *Phocoena sinus*, is the smallest living cetacean, weighing up to 12 pounds and measuring up to 5 feet long. The smaller *P. sinus* differs from the closely related *Phocoena phocoena* by having proportionately larger flippers that are more concave at the back border. *P. sinus'* dorsal fin is also proportionately higher with a more concave back edge than *P. phocoena's* fin. When comparing the heads, *P. sinus* has a smaller skull and a U-shaped indentation in the palate instead of the W-shaped indentation of *P. phocoena's* palate. *P. sinus* has less vertebrae than other species of the genus *Phocoena*.

The most striking features of the color pattern are the large black eye patches and the black upper and lower lip patches. In both areas, the pigmentation contrasts sharply with the surrounding light gray coloration.

Based on one specimen taken in a gill net, young cochitos have fetal folds on the side. Little else is known about this animal's reproduction, growth patterns, and behavior.

P. sinus is one of four species in the genus *Phocoena*, with no recognized subspecies. Other common names for *P. sinus* are the vaquita and Gulf of California harbor porpoise. The specific name sinus means bay and refers to the species' distribution in the Gulf of California.

Behavior

The cochito seems to feed mainly on fish and invertebrates. Remnants of two types of fish, bronze striped grunts and gulf croakers, as well as squid were found in one animal's stomach. Both of these fish are abundant in the northern Gulf of California. It is thought that this animal does not migrate to a large degree but seasonal movements probably do occur. When the waters of the northern Gulf get very warm in summer, the animals are seen less frequently.

Habitat

The cochito lives in the warm waters of the upper quarter of the Gulf of California. The water is shallow, murky, and productive for species able to exploit the shallow lagoons when the tide allows. It has been spotted in mangrove lagoons in water so shallow that their backs protrude above the surface.

Distribution

The cochito occurs in the upper quarter of the Gulf of California, Mexico.

Threats

Threats to the cochito come from human intervention in the forms of over fishing of its home waters and pollution. In the past, the main cause of mortality has been capture in gill nets set by commercial fishermen to catch totoaba, *Cynoscian macdondaldi*. The totoaba, itself, has been fished to the point of extinction and catching it is now against Mexican law. However, many fishermen still set nets for the totoaba illegally and snag the *P. sinus* as well. Individuals of this species have also been occasionally captured in shrimp trawls. Additionally, pesticides entering the Gulf of California from the Colorado River may have an adverse effect on *P. sinus*.

Conservation and Recovery

Educating the local fishermen on illegal catching and the use of certain nets is an important part in the recovery of the cochito.

The Mexican government totally banned both sport and commercial fishing for totoaba in 1975. If this ban is adequately enforced, the accidental deaths of the cochito may decrease. However, gill net fishing for other types of fish and shrimp trawling may also have to be banned to stop more of the accidental deaths.

Indus River Dolphin

Platanista minor

Status	Endangered
Listed	January 14, 1991
Family	Platanistidae (Dolphin)
Description	Light grayish-brown skin, long beak and broad flippers.
Habitat	Deep channels of the Indus River system.
Food	Fish and crustaceans.
Reproduction	Gestation period of 10 months.
Threats	Alteration of habitat and hunting.
Range	Pakistan: Sind and Punjab

Bob Brownell, USFWS

Description

The Indus River dolphin, *Platanista minor*, grows to lengths of 83 to 102 inches and weighs 190 to 285 pounds. Its skin is light grayish-brown, and paler underneath. It is adapted to facilitate fish catching. It has a long, forceps-like, upcurved beak with numerous small teeth in both jaws. It has broad flippers to allow tight turns, and unfused neck vertebrae to allow the head to move in relation to the body.

The Indus River dolphin has evolved small eyes and is essentially blind, as its eyes lack a crystalline lens. It is only able to sense the intensity and perhaps the direction of light. The acoustic sense of this species is paramount. It produces trains of high-frequency pulses, mainly in the range of 15 to 159 kilohertz, and separated by intervals of a minute or less. This nearly constant barrage of echo-ranging sounds allows them to navigate and find food in a habitat where visibility is poor. This species has no recognizable dorsal fin, it has only a fibrous dorsal ridge.

The Indus River dolphin surfaces to breathe in a normal dorso-ventral plane, but it almost always swims on its side under water. One flipper trails along or several centimeters above the bottom, with the body at an oblique angle of approximately 10 degrees with respect to the bottom and the tail held slightly higher than the head. The head nods constantly, making a lateral sweep over the bottom. Usually individuals swim on their right sides. The flippers not only provide stability but also function as tactile organs, giving the individual important information about its position relative to the riverbed.

Some confusion exists on the taxonomic structure of this species. Recently, it has been put in a superfamily called *Platanistoidea*. Within this superfamily, this species rests in the family *Platanistidae*. Other common names include the Sindhi names bhulan and sunsar, or variants of these; Indus susu or the blind river dolphin; and Gangetic dolphin.

Behavior

The Indus River dolphin eats mainly fish and crustaceans. Catfish, carp, gobies, mahseers and clupeids are among those eaten, and prawns apparently can be important prey at times. Adults sometimes take fish as long as 11.8 to 17.5 inches. In captivity, the species can eat 100 to 300 pounds of fish daily. In the wild, much of its feeding activity occurs near the bottom; the species may even root in the bottom sediments for benthic prey. The Indus River dolphin can forage in water as shallow as one foot. It vocalizes and swims almost constantly.

If seasonal migrations occur, it is probably due to the need to search for adequate water and prey.

Gestation in the species is approximately 10 months. The Indus River dolphin can live as long as 28 years.

Habitat

The Indus River dolphin is entirely confined to riverine water, and it is behaviorally adapted to live in the heavily turbid, silt-laden waters of the Indus River system. Fifty percent of this river system's discharge occurs from July to September and only 15 percent

from October to March. The species avoids the narrow, turbulent areas where a river enters foothill country or flows between shingle banks, and it also avoids irrigation canals and small by-rivers. This species prefers deep channels and junctions where tributaries meet the main river.

The Indus River dolphin has been observed in water as cold as 8 degrees Celsius and as warm as 33 degrees Celsius, and it is believed that water temperature is not a large factor in its movements and distribution.

Distribution

The Indus River dolphin is only known from the turbid waters of the Indus River system in Pakistan. The species was known in the Indus River upstream to Attock as well as its major tributaries (Sutlej, Ravi, Chenab and Jhelum). A small population occurred in the pondstream on the Sutlej River until the late 1970s.

The Indus River dolphin is currently confined to an 80 mile stretch of the Indus River. The species is centered in Sind province between the Sukkur and Guddu barrages. The present upstream limit for the species is the Jinnah Barrage in northwestern Punjab. Few or no individuals occur downstream of Kotri Barrage.

Estimates place the population at 500 individuals.

Threats

The main cause of the Indus River dolphin's decline is loss of habitat. The erection of barrages and diversion of water for irrigation has taken away much of the available habitat. The construction of three barrages - Sukkur in 1932, Kotri in 1955, and Guddu in 1969 - had the effect of controlling water levels so that a vast area previously almost uninhabited by man became available for agricultural and other development. The barrages also partitioned the aggregate population into small, virtually isolated groups. The tributary rivers of the Indus, especially the Ravi and Sutlej, and even the Indus itself downstream of Kotri Barrage, virtually dry up during the winter months. The Indus River dolphin must find refuge in deep channels or isolated pools to survive.

Exploitation of the Indus River dolphin is another major cause of its decline. Specially trained otters were once used to help catch dolphins. The feeding otters apparently attracted individuals to an area where they were more easily netted. Other fishermen have used herons and egrets, attached to their boats by a long lead, to track the species. A special net was held by a fisherman standing on a specially erected platform high on the river bank. When an individual approached near enough, the man would throw the net over it and jump into the water to secure the animal. In some cases, a small live fish would be dangled on a line into the water to lure the individual within range.

Most Muslims traditionally shunned dolphin meat and oil, but low-caste Hindus highly valued both products in some areas. They ate the meat and used the oil for cooking. Some of the oil was sold for waterproofing boats and preserving leather, for mixing with flour to make animal food, or as a liniment.

Conservation and Recovery

Accidental capture in fishing nets has long been responsible for a certain amount of dolphin mortality in the Indus. Protection of the remaining individuals and their habitat is necessary in the recovery of the Indus River dolphin. The species has had complete legal protection in Sind province since 1972 and in Punjab since 1973. The stretch of the river from Sukkur to Guddu was declared a dolphin reserve in December 1974. Hunting continued in Sind through the 1970s, but the ban was enforced by the early 1980s. These protective measures need to be continued and strengthened to protect the species. Further water diversions and construction of barrages should not be allowed in the dolphin's range to protect its habitat. Studies into its reproductive requirements should be implemented so that a successful captive breeding program can take place. Some collections were begun in the late 1960's with limited success. Studies of the Indus River dolphin from these collections could also help to implement a captive breeding program.

Amazonian Manatee

Trichechus inunguis

Luiz Claudio Marigo

Status	Endangered
Listed	June 2, 1970
Family	Trichechidae (Manatee)
Description	Robust, compressed body; thick, tough, and nearly hairless grey skin.
Habitat	Protected coastal habitats.
Food	Aquatic plants.
Reproduction	Usually 1 offspring after gestation of 12-14 months.
Threats	Low numbers; human entrapment.
Range	Brazil, Guyana, Colombia, Peru, Ecuador

Description

The Amazonian manatee, *Trichechus inunguis*, is an aquatic mammal with a robust, fusiform body that is adapted for life in the water. The smooth, gray skin is thick, tough, and nearly hairless. On the top of the abdomen, the Amazonian manatee usually has whitish patches. The head is not visibly distinct from the body and small eyes protrude slightly from the side of the head. There are no external ears. Specifically designed for grazing on aquatic vegetation, the small mouth has very mobile lips with a deeply divided upper lip so each side can move independently when feeding. Functional incisors and canines are absent, and the numerous cheek teeth are replaced from the rear in a sequential fashion. These teeth have two crests and are low crowned. The forelimbs are modified into flippers, and there are no hind limbs. Unlike the Caribbean manatee, *T. manatus*, nails are absent from the flippers of the Amazonian manatee. The tail is modified into a horizontally flattened, spatulate paddle.

Adults attain only 9 feet in length at best and weigh a known 1,050 pounds. This smaller size is the primary physical distinguishing factor separating *T. inunguis* from other *Trichechus* species. Genetically, *T. inunguis* is also distinct because it has 56 chromosomes compared with the 48 chromosomes of *T. manatus*.

Sirenians, sea cows, were more diverse in the past with species in the Eocene known from North Africa, Jamaica, and Florida. Now the Order *Sirenia* is reduced to two families, the *Dugongidae* and the *Trichechidae*. *T. inun-*

guis, a member of the Trichechidae family, was originally described in 1883 by Natterer.

Behavior

Like the Caribbean manatee, the Amazonian manatee tends to move singly except during courtship. Individuals of a group contact each other by underwater vocalizations.

In a study conducted in 1975 initiated by the Instituto Nacional de Pesquisas da Amazonia a manatee was tagged and followed for 20 days. During the study period the manatee migrated an average of 8.8 feet a day and activity levels were equal both night and day.

After a gestation period of 13 months, a single calf is born. This calf is dependent on its mother for a long time, so intervals between births may be spaced three and a half years apart or more. These long intervals may also be a function of the carrying capacity of the habitat. Young manatees reach sexual maturity at five to six years of age.

An obligate vegetarian, the Amazonian manatee likes to feed on *Paspalum repens*, the dominant aquatic vegetation in the slow moving Amazon tributaries. This plant forms large "floating meadows" in the Amazon river basin. The Amazonian manatee also eats water grasses such as *Panicum* and *Echiochloa*.

During dry seasons when the river falls, the Amazonian manatees may stop feeding for up to six months as live vegetation is not within the animal's reach; this feature is unique to the Amazonian manatee. During this period the river may drop as much as 20 feet, forcing the manatee population to congregate in deep channels where vegetation is scarce.

Habitat

Unlike other *Trichechus* species which can occupy brackish, and salt water habitats, the Amazonian manatee occupies only freshwater habitats. Manatees generally require warm water with the Amazonian manatee recorded in temperatures of 25-30 degrees Celsius.

Found in the Amazon river system, this species is probably confined to slow moving "black water" rivers. These rivers are believed to be fairly stable and this manatee does not usually migrate over long distances.

Distribution

The Amazonian manatee is distributed through Brazil, Guyana, Colombia, Peru and Ecuador in the Tocantins, Xingu, Tapajo, Nhamunda, Madeira, Negro, Branco, Takatu, Putumayo, Caquetqa, Apaporis, Napo, Tigre, Maranon, Samiria, Pacaya Ucayali, Huallago, Rio Aquarica and Rio Cuyabeno river tributaries of the Amazon River.

Threats

The Amazonian manatee is mainly threatened by hunting. Some deaths may occur because of accidental capture in commercial fishing operations, although these operations may not be large because the blackwater rivers of the Amazon river are so remote.

Heavy logging and clearcutting of forests have increased siltation in the manatee's riverine habitat, which has reduced the aquatic plant life because of a decrease in sunlight blocked by the silt.

Conservation and Recovery

Legal protection of this species is difficult because its river homes are so isolated. The Amazonian manatee is protected in the Pacaya National Reserve between the Ucayali and Maranon rivers in Peru.

Much of the information known about the Amazonian manatee was collected in 1975 during a 20-day study by the Instituto Nacional de pesquisas da Amazonia. The data collected pertained to migration, periodicity, skeletal material and optical anatomy and physiology. This seemingly short-lived study was successful in part due to the fact that captive manatees were maintained and studied as well as those studied in the wild.

This study was directly responsible for the introduction of 42 manatees into the first hydroelectric reservoir on the Amazon, Curua-una in Brazil. What might be considered a destructive tactic to many ecologists, the reservoir provides a stable habitat for the manatees. This area is also protected from human predation and poaching as the natives residing in the area are strictly agrarians.

West African Manatee

Trichechus senegalensis

USFWS

Status	Threatened
Listed	July 20, 1979
Family	Trichechidae (Manatee)
Description	Thick, tough, and nearly hairless grey skin; and a head not visibly distinct from the body.
Habitat	Protected coastal habitats.
Food	Marine plants
Reproduction	Usually 1 offspring after gestation of 12-14 months.
Threats	Low numbers; human entrapment.
Range	Africa: Senegal to Angola

Description

The West African Manatee, *Trichechus senegalensis*, looks very similar to the West Indian manatee, *Trichechus manatus*. It is an obligate aquatic mammal with a robust body that is fusiform and slightly compressed dorsoventrally. The gray-brown skin is thick, tough, and nearly hairless. The head is not visibly distinct from the body. This species of manatee has a downward deflecting rostrum. Two valvular nostrils are located on the top of the thick, truncated muzzle; the snout is distinct from other *Trichechus* species because it is comparably short. Small eyes protrude slightly from the side of the head. The mouth is small with large terminal lips that are very mobile and bear short stiff bristles. There are

no external ears. The forelimbs are modified into flippers with small nails. There are no hind limbs. The tail is modified into a horizontally flattened, spatulate paddle. Adults attain 11 feet in length and weigh up to 2,200 pounds. Neonates are about 4 feet in length and weigh about 55 pounds.

T. senegalensis was originally described by Link in 1795. It is one of 3 species in the genus *Trichechus*, along with *T. manatus* and *T. inunguis* (see separate entry).

Behavior

Although tagged manatees are generally found living a nomadic life, they sometimes congregate in large groups, especially during the wetter seasons.

The West African manatee feeds on aquatic plants and terrestrial plant material that falls from overhanging plants into the water. It also consumes algae and small crustaceans taken incidentally with other foods. Many West African manatees undertake daily and seasonal migrations in response to tides and to salinity and depth changes. These manatees may travel alone or in groups of 4 to 6 individuals.

Breeding occurs year round. One young is born after a gestation period of 12 to 13 months, and remains with the mother for up to two years.

Habitat

The West African manatee occurs in lagoons, coasts, and numerous rivers of West Africa. The West African manatee generally has similar habitat requirements of the West Indian manatee (*T. manatus*).

During dry seasons the river falls and manatees may become trapped in tributaries or lakes that connect to the Senegal River in the wetter seasons. Additionally, with periods of drought not only do the manatees sometimes become isolated, but the vegetation levels decrease due to increases in salinity.

Distribution

The oldest known fossils of manatees were taken from Jamaica. However, it is believed that these species evolved from the Old World during the middle Eocene period.

The West African manatee is distributed among the coastal and riverine habitats of Senegal (all along the coast and in the Senegal River), Gambia (in the Gambia River basin), Liberia, Guinea-Bissau, Guinea, Sierra Leone (Sierra Leone River), the Ivory Coast, Ghana, Togo, Benin, Niger, Mali, Chad, Nigeria, Cameroon, Gabon, Congo, Republic of Congo (formerly Zaire), and Angola.

Threats

The principal reason for the decline of the West African manatee is the constant pressure from substance hunters for feeding their families and for local sales. In fact, the Kabawa tribe in Nigeria relies on fishing and manatee hunting for their existence. The process for hunting the manatees consists of harpooning the animal with a strong, sharp, detachable head possessing three or four barbs. The head of the harpoon is attached to a palm float and baited with grass. When the manatee begins to feed, the hunter strikes. After the manatee is brought to the canoe, it is killed, and the carcass is sold for consumption or other uses.

Additionally, some individuals have been accidentally killed in fixed shark nets. The degree to which accidental deaths from commercial fishing operations contribute to the decline of the West African manatee is not known.

Conservation and Recovery

The government of Gambia is proposing the construction of several dams along the Gambia River. These dams would adversely affect this manatee by crushing them in gates or locks or by altering the habitat.

The West African manatee is protected in many refuges and National Parks, including the Oiseaux du Djoudi and Basse-Casamance National Parks in Senegal, and the Faunal Reserve of Lere-Binder in Chad. When manatees become trapped in tributaries of lakes in the dry seasons, the Ministry of Water and Forests of Senegal will allocate staff to bring the manatees back to the Senegal River.

In 1986 Wildlife Conservation International and the World Conservation Union began a program geared toward public awareness and research, including surveys, radio tracking, interviews with natives, and examination of carcasses. A breakthrough in research has been the development of a trap that does not harm the manatees and allows for minimum trauma both during the scientific examination and afterwards. The traps are somewhat primitive, made of wooden stakes secured with vines opened at one end; once the manatee has entered the structure the front is closed as the manatee hits the trigger stick. Trapping manatees in this manner has given field scientists the capability to treat manatees for diseases and to assist wounded individuals.

References

Albignac, R. "Status of the Aye-Aye in Madagascar." *Primate Conservation* 8 (1987): 44-45.

Alderton, David. *Wildcats of the World*. New York: Facts on File, 1993.

Animal Kingdoms: Wildlife Sanctuaries of the World. Washington, DC: National Geographic Society, Book Division, 1995.

The Australian Wildlife Year: A Month-by-Month Guide to Nature. Sydney: Reader's Digest, 1989.

Banfield, A. W. *The Mammals of Canada*. Toronto: University of Toronto, 1974.

Beacham, Walton, ed. *Beacham's International Threatened, Endangered, and Extinct Species* CD-ROM. Osprey, FL: Beacham Publishing Corp, 1995.

Bertram, B. "Endangered Small Mammals in Zoos." *International Zoo Yearbook* 24/25 (1984/1985): 99-109.

Bogart, M. H., R. W. Cooper, and K. Benirschke. "Reproductive Studies of Black and Ruffed lemurs, *Lemur macao macao* and *Lemur variegatus* Spp." *International Zoo Yearbook* 17 (1977): 177-182.

Boitani, Luigi, and Stefania Bartoli. *Simon & Schuster's Guide to Mammals*. Translated by Simon Pleasance. New York: Fireside (Simon and Schuster), 1983.

Boskoff, K. J. "Aspects of Reproduction in Ruffed Lemurs (*Lemur variegatus*)." *Folia Primatologica* 28 (1977): 241-250.

Bramblett, C. A. *Patterns of Primate Behavior*. Palo Alto, CA: Mayfield, 1976.

Brandes, Kathleen, ed. *Vanishing Species*. New York: Time-Life Books, 1976.

Bryant, S. "Maintenance and Captive Breeding of the Eastern Quoll (*Dasyurus viverrinus*)." *International Zoo Yearbook* 27 (1988): 119-124.

Burton, J. and B. Pearson. *The Collins Guide to the Rare Mammals of the World*. Lexington, MA: Stephen Greene Press, 1987.

Burton, Maurice, ed. *Encyclopedia of Animals in Color*. New York: Exeter Books, 1983.

Burton, Maurice, and Robert Burtons, eds. *Encyclopedia of Mammals*. Hong Kong: Phoebus (Octopus Books), 1975.

Cadieux, C. *These Are the Endangered*. Washington, DC: Stone Wall Press, 1981.

Carman, M. "The Gestation and Rearing Periods of the Mandrill *Mandrillus sphinx* at the London Zoo." *International Zoo Yearbook* 19 (1979): 159-160.

Chevalier-Skolnikoff, S. and F. Poirier, eds. *Primate Bio-Social Development*. New York: Garland, 1977.

Cone, Jeffrey P. "The Return of the Golden Monkey." *Americas* 49, 2 (March-April 1997): 26-31.

Cox, James A. *The Endangered Ones*. New York: Crown, 1975.

Crump, Donald, J. *National Geographic Book of Mammals*. Washington, DC: National Geographic Society, 1981.

Cuury-Lindahl, K. *Let Them Live: A Worldwide Survey of Animals Threatened with Extinction*. New York: William Morrow, 1972.

Dawson, T. *Monotremes and Marsupials: The Other Mammals*. London: Edward Arnold, 1983.

Dawson, T. and A. Hulbert. "Standard Metabolism, Body Temperature, and Surface Areas of Australian Marsupials." *American Journal of Physiology* 218 (1970): 1233-1238.

Day, David. *The Doomsday Book of Animals: A Natural History of Vanished Species*. New York: Viking Press, 1981.

de Waal, Frans. *Peacemaking Among Primates*. Cambridge: Harvard University Press, 1989.

de Waal, Frans. *Chimpanzee Politics: Power and Sex Among Apes*. Baltimore, MD: Johns Hopkins University Press, 1990.

de Waal, Frans. *Good Natured: The Origins of Right and Wrong in Humans and Other Animals*. Cambridge: Harvard University Press, 1996.

Domico, Terry. *Bears of the World*. New York: Facts on File, 1988.

Dominis, J. and Edey, M. *The Cats of Africa*. New York: Time-Life, 1968.

Doyle, G. A. and R. D. Martin, eds. *The Study of Prosimian Behavior*. New York: Academic Press, 1979.

Duplaix, N. and N. Simon. *World Guide to Mammals*. New York: Crown, 1976.

Durrell, L. *State of The Ark: An Atlas of Conservation in Action*. London: Gaia Books, 1986.

Emanoil, Mary, ed. *Encyclopedia of Endangered Species*. Detroit: Gale Research, 1994.

Fisher, J., Simon, N. and J. Vincent. *Wildlife in Danger*. New York: Viking Press, 1969.

Fishman, David J. "The Shyest Monkey of Them All." *Science World* 47, 8 (January 11, 1991): 9.

Foerg, R. "Reproductive Behaviour in *Varecia variegata*." *Folia Primatologica* 38 (1982): 108-121.

Ganzhorn, J. U. "The Aye-Aye (*Daubentonia madagascariensis*) Found in the Eastern Rainforest of Madagascar." *Folia Primatologica* 46 (1986): 125-126.

Gerald-Steklis, Netzin. Pers. Comment. Dian Fossey Gorilla Fund, Atlanta, GA, 1997.

Geroudet, P. and N. Simon. 1970. *Last Survivors: The Natural History of Animals in Danger of Extinction*. New York: The World Publishing Company.

Godfrey, L. and M. Villaume-Randriamanantena. "*Hapalemur simus*: Endangered Lemur Once Widespread." *Primate Conservation* 7 (1986): 2-96.

Goldman, Edward A. *The Puma: Mysterious American Cat: Part II: Classification of the Races of the Puma*. New York: Dover, 1964.

Goodall, Jane. *The Chimpanzees of Gombe: Patterns of Behavior*. Cambridge, MA: Harvard University Press, 1986.

Gould, Edwin, and George McKay, eds. *Encyclopedia of Animals: Mammals*. New York: Gallery Books (W.H. Smith), 1990.

Green, Richard. *Wild Cat Species of the World*. Plymouth, England: Basset, 1991.

The Grolier World Encyclopedia of Endangered Species. Danbury, CT: Grolier Education, 1993.

Groombridge, Brian. *1994 IUCN Red List of Threatened Animals*. Gland, Switzerland: IUCN, 1993.

Groves, C. P., P. Andrews, and J. F. M. Horne. "Tana River Colobus and Mangabey." *Oryx* 12 (1974): 565-575.

Grub, P. "Distribution, Divergence and Speciation of the Drill and Mandrill." *Folia Primatologica* 20 (1973): 161-177.

Grzimek, Bernhard, ed. *Grzimek's Animal Life Encyclopedia*. New York: Van Nostrand Reinhold, 1968.

Guggisberg, C. A. W. *Wild Cats of the World*. New York: Taplinger, 1975.

Gunderson, V. "Some Observations on the Ecology of *Colobus badius temmincki,* Abuko Nature Reserve, The Gambia, West Africa." *Primates* 18, 2 (1975): 305-314.

Haltenorth, T. and H. Diller. *A Field Guide to the Mammals of Africa Including Madagascar.* London: Collins, 1980.

Harcourt, Caroline. *Lemurs of Madagascar and the Comoros: The IUCN Red Data Book.* Gland, Switzerland: IUCN, 1990.

Hershkovitz, P. *Living New World Monkeys (Platyrrhini): With an Introduction to Primates.* Chicago: University of Chicago Press, 1977.

Hoshino, J. "Feeding Ecology of Mandrills (*Mandrillus sphinx*) in Campo Animal Reserve, Cameroon." *Primates* 25 (1985): 248-273.

Humphrey, Stephen R. "How Species Become Vulnerable To Extinction and How We Can Meet the Crisis". *Animal Extinctions: What Everyone Should Know.* Washington, DC: Smithsonian Institution Press, 1985.

Jolly, A. *Lemur Behavior.* Chicago: University of Chicago Press, 1955.

Jolly, A. "Troop Continuity and Troop Spacing in *Propithecus verreauxi* and *Lemur catta* of Berenty (Madagascar)." *Folio Primatologica* 17 (1972): 355-362.

Jolly, A., Oliver, W. L. R, and S. M. O'Connor. "Population and Troop Ranges of *Lemur catta* and *Lemur fulvus* at Berenty, Madagascar: 1980 Census." *Folia Primatologica* 39 (1982): 115-123.

Jolly, Alison. "Madagascar's Lemurs: On the Edge of Extinction." *National Geographic* 174, 2 (August 1988): 132-161.

Kang-Chung, Ng and Gren Manual. "Outrage Over 'Dancing' Tiger." *South China Morning Post* May 13, 1996.

Kappeler, P. and J. Ganzhorn, eds. *Lemur Social Systems and Their Ecological Basis*. New York: Plenum Press, 1993.

Koenders, L., Rumpler, Y. and B. Brun. 1985. "Notes on the Recently Rediscovered Sclater's Lemur (*Lemur macaco flavifrons*)." *Primate Conservation* 6 (1985): 35.

King, C. *The Handbook of New Zealand Mammals*. London: Oxford University Press, 1990.

Kingsmill, S. *Vanishing Wildlife: Endangered Species of the World*. New York: Gallery Books (W.H. Smith), 1990.

Kitchener, A. *The Natural History of the Wild Cats*. Ithaca, NY: Comstock, 1991.

Klopfer, P.H. and K. Boskoff. "Maternal Behavior in Prosimians." In *The Study of Prosimians*. Edited by G. A. Doyle and R. D. Martin. New York: Academic Press, 1979, p. 123-157.

Lampton, C. *Endangered Species*. New York: Franklin Watts, 1988.

Lavanagh, Michael. *A Complete Guide to Monkeys, Apes and Other Primates*. New York: Viking Press, 1984.

Lawlor, T. E. *Handbook to the Orders and Families of Living Mammals*. Eureka, CA: Mad River Press, 1976.

Lee, G., ed. *Endangered Wildlife of the World*. New York: Marshall Cavendish, 1993.

Lee, Phyllis C., Jane Thornback, and Elizabeth L. Bennett. *Threatened Primates of Africa: The IUCN Red Data Book*. Gland, Switzerland: IUCN, 1988.

Littlewood, A. and J. Smith. "Breeding and Hand-Rearing Mandrills *Mandrillus sphinx* at Portland Zoo." *International Zoo Yearbook* 19 (1979): 161-165.

Macdonald, David, ed. *The Encyclopedia of Mammals*. Oxford, England: Andromeda, 1985.

MacKinnon, John. *In Search of the Red Ape*. New York: Holt, Rinehart and Winston, 1974.

Marsh, C. W. "Ranging Behavior and Its Relation to Diet Selection in Tana River Red Colobus (*Colobus badius rufomitratus*)." *Journal of Zoology* 195 (1981): 473-492.

Marsh, C. W. and R. Mittermeier, eds. *Primate Conservation in the Tropical Forest*. New York: Alan R. Liss, 1987.

Martin, V. ed. *For the Conservation of the Earth*. Golden, CO: Fulcrum, 1988.

McClung, R. *The Story of Extinct and Vanishing Wildlife of the Eastern Hemisphere: Lost Wild Worlds*. New York: William Morrow, 1976.

McClung, R. *Vanishing Wildlife of Latin America*. New York: William Morrow, 1981.

Meester, J. and H. Setzer. *The Mammals of Africa: An Identification Manual*. Washington, DC: Smithsonian Institution Press, 1971.

Meier, B., R. Albignac, A. Peyrieras, Y. Rumpler, and P. Wright. "A New Species of *Hapalemur* (Primates) from South East Madagascar." *Folia Primatologica* 48 (1987): 211-215.

Meier, B. and Y. Rumpler. "Preliminary Survey of *Hapalemur simus* and of a New Species of Hapalemur in Eastern Betsileo, Madagascar." *Primate Conservation* 8 (1987): 40-43.

Moore, Peter D. *Encyclopedia of Animal Ecology*. Oxford, England: Equinox, 1987.

Moynihan, M. *The New World Primates: Adaptive Radiation and the Evolution of Social Behavior, Languages, and Intelligence*. Princeton, NJ: Princeton University Press, 1976.

Napier, P. and J. Napier. *The Natural History of the Primates*. The MIT Press. Cambridge, MA: MIT Press, 1985.

National Geographic. Vol. 174, No. 2 (August 1988).

Natural History. Vol. 97, No. 7 (July 1988).

Nowak, Ronald M., and John L. Paradiso. *Walker's Mammals of the World*. Baltimore: Johns Hopkins University Press, 1983.

Parker, Sybil P., ed. *Grzimek's Encyclopedia of Mammals*. New York: McGraw-Hill, 1989.

Pereira, M. E., A. Klepper, and E. L. Simons. "Tactics of Care for Young Infants by Forest-Living Ruffed Lemurs (*Varecia variegata variegata*): Ground Nests, Parking and Biparental Care." *American Journal of Primatology* 13 (1987): 129-144.

Pereira, M. E., M. L. Seeligson, and J. M. Macedonia. "The Behavioral Repertoire of the Black-and-White Ruffed Lemur, *Varecia variegata variegata* (Primates: Lemuridae)." *Folia Primatologica* 52 (1988): 1-32.

Philomena, Alice, ed. *The Reader's Digest Illustrated Book of Cats*. Montreal: Reader's Digest Association, 1992.

Pollock, J. "A Note on the Ecology and Behavior of *Hapalemur griseus.*" *Primate Conservation* 7

(1986): 97-100.

Pollock, J. "Primates and Conservation Priorities in Madagascar." *Oryx* 20 (1986): 209-216.

Pollock, J. "Spatial Distribution and Ranging Behavior in Lemurs." In *The Study of Prosimian Behavior*. Edited by G. A. Doyle and R. D. Martin. London: Academic Press, 1979.

Preston-Mafham, Ken. *Madagascar: A Natural History*. New York: Facts on File, 1991.

Preston-Mafham, Rod and Ken Preston-Mafham. *Primates of the World*. New York: Facts on File, 1992.

Quigley, Howard, and Maurice Hornocker. "The Siberian Tiger Project: Saving Endangered Species through International Cooperation." *Endangered Species Bulletin* 19, 3 (May/June 1994).

Reynolds, J. E. and D. K. Odell. *Manatees and Dugongs*. New York: Facts on File, 1991.

Rainier III, Prince, and G. H. Bourne, ed. *Primate Conservation*. New York: Academic Press, 1977.

Rohlf, D. *The Endangered Species Act: A Guide to Its Protections and Implementation*. Stanford, CA: Stanford Environmental Law Society, 1988.

Rowe, Noel. *The Pictorial Guide to the Living Primates*. East Hampton, NY: Pogonias Press, 1996.

Rutherford, Alice Philomena. *The Reader's Digest Illustrated Book of Cats*. Montreal: Reader's Digest Association, 1992, p. 23.

Savage, R. J. G., and M. R. Long. *Mammal Evolution: An Illustrated Guide*. New York: Facts on File, 1986.

Schaller, George B. "Saving China's Wildlife." *International Wildlife* 20, 1 (January-February 1990): 30-41.

Schaller, G. B. *The Mountain Gorilla: Ecology and Behaviour*. Chicago: University of Chicago Press, 1963.

Schmidt, C. "A Review of Zoo Breeding Programs for Primates." *International Zoo Yearbook* (1986) 24/25 (1984/1985): 107-123.

Scientific American. Vol. 268, No. 1 (January 1993).

Shackleton, D. M., ed. *Wild Sheep and Goats, and their Relatives: Status Survey and Conservation Action Plan for Caprinae*. Gland, Switzerland: IUCN, 1997.

"Shenzhen Officials Raid Nightclub to Free Tiger." Reuters World Service, June 1, 1996.

Silkilwasha, F. "The Distribution and Conservation Status of the Zanzibar Red Colobus." *African Journal of Ecology* 19 (1981): 187-194.

Simon, N. and P. Geroudet. *Last Survivors: The Natural History of Animals in Danger of Extinction*. Cleveland: World, 1970.

Simons, E. L. "A New Species of *Propithecus* (Primates) from Northeast Madagascar." *Folia Primatologica* 50 (1988): 143-151.

Simons Morland, H. "Infant Survival and Parental Care in Ruffed Lemurs (*Varecia variegata*) in the Wild." *American Journal of Primatology* 18 (1989): 157.

Singh, Billy Arjan. "Save the Tiger—The Last Ditch." Tiger Information Center: www.tiger.com.

Stolzenberg, William. "Tamarin Tale: Tracking Down a New Species." *Science News* 137, 26 (June 30, 1990): 406.

Stonehouse, B. and D. Gilmore, ed. *The Biology of Marsupials*. London: Macmillan Press, 1977.

Strahan, Ronald, ed. *The Australian Museum Complete Book of Australian Mammals: The National Photographic Index of Australian Wildlife*. London: Angus & Robertson, 1983, p. 390.

Strahan, Ronald, ed. *Mammals of Australia*. Chatswood, New South Wales: Reed Books, 1995.

Struhsaker, T. T. and L. Leland. "Observations on Two Rare and Endangered Populations of Red Colobus Monkeys in East Africa: *Colobus badius gordonorum* and *Colobus badius kirkii*." *Africa Journal of Ecology* 18 (1980): 191-216.

Sussman, R. W. "Demography of *Lemur catta* on Southern Madagascar." *American Journal of Physical Anthropology* 78, 2 (1989): 312.

Sussman, R.W. and A. Richard. "Lemur Conservation in Madagascar: The Status of Lemurs in the South." *Primate Conservation* 7 (1986): 85-92.

Swaney, Deanna and Robert Willox. *Madagascar & Comoros: A Travel Survival Kit*. Hawthorn, Victoria, Australia: Lonely Planet Publications, 1994.

"Tales of Tails Hitherto Unseen." *U.S. News & World Report* 109, 1 (July 2, 1990): 14.

Tattersall, Ian. "Cathemeral Activity in Primates: A Definition." *Folia Primatologica* 49 (1987): 200.

Tattersall, Ian. "Madagascar's Lemurs." *Scientific American* 268, 1 (January 1993): 110-117.

Tattersall, Ian. *The Primates of Madagascar.* New York: Columbia University Press, 1982.

Tattersall, Ian. and R. W. Sussman, ed. *Lemur Biology.* New York: Plenum Press, 1975.

Thapar, Valmik. *Tiger: Portrait of a Predator.* New York: Facts on File, 1986.

U. S. Fish & Wildlife Service. "Three Primates and Seven Cacti Considered for Transfer to Appendix I." *Endangered Species Bulletin* 5, 2 (February 1980).

U.S. Fish & Wildlife Service. "Endangered Classification Extended to Ocelots in the U.S." *Endangered Species Bulletin* 7 (August 1982).

U.S. Fish & Wildlife Service. "Ten Foreign Mammals Listed as Endangered." *Endangered Species Bulletin* 9, 2 (February 1984).

U.S. Fish & Wildlife Service. "Eight Foreign Mammals Proposed for Listing as Endangered." *Endangered Species Bulletin* 10, 11 (November 1985).

U.S. Fish & Wildlife Service. *Endangered Species Bulletin* 15, 10 (October 1990).

U.S. Fish & Wildlife Service. *Endangered Species Bulletin,* 17: 1,2 (January/February 1992).

Valdez, Raul. "Where the Bharals and the Argalis Roam." *International Wildlife* 12, 2 (March-April 1982): 36-41.

White, F. J. "Diet, Ranging Behavior and Social Organisation of the Black and White Ruffed Lemur, *Varecia variegata variegata,* in Southeastern Madagascar." *American Journal of Physical Anthropology* 78, 2 (1989): 323.

Wright, Patricia. "Lemurs Lost and Found." *Natural History* 97, 7 (July 1988): 56-60.

Wright, P. C. "Primate Ecology, Rainforest Conservation and Economic Development: Building a National Park in Madagascar." *Evolutionary Anthropology* 1 (1992): 25-33.

Zimmer, Carl. "The Face of Discovery." *Discover* 12, 1 (January 1991): 57-58.

Glossary

Adaptation: The features of an animal that enable it to survive in its environment.

Adaptive radiation: A genetic, morphological, or behavioral change that a species makes to help it survive in its environment.

Adult: A fully developed and mature individual, capable of breeding.

Adventitious: Appearing in an unusual place or in an irregular or sporadic manner.

Aestivation: State of dormancy or torpor during summer or periods of drought.

Agouti: A fur color in which each hair has alternating light and dark bands, giving the fur a streaked appearance.

Aggregrate: Crowded in a dense cluster.

Air sac: A side-pouch of the larynx (the upper part of the windpipe), used in some primates and male walruses as resonating chambers in producing calls.

Alarm call: A loud vocalization given by all ages and genders in response to a disturbance such as the appearance of a predator or another group.

Allochthonous: originating elsewhere, or living in a different habitat.

Allogrooming: Reciprocal cleaning of the fur.

Allomothering: Care of an invant by a group member other than its mother.

Allopatric: Not sharing the same geographic range.

Alluvial deposits: Sediment deposited by flowing water.

Alluvion: Flow of water against a shore or bank.

Alluvium: Sediment deposited by a flowing river.

Alpine: A region that occurs above the tree-line and below the snow-line on temperate and tropical mountains; usually pertaining to altitudes above 1,500 meters (4,900 feet).

Alveolar: Pertaining to the jaw section containing the tooth sockets.

Anestrus: An interval of sexual dormancy between two periods of estrus (period of sexual activity).

Animal: A generically used term to designate all species other than plants.

Anterior: To the front.

Antiphonal: Alternating, as in a call and response.

Aperture: Orifice, hole or opening.

Apical: Pertaining to or located at the apex (tip).

Apocrine glands: Specialized sweat glands in the armpits and the perineum. Bacteria act upon apocrine secretions, resulting in perspiration odor.

Apomixis: A rare reproductive process in which a new individual is produced from a female cell other than an egg cell.

Aquatic: Living in water.

Arboreal: Living in trees.

Arboricide: Chemicals used to defoliate or kill trees, usually in clearing land for agriculture.

Argiustoll: A soil that is darkly colored with an accumulation of silicate clay layers with an average temperature between 5 and 8 degrees Celsius.

Association: A grouping of two or more species that travel and/or feed together.

Baculum: A bone in the penis of some mammals. Its size and shape is sometimes used in identification, i.e., bats.

Baleen: Plates located in the upper jaws of whales that filter plankton from sea water.

Basal: Located at or pertaining to the base.

Bask: Behavior in animals of absorbing sunlight for extended periods.

Benthic: Pertaining to organisms living on the bottom of a lake or sea.

Bezoar stones: Gallstones of primates that live in limestone-rich habitats.

Bicornuate: Having two crescent-shaped parts.

Bicuspid: Having two points at the cusp; a tooth with two points.

Bifid: Divided into two equal parts or lobes.

Bifurcate penis: Male sexual organ with two forks.

Bipedal: Using only two limbs for locomotion, as in humans and birds.

Blowhole: The breathing hole located on the head of a whale.

Blubber: A thick layer of fat beneath the skin of a whale.

Boreal: A conifer-dominate forest occurring in the northern high latitudes, bounded on the north by tundra (treeless plain) and to the south by broad-leaved, deciduous forests.

Brachial gland: A gland on the arm or wrist.

Brachiation: Moving through trees by swinging with arms from limb to limb.

Breaching: Leaping of a whale from the water.

Brood: Offspring raised together.

Browsing: Feeding by plant-eating animals.

Bursa copulatrix: A saclike, bodily cavity used in copulation.

Bursa: A saclike bodily cavity.

Caatinga: Brazilian rain forest characterized by low trees growing on sandy soils that lack nutrients.

Calcareous: Composed of calcium carbonate.

Canines: Pointed teeth; eye-teeth.

Cannibalistic: The practice among some animals of eating the flesh of their own species.

Canthal: Cither of two angles formed by the junction of the eyelids.

Canting: Springing out from a branch to catch prey with the hands while the hind legs hold onto the branch.

Carnivore: An animal that eats the flesh of other animals as a major percentage of its diet.

Cathemeral: Active periodically throughout the day and night, as in lemurs.

Cecum: A sacklike appendage between the small and large intestines.

Cellulose: The fundamental constituent of the cell walls of all green plants, and some algae and fungi. It can only be digested by the intestinal flora in mammalian guts.

Cementum: Hard material which coats the roots of mammalian teeth. In some species, cementum is laid down in annual layers which, under a microscope, can be counted to estimate the age of individuals.

Cephalic: Pertaining to the head or skull.

Channel: The bed or deeper part of a stream, river or harbor.

Channelization: The process of deepening a river bed.

Chaparral: A dense thicket of shrubs and small trees.

Cheek pouch: A structure in the mouth used to store food temporarily; found in Old World monkeys but not in colobines.

Chemoreception: The reaction of a sense organ to a chemical stimulus.

Circumocular ring: A ring around the eye.

CITES: An international treaty, the purpose of which is to protect endangered species. This is accomplished through the illegalization of trade of these species across international boundaries.

Class: a taxonomic classification of organisms belonging to related orders. This is the common category by which most animals are referred, such as birds, reptiles, insects, crustaceans, arachnids, amphibians, snails, and mammals; or plants, such as ferns, mosses, and mushrooms.

Cloud forest: High-altitude forest with a dense undergrowth of dwarf trees, ferns, mosses, and other plants that grow on the trunks of the trees.

Clump: A thick grouping of plants or trees.

Clutch: The number of eggs laid in one breeding.

Colonial: Forming colonies; an inhabitant of a colony.

Colonize: To establish a population in a new territory.

Colony: Group of the same species living or growing together.

Competition: The interaction between different species vying for the same ecological niche, habitat or food supply.

Congener: A member of the same kind, class or group; an organisim belonging to the same genus as another.

Coniferous forest: Comprised primarily of cone-bearing evergreens, usually located in cool, dry climates.

Consort: With regard to a male and an estrus female, to temporarily associate and travel together to enhance the male's chances of paternity. Consortion is found in baboons and chimpanzees.

Conspecific: Belonging to the same species.

Copulation: The process by which sperm is transferred from the male to the female.

Courtship: behavior in animals prior to mating.

Crepuscular: Becoming active in the twilight mostly at dawn and dusk.

Crypsis: An aspect of the appearance of an organism which camouflages it from the view of others, such as predators or competitors.

Cusp: The fold or flap of a heart valve; also, a pointed end.

Cycle: A series of events that occurs repeatedly in the same sequence.

Deciduous: Shedding or losing foliage at the end of a growing season, such as trees losing leaves in the fall.

Deforestation: The process of clearing forests.

Derived feature: A specialized adaptation (behavioral or morphological characteristic) that differs from that of the taxon's ancestors.

Dermatoglyphic: Having skin patterns on the fingers, palms, or feet.

Desert: Habitat with low rainfall and sparse vegetation.

Desiccation: The process of drying out.

Detritus: Decomposing organisms that serve as a food supply to many species.

Diastema: A considerable gap between the front (cutting) teeth and the rear (grinding) teeth, characteristic of many grazing and browsing animals.

Dichromatize: To become divided into parts or branches.

Digitate: Originating from one point.

Digitigrade: Walking so that only the toes touch the ground.

Dimorphic: Having two distinct forms.

Diploid: Having a homologous (genetically the same) pair of chromosomes for each characteristic except sex.

Dispersal: Migration of individuals from their home range.

Display: A pattern of behavior involving posture, action, and/or vocalization that serves as communication between species, such as mating rituals.

Distal: Toward the distant end of a structure such as a limb or digit. Opposite of proximal.

Distribution: The overall area in which a species is known to occur. It is not implied, and is very rarely the case, that a species occurs in all parts of the area defined by its distribution.

Disturbed area: Habitat whose native vegetation has been altered.

Diurnal: Active during the day.

Diversity: The number of differing species in a habitat.

Dominant: Higher ranking in a hierarchy, as determined by the displacement of other troop members for priority of access to food, mates, or resting places.

Dorsal: Situated at the rear of an animal.

Dorsum: A part of an organ analogous to the back.

Eccrine glands: Sweat glands whose secretions are by ducts and do not contain portions of the secretory cells themselves; important to body heat regulation.

Echolocation: the ability of an animal, such as a bat or dolphin, to orient itself by the reflection of sound it has produced.

Ecosystem: The interrelationships among the living organisms and the chemical and physical components of a given environment.

Edaphic: Pertaining to the soil as it affects living organisms.

Embryo: An organism in the early stages of development; unhatched.

Embryonic diapose: The temporary cessation of development of an embryo. This phenomenon occurs in many bats, seals and macropods. Also referred to as delayed implantation.

Emergent trees: Trees that grow above the top of the canopy.

Endangered Species Act of 1973: The purposes of the Act are to determine on the basis of scientific evidence alone whether any species is endangered or threatened and to "list" the ones that are; to prohibit anyone from harming a listed species; protect the species from illegal trade; and to prevent government programs from jeopardizing a listed species.

Endemic: Species that are native to a specific region; non-endemic species are called "exotic."

Entisols: Soils without natural genetic horizons or with weakly developed horizons.

Environment: All the conditions that affect the growth and sustenance of organisms.

Environmental stress: Stress on a species caused by the dwindling of resources necessary to sustain an organism's survival.

Epiphyseal: Part of the bone, often the end of a long bone, that develops separated from the main portion of the cartilage.

Estrus: The period around ovulation when females are willing to mate, as indicated by perineal swellings or pheromonal or behavioral signals.

Extinct: A species that has no surviving individuals.

Extirpate: To eliminate a population.

Faculatatively: Adaptive to varying environments.

Family: A taxonomic category below Order and above Genus based on the grouping of related genera.

Fauna: Animal life.

Faunivore: An animal that eats oher animals as a major percentage of its diet.

Femoral: Pertaining to the thigh.

Fen: Low, flat, swampy land; a bog.

Feral: Living in the wild (of domesticated animals, i.e., cats or dogs).

Fertilization: The union of a sperm and egg that stimulates growth of the embryo.

Filter feeding: In marine life, the process of filtering food from water through a siphoning organ.

Flank: The side or lateral part of the body.

Fluke: One of the lobes of a whale's tale; referring to their broad triangular shape.

Folivore: An animal that eats leaves as a major percentage of its diet.

Fontanelle: The soft membranous intervals between the incompletely ossified cranial bones of a fetus or infant.

Food chain: Interdependence of feeding organisms that prey upon lower or more vulnerable species. Frequently, if one species in a food chain is eliminated, all species within the chain are affected.For example, when farmers exterminated prairie dogs in the midwest, a dramatic decline in the black footed ferret occurred.

Fossil: An impression or cast of a plant or animal preserved in rock.

Fossorial: Adapted to burrowing or digging.

Fostering: When the young of one species are raised by parents of a related species.

Frugivore: An animal that eats fruit as a major percentage of its diet.

Furbearer: Term applied to mammals whose pelts have commercial value and form part of the fur harvest.

Fuscous: Dusky; dark gray or grayish brown.

Fusiform: Tapering at each end; spindle shaped.

Gallery: Forest found along streams and rivers.

Gamete: A mature sperm or egg capable of participating in fertilization.

Ganglia: In anatomy, a group of nerve cells located outside the brain or spinal cord in vertebrates; in pathology, a cystic lesion resembling a cyst-like tumor.

Genetic: Pertaining to characteristics that are passed by chromosomes from one generation to the next.

Genotype: The genetic constitution of an organism, determining all aspects of its appearance, structure and function.

Genus: The taxonomic classification below family and above species; indicated by italics and capitalization (e.g., *Felis*).

Geomorphologic agent: a force causing change in land forms.

Gestation period: The period between conception and birth.

Glabrous: Having no hairs; smooth.

Glaciate: To subject to glacial action; to cover with ice or a glacier.

Gonad: Testicle or ovary; an organ that produces reproductive cells.

Gonopodium: A penetrating organ used in copulation.

Graminoids: The food of graminivorous species that includes grasses, seeds, and grain.

Graminivore: An animal that eats grass seeds and grains as a major percentage of its diet.

Grasslands: Ground dominated by grasses and lacking in trees as a result of the amount of rainfall.

Gravid: Pregnant.

Graviportal: Animals in which the weight is carried by the limbs acting as rigid, extensible struts, powered by extrinsic muscles; i.e., elephants and rhinos.

Great call: The territorial song produced by gibbons.

Group: In the animal kingdom, the division of species into amphibians, arachnids, birds, crustaceans, fishes, insects, mammals, mussels, reptiles, and snails.

Guard hair: An element of the coat of seals consisting of a longer, stiffer, more bristle-like hair which lies outside and supports the warmer, softer underfur.

Gular: Pertaining to or located on the throat.

Habitat: An area providing the physical (rainfall, temperature, rock or soil structure, etc) and biological (plants and animals) conditions required by a particular species.

Habituated troop: Animals that have gradually learned to trust researchers and can be followed and studied.

Haploid: Having half the number of normal chromosomes.

Haplustolls: a well- to moderately well-drained darkly colored soil that is textured of loamy, very fine sand.

Harem group: A social group consisting of a single adult male, at least two adult females and immature animals: a common pattern of social organization among mammals.

Haul-out: Behavior of sea mammals pulling themselves ashore.

Herbivore: An animal that feeds on plants as a major percentage of its diet.

Heterothermy: A condition in which the internal temperature of the body follows the temperature of the outside environment.

Hierarchy (social or dominance): The existence of divisions within society, based on the outcome of interactions which show some individuals to be consistently dominant to others. Higher-ranking individuals thus have control of aspects (i.e. access to food or mates) of the life and behavior of low-ranking ones.

Hispid: Covered with stiff or rough hair, or bristles.

Holotype: The specimen used as the basis of the original published description of a taxonomic species.

Home range: An area defined by the habitual movements of an animal or troop over an annual cycle; usually expressed in hectares (ha). 1 ha = approximately 2.5 acres.

Hummock: A low mound, ridge or knoll.

Humults: Freely drained ultisols which have a high content of organic matter.

Hybrid: An offspring produced by parents of different species; for example, a donkey and a horse produce a mule.

Hypothermic: Abnormally low body temperature.

Impoundment: Accumulation of water in a reservoir.

Incubation: Keeping eggs warm until they hatch.

Individual: A single member of a population.

Infanticide: The deliberate killing of infants by members of their own species.

Invasion: The migration of a species into a new area, usually to the detriment of organisms already living there.

IPS Congress: International Primatological Society Congress, a conference held in even-numbered years.

Ischial callosities: The two pads on the rump, upon which Old World monkeys and gibbons sit. Each pad of tissue overlies a flattened projection of the ischium bone of the pelvis.

Isolated: A portion of a breeding population that is cut off from the rest of the population.

IUCN Red Data Book: The official listing document of threatened species worldwide by the Swiss organization, International Union for Conservation of Nature and Natural Resources, now known as the World Conservation Union.

Juvenile: An individual between infancy and sexual maturity.

Karst: A region of eroded limestone formations with caves and cracks.

Keel: A prominent ridge on the back of an animal.

Keratin: A tough, fibrous protein substance that forms the outer layer of epidermal structures (protective covering) such as hair, nails, horns and hoofs.

Keystone foods: A small number of foods upon which a species depends to survive the harshest conditions of the year.

Kingdom: The highest taxonomic division into which organisms are classified, as either animals or plants. Some organisms not readily classified as plants or animals, such as amoebae and paramecium, are sometimes classified in a third kingdom called Protista.

Knuckle walking: A type of four-limbed locomotion used by gorillas and chimpanzees in which the weight of the head and torso is borne on the knuckles.

Lactation: The secretion of milk from mammary glands.

Lateral: Pertaining to the side of an animal.

Lip smacking: A gesture indicating a friendly signal that many primate species use when approaching another individual.

Life cycle: The sequence of events in the progression of an organism from birth to death.

Limnetic: Pertaining to the deeper, open waters or lakes or ponds.

Littoral: A shore or coastal region.

Localized: Found within a limited geographic area.

Maculation: the spotted markings on a plant or animal, such as the spots on a leopard.

Mamma: An organ of female mammals that contains milk-producing glands.

Mammal: Vertebrates that are warm-blooded, usually possess hair, and nourish their young on the mother's milk.

Mangabey: A monkey of equatorial Africa, having a long tail and relatively long muzzle.

Mangrove: A tropical tree with exposed roots forming an interlocking mass; often vital to stabilizing shore lines.

Marsupial: A mammal of the order Marsupialia, found mainly in Australia, that includes kangaroos, opossums and wombats; set apart by urogenital and skeletal differences.

Marsupium: An external abdominal pouch in female marsupials that contains mammary glands (breasts) and that shelters the young; also, a temporary egg pouch in animals.

Matrifocal: Pertaining to a social structure in which females are the center of the group and males are peripheral.

Medial: Situation in or extending toward the middle.

Melanistic: Darkness of the skin, hair or eyes resulting from high pigmentation (coloration).

Membrane: A thin, pliable layer of tissue covering surfaces or connecting regions, structures or organs of a plant or animal.

Membranous: pertaining to a membrane, a thin, pliable layer of tissue covering surfaces or connecting regions, structures or organs of a plant or animal.

Mesic: Between dry and wet.

Mesocone: Protrusion in gastropods.

Metabolism: Chemical process within an organism to release energy.

Metamorphosis: Development from one stage of maturity to the next, usually with marked change in appearance.

Microclimate: The conditions immediately surrounding an organism, often differing significantly from the environment as a whole.

Migration: The seasonal movement of animals from one territory to another for the purposes of feeding or breeding.

Monogamous: Having one mate for life.

Monophagous: Eating only one kind of food.

Monotypic: Pertaining to a taxon with only one representative, such as a genus with only one species or a species with no subspecies.

Montane forest: Forest occurring at middle altitudes on the slopes of mountains, below the alpine zone but above the lowland forests.

Moraines: Accumulation of boulders, stones, or other debris carried and deposited by a glacier.

Morph: Any individual of a polymorphic (the occurrence of different forms, stages, or color types in organisms of the same species) group.

Morphology: The biological study of the form and structure of living organisms.

Mosaic bones: Bone tissue composed of somatic cells of genetically different types; this phenomenon is caused by gene or chromosome mutations.

Native: Indigenous; original to the region; not introduced from another region; endemic.

Natural selection: The evolutionary process by which better-adapted individuals have more offspring that survive and reproduce than less well adapted individuals do. In the long term this process leads to genetic changes in a population.

Nester: A species that nests.

New World Monkey: Monkeys inhabiting the tropical forests of the Western hemisphere, primarily South and Central America.

Niche: Tthe adaptive position of a species within the ecosystem.

Nocturnal: Active at night.

Non-native: Alien to an area; sometimes called "exotic"; not endemic.

Nuchal: Pertaining to the neck; in insects, the dorsal region of the thorax.

Nuehal hump: Any hump on the nape of the neck.

Nutrient: Food substance that promotes growth.

Omnivore: An animal that eats both animal and vegetable matter as major percentages of its diet.

Opportunistic: A species that adapts its feeding habits to the most available food source.

Order: A systematic grouping of organisms belonging to similar families. The order divides the class into animals that share many common characteristics.

Ossify: To change into bone.

Overgrazing: Occurs when animals feed too long in one area, causing destruction of vegetation and erosion of soil.

Oviposition: To lay eggs.

Ovoviparous: The condition in which eggs are hatched within the mother and born alive.

Ovum: The female reproductive cell (eggs) in animals.

Pair bond: A long-term relationship between a male and a female. Pair bond species mate for one or several breeding seasons while monogamous species mate for life.

Paratypes: A specimen other than the holotype which was collected before the original description but has been deemed one of the specimens upon which the original description was based.

Parietal: In anatomy, relating to either of the parietal bones, which are two large, irregularly quadrilateral bones that form, with the occipital bones, the sides and top of the skull.

Parturition: Pertaining to childbirth or labor.

Patagium: An expanse of skin between the fore- and hindlimbs used in gliding (some marsupials) or flying (bats).

Pelage: The coat of a mammal consisting of hair, fur, wool or other soft covering as distinct from bare skin.

Pelagic: The upper part of the open sea, above the benthic zone.

Pendent: Hanging down, dangling or suspended.

Pendulous: Hanging loosely so as to swing or sway.

Periodicity: Recurring patterns of behavior.

Periphyton: Stationery organisms that live attached to surfaces projecting from the bottom of a freshwater environment.

Peritoneum: Abdominal cavity.

pH: a measure of the acidity or alkalinity of a solution, numerically equivalent to 7 for neutral solutions; the numerical scale increases with alkalinity and decreases with acidity.

Phacelia: Gastric filament; functions to kill or paralyze live prey taken into the stomach of the species.

Phalanger: A small, arboreal marsupial of Australia having a long tail and dense wooly fur.

Phenology: The study of periodic biological occurrences and behavior, such as flowering, breeding, and migration.

Phenotype: Organisms exhibiting similar environmentally and genetically observable appearances.

Pheromone: Secretions whose odors act as chemical messengers to animal communication and which prompt a specific response on behalf of the animal receiving the message.

Photoperiod: The number of hours of light in a given day.

Phreatic water: Ground water.

Phylum: After dividing organisms by their kingdoms–animals and plants–the phylum distinguishes organisms by their bodily structure; for example, sponges form one group within the phylum while mollusks and arthropods form two other groups. Vertebrates (animals with backbones) are grouped into a separate phylum, called a subphylum, which includes mammals and birds; the divisions of the animal kingdom, synonymous to the division of plants.

Piscivorous: Feeding on fish.

Pleistocene: Belonging to the geologic period characterized by northern glaciation and the appearance of early forms of humans.

Pocosin: A swamp in an upland coastal region.

Poikilothermic: Having a body temperature that varies with the external environment, sometimes called "cold blooded."

Pollution: The disruption of an ecosystem by contaminants.

Polyembryonic: Having multiple embryos.

Polygyny: A social structure in which one breeding male mates with more than one female in the group during a given mating season.

Population: A group of individuals within a defined area that is capable of interbreeding.

Posterior: The rear or tail region of an animal.

Postocular: Behind the eyes.

Pouch (marsupial): A flap of skin on the underbelly of female marsupials, which covers the mammillae. The pouch may be a simple, open structure as in most carnivorous marsupials, or a more enclosed pocket-like structure as in phalangers and kangaroos.

Precambrian: The oldest and most expansive of geological periods characterized by the appearance of primitive life forms.

Precocial: Well furred at birth adn able to move about independently.

Predator: An animal that hunts other animals for food.

Prehensile: Able to grip; mainly in respect of the tail of a mammal.

Premaxillae: Bones located in front of and between the maxillary bones in the upper jaw of vertebrates.

Prey: Aanimals that are hunted by predators.

Primary forest: Forest that has matured and remained undisturbed for several centuries.

Proboscis: A long flexible snout or trunk, as of an elephant; the slender, tubular feeding and sucking structure of some insects.

Process: An appendage; a part extending or projecting from an organ or organism.

Progenitor: A direct ancestor or originator of the line of descent.

Prosimian: Literally "before the monkeys"; a member of the relatively primitive primate suborder Prosimii (lemurs, lorises and tarsiers).

Protozoa: Single-shelled, usually microscopic organisms of the phylum or sub kingdom Protozoa, which included the most primitive forms of animal life.

Protractile premaxillaries: Bones located in the upper jaw of vertebrates that are capable of being extended.

Proximal: Toward the near or fixed end of a structure. Opposite of distal.

Pulmonate: Having lungs or a lunglike structure.

Quadrupedal: Using four limbs for locomotion.

Rack: The antlers of mammals in the family Cervidae, including deer and moose.

Radio tracking: Using an affixed transmitter to follow the movements of an animal.

Range: Geographical area wherein a species resides.

Refugial population: The animals protected in a refuge.

Relict: A localized species or population that has survived from an earlier epoch.

Reproductive phenology: The study of breeding as related to weather.

Rhinarium: The moist part around the nose that enhances smell in some animals, including dogs and prosimians.

Riffle: A rocky shoal or sandbar lying just below the surface of a river.

Riparian: Pertaining to the bank of a natural course of water.

Rufous: Strong yellowish pink to moderate orange or reddish-brown color.

Rumen: A compartment in the complex stomach of sheep, cattle and other ruminant animals where fibrous plant material is partially digested by the action of micro-organisms.

Rut: A period of sexual excitement; the mating season.

Sagittal: Relating to the structure that unites the two parietal bones of the skull that is most prominent in male gorillas..

Savanna (savannah): An extensive tropical vegetation dominated by grasses with varying mixtures of bushes and trees in open, wet land.

Scavenger: An animal that feeds on dead animals it did not kill.

Scrub: A plant community characterized by scattered, low-growing trees and shrubs, interspersed with herbs, grasses, and patches of bare soil.

Sebaceous: Pertaining to oily or greasy substances. Sebaceous glands in the skin produce a secretion that lubricates hairs and renders them water-resistant.

Sectorial: Cutting; in reference to teeth that are adapted to cutting flesh or the bodies of invertebrate animals by a shearing action.

Seepage water: Water flowing toward stream channels after infiltration into the ground.

Sexual dichromatism: Color pattern variation between the genders of the same species.

Sexual dimorphism: Size, color, or weight variation between genders of the same species.

Siltation: The process of depositing silt.

Solitary: Living alone. Animals that do not socialize.

Specialization: Evolution of a species so that it occupies a narrow place or niche in the community.

Species: A group of organisms with distinct characteristics that is capable of interbreeding and producing like offspring; the basic taxonomic category. The species epithet is the uncapitalized word that follows the genus name, as in *Phaner furcifer*.

Spine: In zoology, the spinal column of a vertebrate.

Stochastic: Chance or random events that could lead to the extinction or extirpation of a species.

Subalpine: A conifer-dominated forest which occurs in temperate latitudes; related to the boreal forest.

Subgenus: Taxonomical category between a genus and a species, such as dogs (**genus**) being divided to spaniels and terriers.

Subphylum: Subdivision of phylum composed of closely related groups of animals, such as vertebrates.

Subspecies: A classification level for a species subgroup that lives in a different geographical region which possess characteristics that are biologically different. The second uncapitalized word after the genus name designates the subspecies, as in *Gorilla gorilla beringei*.

Sulcus: Narrow fissures separating cerebral convolutions (convex folds on the surface of the brain).

Sympatric: Occupying the same geographic area without interbreeding.

Synchronous: In biology, the birth of all the young, usually hatching from eggs, at the same time.

Syndactylous: Having the third and fourth toes of the hindfoot joined together except at the tip, where there are two claws (as in bandicoots and diprotodont marsupials).

Synonyms: A taxonomic name that is equivalent to or replaced by another name.

Tarsus: In vertebrates, the section of the foot between the leg and metatarsus.

Tautonym: A taxonomic designation, such as *Gorilla gorilla*, commonly used in zoology in which the genus and species names are the same.

Taxon: A named group of organisms with common characteristics constituting one of the categories in taxonomic classification, such as phylum, order or family.

Taxonomy: The descriptive science of classifying and naming of organisms.

Terrestrial: Adapted to life on the ground.

Territory: The area that an animal or group actively defends from other members of its species.

Tolerance limit: Physical extremities beyond which a species cannot survive.

Turbid: Muddy; having sediment or foreign particles stirred up.

Type specimen: When a species is formally described for the first time, one of the specimens described is lodged in a museum to provide a permanent reference. It is known as the type, holotype or type specimen. Other specimens of the species, lodged at the same time as the holotype, are referred to as paratypes.

Ultisol: A type of mineral soil with an accumulation of silicate clay layers with an average soil temperature of 8 degrees Celsius or higher.

Understory: The lowest forest level, between the ground and 10 meters (33 feet).

Undulate: Moving in a smooth, wave-like motion.

Ungulate: having hoofs.

Ustic: a soil temperature regime common to subhumid and semiarid regions; moisture is limited; temperatures range between 5 degrees Celsius and 8 degrees Celsius at 50 centimeters depth.

Venter: In anatomy, the abdomen or belly; in biology, a swollen structure or part similar to a belly.

Ventral clinging and leaping: A type of locomotion in primates whose hind limbs are usually longer than their forelimbs, where the posture is parallel to the trunk of a tree when clinging and leaping from one trunk to another.

Ventrum: The belly region.

Vertebrate: An animal with a backbone.

Vibrissae: Long, stiff hairs, particularly on the face but also on the limbs, which extend the sense of touch or a mammal, i.e., the "whiskers" of a cat or mouse.

Viviparous: In zoology, giving birth to living offspring that develop within the mother's body.

Xeric: Adaptable to an extremely dry habitat.

Xeromorphic: Adaptable to drought conditions.

Yolk sac: A sac, usually containing yolk, which hangs from the ventral surface of the vertebrate fetus. In mammals, the yolk sac contains no yolk, but helps to nourish the embryonic young via a network of blood vessels.

Zygomatic arch: The bony arch in vertebrates that extends along the side or front of the skull beneath the orbit.

Zygotes: The cell formed through sexual union.

Country Index

Argentina

Blastocerus dichotomus	Marsh Deer	498
Chlamyphorus truncatus	Pink Fairy Armadillo	946
Chrysocyon brachyurus	Maned Wolf	758
Felis jacobita	Andean Cat	667
Felis [=Leopardus] pardalis	Ocelot	677
Felis [=Leopardus] tigrinus	Tiger Cat	694
Felis [=Leopardus] wiedi	Margay	699
Hippocamelus bisculus	South Andean Huemul	536
Lutra longicaudis	Long-tailed Otter	880
Lutra provocax	Southern [=Patagonian] River Otter	882
Ozotoceros bezoarticus	Pampas Deer	544
Panthera onca	Jaguar	715
Pteronura brasiliensis	Giant Otter	884
Pudu pudu	Pudu	547
Tapirus terrestris	Brazilian [=South American] Tapir	430

Australia

Antechinomys laniger	Eastern Jerboa Marsupial [=Kultarr]	784
Bettongia gaimardi	Gaimard's Rat-kangaroo	786
Bettongia lesueur	Lesueur's Rat-kangaroo [=Burrowing Bettong]	788
Bettongia penicillata	Brush-tailed Rat-kangaroo [=Bettong]	790
Bettongia tropica	Queensland Rat-kangaroo	792
Burramys parvus	Mountain Pygmy Possum	794
Caloprymnus campestris	Plains Rat-kangaroo	797
Chaeropus ecaudatus	Pig-footed Bandicoot	799
Dasyurus viverrinus	Eastern Native-cat [=Eastern Quoll]	801
Gymnobelideus leadbeateri	Leadbeater's Possum	805
Lagorchestes hirsutus	Western [=Rufous] Hare Wallaby	807
Lagostrophus fasciatus	Banded Hare Wallaby	810
Lasiorhinus krefftii	Hairy-nosed Wombat	812
Leporillus conditor	Greater Stick-nest Rat	918
Macropus giganteus	Eastern Gray Kangaroo	814
Macropus giganteus tasmaniensis	Tasmanian Forester Kangaroo	818
Macropus parma	Parma Wallaby	820
Macrotis lagotis	Greater Rabbit Bandicoot	822
Macrotis leucura	Lesser Rabbit Bandicoot	825
Myrmecobius fasciatus	Numbat	827
Notomys aquilo	Australian Native Mouse	920
Onychogalea fraenata	Bridled Nail-tailed Wallaby	830
Onychogalea lunata	Crescent Nail-tailed Wallaby	832
Parantechinus apicalis	Dibbler	834
Perameles bougainville	Barred Bandicoot	836

Perameles eremiana	Desert Bandicoot	838
Petrogale xanthopus	Yellow-footed Rock Wallaby	840
Planigale ingrami subtilissima	Little Planigale	842
Planigale tenuirostris	Southern Planigale	844
Pseudomys fieldi	Field's Mouse	922
Pseudomys fumeus	Smoky Mouse	924
Pseudomys gouldii	Gould's Mouse	926
Pseudomys occidentalis	Western Mouse	930
Pseudomys praeconis [=fieldi]	Shark Bay Mouse	932
Pseudomys shortridgei	Shortridge's Mouse	934
Pseudomys [=Gyomys] novaehollandiae	New Holland Mouse	928
Setonix brachyurus	Quokka	847
Sminthopsis longicaudata	Long-tailed Marsupial-mouse	849
Sminthopsis psammophila	Large Desert Marsupial-mouse	851
Thylacinus cynocephalus	Tasmanian Wolf [=Tasmanian Tiger]	853
Wyulda squamicaudata	Scaly-Tailed Possum	855
Xeromys myoide	False Water-rat	937
Zyzomys [=Laomys] pendunculatus	Central Rock-rat	
	[=Australian Native-mouse]	939

Bangladesh

Bos gaurus	Seledang [=Gaur]	569
Hylobates hoolock	Hoolock Gibbon	61
Panthera tigris tigris	Bengal Tiger	742
Presbytis [=semnopithecus] entellus	Entellus [=Sacred] Langur	99
Rhinoceros unicornis	Indian Rhinoceros	414
Trachypithecus pileatus	Capped Langur	108

Belize

Alouatta pigra [=villosa]	Guatemalan Howler Monkey	324

Benin

Cercopithecus erythrogaster	Red-bellied Monkey	
	[=White-throated Guenon]	265
Loxodonta africana	African Elephant	394
Pan troglodytes verus	Western Chimpanzee	42
Trichechus senegalensis	West African Manatee	999

Bhutan

Bos gaurus	**Seledang [=Gaur]**	569
Cervus elaphus wallichi	**Shou [=Sikkim Deer]**	515
Moschus spp.	**Musk Deer**	538
Panthera uncia	**Snow Leopard**	749
Rhinoceros unicornis	**Indian Rhinoceros**	414
Trachypithecus [=Presbytis] geei	**Golden Langur**	106

Bolivia

Blastocerus dichotomus	**Marsh Deer**	498
Callimico goeldii	**Goeldi's Marmoset**	361
Chinchilla brevicaudata boliviana	**Chinchilla**	911
Chrysocyon brachyurus	**Maned Wolf**	758
Felis jacobita	**Andean Cat**	667
Ozotoceros bezoarticus	**Pampas Deer**	544
Tapirus terrestris	**Brazilian [=South American] Tapir**	430
Vicugna vicugna	**Vicuna**	468

Botswana

Acinonyx jubatus	**Cheetah**	657
Diceros bicornis	**Black Rhinoceros**	405
Felis nigripes	**Black-footed Cat**	674
Hyaena brunnea	**Brown Hyena**	769
Loxodonta africana	**African Elephant**	394

Brazil

Blastocerus dichotomus	**Marsh Deer**	498
Brachyteles arachnoides	**Woolly Spider Monkey**	337
Bradypus torquatus	**Three-toed Brazilian [=Maned] Sloth**	942
Cacajao calvus calvus	**White Uakari**	339
Cacajao calvus rubicundus	**Red Uakari**	342
Cacajao melanocephalus	**Black [=Black-headed] Uakari**	345
Callimico goeldii	**Goeldi's Marmoset**	361
Callithrix aurita	**Buffy Tufted-ear Marmoset**	364
Callithrix flaviceps	**Buffy-headed Marmoset**	367
Chaetomys subspinosus	**Thin-spined Porcupine**	909
Chiropotes albinasus	**White Nosed Saki**	347
Chiropotes satanas satanas	**Southern Bearded Saki**	349
Chrysocyon brachyurus	**Maned Wolf**	758
Felis [=Leopardus] pardalis	**Ocelot**	677

Felis [=Leopardus] tigrinus	Tiger Cat	694
Leontopithecus caissara	Black-faced Lion Tamarin	370
Leontopithecus chrysomelas	Golden-headed Lion Tamarin	372
Leontopithecus chrysopygus	Golden-rumped [=Black] Lion Tamarin	375
Leontopithecus rosalia	Golden Lion Tamarin	378
Lutra longicaudis	Long-tailed Otter	880
Ozotoceros bezoarticus	Pampas Deer	544
Panthera onca	Jaguar	715
Priodontes maximus [=giganteus]	Giant Armadillo	951
Saguinus bicolor	Bared-faced [=Pied] Tamarin	381
Tapirus terrestris	Brazilian [=South American] Tapir	430
Trichechus inunguis	Amazonian Manatee	996

Burkina Faso

Loxodonta africana	African Elephant	394

Burma

Cervus eldi	Eld's Brow-Antlered Deer	519
Didermocerus sumatrensis	Sumatran Rhinoceros	408
Felis planiceps	Flat-headed Cat	683
Hylobates hoolock	Hoolock Gibbon	61
Moschus spp.	Musk Deer	538
Panthera tigris corbetti	Indochinese Tiger	733
Presbytis [=Semnopithecus] entellus	Entellus [=Sacred] Langur	99
Prionodon pardicolor	Spotted Linsang	870
Tapirus indicus [=Acrocodia indica]	Asian [=Malayan] Tapir	422
Trachypithecus pileatus	Capped Langur	108

Burundi

Cercopithecus lhoesti	L'hoest's Guenon	270
Lycacon pictus	African Wild Dog	765
Pan troglodytes schweinfurthi	Eastern Chimpanzee	33

Cambodia

Bos sauveli	Kouprey	576
Hylobates concolor	Crested [=Black] Gibbon	57
Hylobates pileatus	Pileated [= Capped] Gibbon	74
Nycticebus pygmaeus	Lesser Slow [=Pgymy] Loris	311
Prionodon pardicolor	Spotted Linsang	870

Pygathrix nemaeus	Douc [=Red-shanked Douc] Langur	94
Tapirus indicus [=Acrocodia indica]	Asian [=Malayan] Tapir	422

Cameroon

Aonyx [=Paraonyx] congica microdon	Cameroon Clawless Otter	876
Cercocebus torquatus	White-collared Mangabey	258
Cercopithecus erythrotis	Red-eared Nose-spotted Monkey [=Red-eared Guenon]	268
Colobus satanas	Black Colobus	116
Diceros bicornis	Black Rhinoceros	405
Gorilla gorilla gorilla	Western Lowland Gorilla	8
Loxodonta africana	African Elephant	394
Lycacon pictus	African Wild Dog	765
Mandrillus leucophaeus	Drill	247
Mandrillus sphinx	Mandrill	250
Pan troglodytes	Chimpanzee	30
Pan troglodytes troglodytes	Central Chimpanzee	37
Procolobus preussi	Preuss's Red Colobus	144
Trichechus senegalensis	West African Manatee	999

Canada

Bison bison athabascae	Wood Bison	566
Ursus americanus	American Black Bear	443

Central African Republic

Diceros bicornis	Black Rhinoceros	405
Gorilla gorilla gorilla	Western Lowland Gorilla	8
Loxodonta africana	African Elephant	394
Pan troglodytes	Chimpanzee	30
Pan troglodytes troglodytes	Central Chimpanzee	37

Central America

Ateles geoffroyi	Black-handed Spider Monkey	327
Felis [=Leopardus] pardalis	Ocelot	677
Felis [=Leopardus] tigrinus	Tiger cat	694
Felis [=Leopardus] wiedi	Margay	699
Tapirus bairdi	Central American Tapir	419

Chad

Diceros bicornis	Black Rhinoceros	405
Gazella leptoceros	Slender-horned (=Rhim) Gazelle	610
Loxodonta africana	African Elephant	394
Oryx dammah [=Oryx tao]	Scimitar-horned Oryx	625
Trichechus senegalensis	West African Manatee	999

Chile

Felis jacobita	Andean Cat	667
Hippocamelus antisensis	North Andean Huemul	534
Hippocamelus bisculus	South Andean Huemul	536
Lutra felina	Marine Otter	878
Lutra provocax	Southern [=Patagonian] River Otter	882
Pudu pudu	Pudu	547

China

Ailuropoda melanoleuca	Giant Panda	440
Bos grunniens mutus	Wild Yak	571
Camelus bactrianus	Wild Bactrian camel	466
Cervus elaphus macneilli	McNeill's [=Szechwan] Deer	513
Cervus elaphus yarkandensis	Yarkand Deer	517
Cervus nippon kopschi	South China Sika Deer	526
Equus hemionus	Asian Wild Ass	481
Equus przewalskii	Przewalski's Horse	483
Felis [=Prionailurus] bengalensis bengalensis	Leopard Cat	660
Felis [=Prionailurus] viverrinus	Fishing Cat	696
Felis [=Profelis] temmincki	Temminck's Cat	691
Lipotes vexillifer	Chinese River Dolphin	983
Macaca arctoides	Stump-tailed Macaque	232
Macaca thibetana	Tibetan Macaque	245
Neofelis nebulosa	Clouded Leopard	711
Ovis ammon	Argali	630
Panthera tigris	Tiger	721
Panthera tigris corbetti	Indochinese Tiger	733
Trachypithecus [=Presbytis] francoisi	Francois' Langur	104
Ursus arctos pruinosus	Horse[=Brown] Bear	455
Ursus [=Selenarctos] thibetanus	Asian Black Bear	458

China: Guizhou Province

Pygathrix [=Rhinopithecus] brelichi	Guizhou Snub-nosed Monkey	92

China: Hainan and Yunnan Provinces
Hylobates concolor

Crested [=Black] Gibbon

57

China: Hubei, Shaanxi, Gansu, Sichuan Provinces
Pygathrix [=Rhinopithecus] roxellana

Sichuan Snub-nosed Monkey

97

China: Manchuria
Panthera tigris amoyensis

Chinese Tiger

729

China: Shansi Province
Cervus nippon grassianus
Cervus nippon mandarinus

Shansi Sika Deer
North China Sika Deer

522
528

China: Tibet
Nemorhaedus goral

Goral

621

China: Yunnan Province
Elephas maximus
Hylobates hoolock
Hylobates lar
Moschus spp.
Pygathrix [=Rhinopithecus] bieti

Asian Elephant
Hoolock Gibbon
Lar Gibbon
Musk Deer
Yunnan Snub-nosed Monkey

391
61
67
538
90

Colombia

Ateles geoffroyi
Cacajao melanocephalus
Callimico goeldii
Chrysocyon brachyurus
Panthera onca
Pteronura brasiliensis
Saguinus leucopus

Saguinus oedipus
Tapirus bairdi
Tapirus pinchaque
Tapirus terrestris
Trichechus inunguis

Black-handed Spider Monkey
Black-headed Uakari
Goeldi's Marmoset
Maned Wolf
Jaguar
Giant Otter
Silvery-brown Bare-faced
  [=White-footed] Tamarin
Cotton-top Tamarin
Central American Tapir
Mountain Tapir
Brazilian [=South American] Tapir
Amazonian Manatee

327
345
361
758
715
884

383
385
419
427
430
996

Congo

Colobus satanas
Gorilla gorilla gorilla
Lycacon pictus
Mandrillus sphinx

Black Colobus
Western Lowland Gorilla
African Wild Dog
Mandrill

116
8
765
250

Pan troglodytes	Chimpanzee	30
Pan troglodytes troglodytes	Central Chimpanzee	37
Panthera pardus	Leopard	718
Procolobus badius bouvieri	Bouvier's Red Colobus	120
Trichechus senegalensis	West African Manatee	999

Congo, Republic of (formerly Zaire)

Acinonyx jubatus	Cheetah	657
Ceratotherium simum cottoni	Northern White Rhinoceros	401
Cercopithecus lhoesti	L'hoest's Guenon	270
Gorilla gorilla beringei	Mountain Gorilla	5
Gorilla gorilla graueri	Eastern Lowland Gorilla	14
Kobus leche	Lechwe	618
Loxodonta africana	African Elephant	394
Pan paniscus	Pygmy Chimpanzee	27
Pan troglodytes	Chimpanzee	30
Pan troglodytes schweinfurthi	Eastern Chimpanzee	33
Panthera pardus	Leopard	718
Procolobus badius ellioti	Elliot's Red Colobus	122
Procolobus badius oustaleti	Oustalet's Red Colobus	124
Procolobus pennantii tholloni	Thollon's Red Colobus	142
Procolobus rufomitratus foai	Foa Red Colobus	149
Trichechus senegalensis	West African Manatee	999

Costa Rica

Alouatta palliata	Mantled Howler Monkey	320
Ateles geoffroyi frontatus	Black-browed Spider Monkey	331
Ateles geoffroyi panamensis	Red Spider Monkey	334
Felis [=Herpailurus] yagouaroundi panamensis	Panamanian Jaguarundi	706
Felis [=Leopardus] tigrinus	Tiger Cat	694
Felis [=Profelis] concolor costaricensis	Costa Rican Puma	662
Saimiri oerstedii	Red-backed Squirrel Monkey	354

Cuba

Capromys angelcabrerai	Cabrera's Hutia	897
Capromys auritus	Large-eared Hutia	899
Capromys nana	Dwarf Hutia	901
Capromys sanfelipensis	Little Earth Hutia	903
Solenodon cubanus	Cuban Solenodon	889

Cyprus

Ovis gmelini ophion   **Cyprian Mouflon**   633

Dominican Republic

Solenodon paradoxus   **Haitian Solenodon**   891

Ecuador

Alouatta palliata	**Mantled Howler Monkey**	320
Hippocamelus antisensis	**North Andean Huemul**	534
Tapirus bairdi	**Central American Tapir**	419
Tapirus pinchaque	**Mountain Tapir**	427
Tapirus terrestris	**Brazilian [=South American] Tapir**	430
Trichechus inunguis	**Amazonian Manatee**	996

Egypt

Gazella leptoceros   **Slender-horned (=Rhim) Gazelle**   610

Equatorial Guinea (Island populations)

Cercopithecus erythrotis	**Red-eared Nose-spotted Monkey**	
	[=Red-eared Guenon]	268
Colobus satanas	**Black Colobus**	116
Loxodonta africana	**African Elephant**	394
Mandrillus leucophaeus	**Drill**	247
Mandrillus sphinx	**Mandrill**	250

Equatorial Guinea: Rio Muni (Mainland populations)
Gorilla gorilla gorilla	**Western Lowland Gorilla**	8
Pan troglodytes troglodytes	**Central Chimpanzee**	37

Eritrea

Alcelaphus buselaphus tora   **Tora Hartebeest**   559

Ethiopia

Acinonyx jubatus   **Cheetah**   657

Alcelaphus buselaphus swaynei	**Swayne's Hartebeest**	557
Alcelaphus buselaphus tora	**Tora Hartebeest**	559
Ammodorcas clarkei	**Clark's Gazelle [=Dibatag]**	561
Canis simensis	**Simien Fox**	755
Capra walie	**Walia Ibex**	590
Diceros bicornis	**Black Rhinoceros**	405
Equus africanus [=asinus]	**African Ass**	474
Loxodonta africana	**African Elephant**	394
Theropithecus gelada	**Gelada Baboon**	253

Finland

Phoca hispida saimensis	**Saimaa Seal**	989

Gabon

Cercocebus torquatus	**White-collared Mangabey**	258
Colobus satanas	**Black Colobus**	116
Gorilla gorilla gorilla	**Western Lowland Gorilla**	8
Loxodonta africana	**African Elephant**	394
Mandrillus sphinx	**Mandrill**	250
Pan troglodytes	**Chimpanzee**	30
Pan troglodytes troglodytes	**Central Chimpanzee**	37
Panthera pardus	**Leopard**	718
Trichechus senegalensis	**West African Manatee**	999

Gambia

Colobus polykomos	**Western Black-and-white Colobus**	113
Pan troglodytes verus	**Western Chimpanzee**	42
Procolobus badius temminckii	**Temminck's Red Colobus**	127
Trichechus senegalensis	**West African Manatee**	999

Ghana

Cercocebus torquatus	**White-collared Mangabey**	258
Cercocebus torquatus atys	**Sooty Mangabey**	260
Cercopithecus diana	**Diana Monkey**	262
Loxodonta africana	**African Elephant**	394
Pan troglodytes	**Chimpanzee**	30
Pan troglodytes verus	**Western Chimpanzee**	42
Procolobus badius waldroni	**Miss Waldron's Bay Colobus**	130
Procolobus verus	**Olive [=Van Beneden's] Colobus**	151
Trichechus senegalensis	**West African Manatee**	999

Guam

Pteropus mariannus mariannus	**Mariana Fruit Bat**	962

Guatemala

Alouatta palliata	**Mantled Howler Monkey**	320
Alouatta pigra [=villosa]	**Guatemalan Howler Monkey**	324
Felis [=Herpailurus] yagouaroundi tolteca	**Sinaloan Jaguarundi**	709
Panthera onca	**Jaguar**	715

Guinea

Cercopithecus diana	**Diana Monkey**	262
Colobus polykomos	**Western Black-and-white Colobus**	113
Loxodonta africana	**African Elephant**	394
Pan troglodytes	**Chimpanzee**	30
Pan troglodytes verus	**Western Chimpanzee**	42
Procolobus badius temminckii	**Temminck's Red Colobus**	127
Procolobus verus	**Olive [=Van Beneden's] Colobus**	151
Trichechus senegalensis	**West African Manatee**	999

Guinea-Bissau

Colobus polykomos	**Western Black-and-white Colobus**	113
Loxodonta africana	**African Elephant**	394
Pan troglodytes verus	**Western Chimpanzee**	42
Procolobus badius temminckii	**Temminck's Red Colobus**	127
Trichechus senegalensis	**West African Manatee**	999

Guyana

Priodontes maximus [=giganteus]	**Giant Armadillo**	951
Pteronura brasiliensis	**Giant Otter**	884
Trichechus inunguis	**Amazonian Manatee**	996

Haiti

Solenodon paradoxus	**Haitian Solenodon**	891

India

Bos grunniens mutus	Wild Yak	571
Caprolagus hispidus	Hispid Hare [=Bristly Rabbit]	859
Cervus duvauceli	Swamp Deer [=Barasingha]	503
Cervus eldi	Eld's Brow-Antlered Deer	519
Cuon alpinus	Dhole [=Asiatic Wild Dog]	760
Equus hemionus	Asian Wild Ass	481
Felis margarita scheffeli	Pakistan Sand Cat	669
Felis [=Prionailurus] bengalensis bengalensis	Leopard Cat	660
Felis [=Prionailurus] viverrinus	Fishing Cat	696
Macaca arctoides	Stump-tailed Macaque	232
Macaca silenus	Lion-tailed Macaque	240
Ovis vignei vignei	Shapo	636
Panthera leo perscia	Asiatic Lion	713
Panthera tigris	Tiger	721
Panthera tigris tigris	Bengal Tiger	742
Panthera uncia	Snow Leopard	749
Presbytis [=Semnopithecus] entellus	Entellus [=Sacred] Langur	99
Rhinoceros unicornis	Indian Rhinoceros	414
Sus salvanius	Pygmy Hog	650
Trachypithecus pileatus	Capped Langur	108
Trachypithecus [=Presbytis] geei	Golden Langur	106
Ursus [=Selenarctos] thibetanus	Asian Black Bear	458
Viverra megaspila civettina	Malabar Large-spotted Civet	872

India: Assam region

Hylobates hoolock	Hoolock Gibbon	61
Prionodon pardicolor	Spotted Linsang	870

India: Kashmir region

Ovis ammon	Argali	630
Cervus elaphus hanglu	Hanglu [=Kashmir Stag}	511

Indochina

Elephas maximus	Asian Elephant	391
Felis [=Pardofelis] marmorata	Marbled Cat	672
Felis [=Prionailurus] viverrinus	Fishing Cat	696
Felis [=Profelis] temmincki	Temminck's Cat	691

Indonesia

Babyrousa babyrussa	Babirusa	648

Elephas maximus	Asian Elephant	391
Felis [=Pardofelis] marmorata	Marbled Cat	672
Panthera tigris	Tiger	721

Indonesia: Bawean Islands

Axis porcinus kuhli	Bawean [=Kuhl's] deer	496

Indonesia: Borneo

Hylobates agilis	Agile Gibbon	54
Hylobates muelleri	Mueller's Gibbon	72
Pongo pygmaeus	Borneo [=Common] Orangutan	22

Indonesia: Borneo, Bali, and Java

Bos gaurus	Seledang [=Gaur]	569
Bos javanicus	Banteng	574

Indonesia: Borneo: Brunei

Nasalis larvatus	Proboscis Monkey	86

Indonesia: Java

Cuon alpinus	Dhole [=Asiatic Wild Dog]	760
Hylobates moloch	Moloch Gibbon	70
Panthera [=Neofelis] tigris sondaica	Javan Tiger	736
Rhinoceros sondaicus	Javan Rhinoceros	411

Indonesia: Java and Sumatra

Felis [=Prionailurus] viverrinus	Fishing Cat	696

Indonesia: Mentawai Islands

Hylobates klossii	Kloss' [= Mentawai] Gibbon	64
Nasalis (Simias) concolor	Pagai Island Mangabey	84
Presbytis potenziani	Mentawai Island Langur	102

Indonesia: Sulawesi Island

Bubalus depressicornis	Lowland Anoa	578
Bubalus quarlesi	Mountain Anoa	582

Indonesia: Sumatra

Capricornis sumatraensis	Serow	592
Hylobates agilis	Agile Gibbon	54
Hylobates lar	Lar Gibbon	67
Hylobates syndactylus	Siamang Gibbon	76
Panthera [=Neofelis] tigris sumatrae	Sumatran Tiger	739
Pongo abelii	Sumatran [=Abel's] Orangutan	18
Tapirus indicus [=Acrocodia indica]	Asian [=Malayan] Tapir	422

Indonesia: Sumatra and Borneo

Didermocerus sumatrensis	Sumatran Rhinoceros	408
Felis planiceps	Flat-headed Cat	683
Felis [=Profelis] temmincki	Temminck'sCat	691
Neofelis nebulosa	Clouded Leopard	711

Iran

Equus hemionus	Asian Wild Ass	481
Felis margarita scheffeli	Pakistan Sand Cat	669
Dama dama mesopotamica	Persian Fallow Deer	532
Panthera tigris	Tiger	721
Panthera tigris virgata	Caspian [=Turanian] Tiger	747
Acinonyx jubatus	Cheetah	657
Ursus [=Selenarctos] thibetanus gedrosianus	Baluchistan Bear	462

Iraq

Dama dama mesopotamica	Persian Fallow Deer	532

Israel

Gazella dorcas saudiya	Saudi Arabian Gazelle	606
Gazella gazella	Arabian Gazelle	608
Oryx leucoryx	Arabian Oryx	628

Italy

Rupicapra rupicapra ornata	Chamois	638
Ursus arctos arctos	Brown Bear (Italian population)	447

Italy: Sardinia

Cervus elaphus corsicanus	Corsican Red Deer	509

Ivory Coast

Cephalophus jentinki	Jentink's Duiker	594
Cercocebus torquatus	White-collared Mangabey	258
Cercocebus torquatus atys	Sooty Mangabey	260
Cercopithecus diana	Diana Monkey	262
Colobus polykomos	Western Black-and-white Colobus	113
Loxodonta africana	African Elephant	394
Pan troglodytes verus	Western Chimpanzee	42

Procolobus badius waldroni	Miss Waldron's Bay Colobus	130
Procolobus verus	Olive [=Van Beneden's] Colobus	151
Trichechus senegalensis	West African Manatee	999

Japan

Macaca fuscata	Japanese Macaque	237
Ursus [=Selenarctos] thibetanus	Asian Black Bear	458

Japan: Iriomote Island
Felis [=Prionailurus] iriomotensis	Iriomote Cat	665

Japan: Ryukyu Islands
Cervus nippon keramae	Ryukyu Sika Deer	524
Pentalagus furnessi	Ryukyu [=Amami] Rabbit	861

Jordan

Gazella dorcas saudiya	Saudi Arabian Gazelle	606
Gazella subgutturosa marica	Sand Gazelle	612
Oryx leucoryx	Arabian Oryx	628

Kazakhstan

Ovis ammon	Argali	630
Panthera uncia	Snow Leopard	749

Kenya

Acinonyx jubatus	Cheetah	657
Cercocebus galeritus	Tana River Mangabey	256
Equus grevyi	Grevy's Zebra	477
Loxodonta africana	African Elephant	394
Panthera pardus	Leopard	718
Procolobus rufomitratus	Tana River Red Colobus	146

Korea

Eschrichtius robustus	Gray Whale	980
Moschus spp.	Musk Deer	538

Laos

Bos gaurus	Seledang [=Gaur]	569
Bos javanicus	Banteng	574
Hylobates concolor	Crested [=Black] Gibbon	57
Nycticebus pygmaeus	Lesser Slow [=Pgymy] Loris	311
Prionodon pardicolor	Spotted Linsang	870
Pygathrix nemaeus	Douc [=Red-shanked Douc] Langur	94
Tapirus indicus [=Acrocodia indica]	Asian [=Malayan] Tapir	422
Trachypithecus [=Presbytis] francoisi	Francois' Langur	104
Ursus [=Selenarctos] thibetanus	Asian Black Bear	458

Liberia

Cephalophus jentinki	Jentink's Duiker	594
Cercocebus torquatus	White-collared Mangabey	258
Cercocebus torquatus atys	Sooty Mangabey	260
Cercopithecus diana	Diana Monkey	262
Colobus polykomos	Western Black-and-white Colobus	113
Loxodonta africana	African Elephant	394
Pan troglodytes verus	Western Chimpanzee	42
Procolobus verus	Olive [=Van Beneden's] Colobus	151
Trichechus senegalensis	West African Manatee	999

Libya

Gazella leptoceros	Slender-horned (=Rhim) Gazelle	610

Madagascar

Allocebus trichotis	Hairy-eared Dwarf Lemur	155
Avahi laniger	Avahi [=Woolly Lemur]	281
Cheirogaleus major	Greater Dwarf Lemur	158
Cheirogaleus medius	Fat-tailed Dwarf Lemur	161
Daubentonia madagascariensis	Aye-Aye	274
Eulemur coronatus	Crowned Lemur	179
Eulemur fulvus collaris	Brown-collared Lemur	182
Eulemur macaco flavifrons	Sclater's [=Blue-eyed] Lemur	184
Eulemur macaco macaco	Black Lemur	186
Eulemur mongoz	Mongoose Lemur	188
Eulemur rubriventer	Red-bellied Lemur	191
Hapalemur aureus	Golden Bamboo Lemur	194
Hapalemur griseus alaotrensis	Alaotran [=Grey] Gentle Lemur	197

Hylobates syndactylus	**Siamang Gibbon**	76
Macaca arctoides	**Stump-tailed Macaque**	232
Nasalis larvatus	**Proboscis Monkey**	86
Panthera tigris corbetti	**Indochinese Tiger**	733
Tapirus indicus [=Acrocodia indica]	**Asian [=Malayan] Tapir**	422

Mali

Loxodonta africana	**African Elephant**	394
Pan troglodytes verus	**Western Chimpanzee**	42
Taurotragus derbianus derbianus	**Western Giant Eland**	643
Trichechus senegalensis	**West African Manatee**	999

Mariana Islands (Guam)

Pteropus tokudae	**Little Mariana Fruit Bat**	969

Mato Grosso

Ozotoceros bezoarticus	**Pampas Deer**	544

Mauritius

Pteropus rodricensis	**Rodrigues Island Flying Fox Fruit Bat**	967

Mexico

Alouatta palliata	**Mantled Howler Monkey**	320
Alouatta pigra [=villosa]	**Guatemalan Howler Monkey**	324
Antilocapra americana peninsularis	**Peninsular Pronghorn**	563
Ateles geoffroyi	**Black-handed Spider Monkey**	327
Cynomys mexicanus	**Mexican Prairie Dog**	763
Felis rufus escuinapae [=Lynx rufus]	**Bobcat**	685
Felis [=Herpailurus] yagouaroundi cacomitli	**Gulf Coast Jaguarundi**	701
Felis [=Herpailurus] yagouaroundi fossata	**Jaguarundi**	704
Felis [=Herpailurus] yagouaroundi tolteca	**Sinaloan Jaguarundi**	709
Felis [=Leopardus] wiedi	**Margay**	699

Mexico

Felis [=Leopardus] pardalis	**Ocelot**	677

Odocoileus hemionus cedrosensis	Cedros Island Mule Deer	542
Panthera onca	Jaguar	715
Phocoena sinus	Cochito [=Vaquita]	991
Romerolagus diazi	Volcano Rabbit	863
Tapirus bairdi	Central American Tapir	419
Ursus americanus	American Black Bear	443
Ursus arctos nelsoni	Mexican Silver Grizzly	453

Mongolia

Camelus bactrianus	Wild Bactrian camel	466
Castor fiber birulai	Mongolian Beaver	905
Equus przewalskii	Przewalski's Horse	483
Moschus spp.	Musk Deer	538
Panthera tigris virgata	Caspian [=Turanian] Tiger	747
Panthera uncia	Snow Leopard	749
Saiga tatarica mongolica	Mongolian Saiga	640

Morocco

Gazella cuvieri	Cuvier's Gazelle	598
Gazella dama lozanoi	Rio de Oro Dama Gazelle	600
Gazella dama mhorr	Mhorr Gazelle	600
Gazella dorcas massaesyla	Moroccan (=Dorcas) Gazelle	602
Hyaena hyaena barbara	Barbary Hyena	772

Mozambique

Acinonyx jubatus	Cheetah	657
Diceros bicornis	Black Rhinoceros	405
Hyaena brunnea	Brown Hyena	769
Loxodonta africana	African Elephant	394
Lycacon pictus	African Wild Dog	765

Myanmar

Bos javanicus	Banteng	574
Hylobates lar	Lar Gibbon	67
Muntiacus feae	Fea's Muntjac	540

Namibia

Acinonyx jubatus	Cheetah	657
Aepyceros melampus petersi	Black-faced Impala	554
Diceros bicornis	Black Rhinoceros	405
Equus zebra hartmannae	Hartmann's Mountain Zebra	485
Felis nigripes	Black-footed Cat	674
Hyaena brunnea	Brown Hyena	769
Kobus leche	Lechwe	618
Loxodonta africana	African Elephant	394

Natal

Hyaena brunnea	Brown Hyena	769

Nepal

Bos gaurus	Seledang [=Gaur]	569
Cervus duvauceli	Swamp Deer [=Barasingha]	503
Felis [=Pardofelis] marmorata	Marbled Cat	672
Felis [=Profelis] temmincki	Temminck's Cat	691
Moschus spp.	Musk Deer	538
Neofelis nebulosa	Clouded Leopard	711
Panthera tigris tigris	Bengal Tiger	742
Panthera uncia	Snow Leopard	749
Prionodon pardicolor	Spotted Linsang	870
Rhinoceros unicornis	Indian Rhinoceros	414
Ursus [=Selenarctos] thibetanus	Asian Black Bear	458

Nicaragua

Ateles geoffroyi frontatus	Black-browed Spider Monkey	331
Felis [=Herpailurus] yagouaroundi fossata	Jaguarundi	704
Felis [=Herpailurus] yagouaroundi panamensis	Panamanian Jaguarundi	706

Niger

Gazella leptoceros	Slender-horned (=Rhim) Gazelle	610
Loxodonta africana	African Elephant	394
Trichechus senegalensis	West African Manatee	999

Nigeria

Aonyx [=Paraonyx] congica microdon	Cameroon Clawless Otter	876
Cercocebus torquatus	White-collared Mangabey	258
Cercocebus torquatus atys	Sooty Mangabey	260
Cercopithecus erythrogaster	Red-bellied Monkey [=White-throated Guenon]	265
Cercopithecus erythrotis	Red-eared Nose-spotted Monkey [=Red-eared Guenon]	268
Gorilla gorilla gorilla	Western Lowland Gorilla	8
Mandrillus leucophaeus	Drill	247
Pan troglodytes	Chimpanzee	30
Pan troglodytes troglodytes	Central Chimpanzee	37
Procolobus verus	Olive [=Van Beneden's] Colobus	151
Trichechus senegalensis	West African Manatee	999

Oman

Gazella gazella	Arabian Gazelle	608
Hemitragus jayakari	Arabian Tahr	614
Oryx leucoryx	Arabian Oryx	628

Orange Free State (South Africa)

Hyaena brunnea	Brown Hyena	769

Pacific Ocean (South)

Dugong dugon	Dugong	975

Pakistan

Capra falconeri	Markhor Goat	584
Equus hemionus	Asian Wild Ass	481
Felis margarita scheffeli	Pakistan Sand Cat	669
Ovis ammon	Argali	630
Platanista minor	Indus River Dolphin	993
Presbytis [=Semnopithecus] entellus	Entellus [=Sacred] Langur	99
Rhinoceros unicornis	Indian Rhinoceros	414
Ursus [=Selenarctos] thibetanus gedrosianus	Baluchistan Bear	462

Panama

Ateles geoffroyi panamensis	Red Spider Monkey	334
Felis [=Herpailurus] yagouaroundi panamensis	Panamanian Jaguarundi	706
Saguinus oedipus	Cotton-top Tamarin	385
Saimiri oerstedii	Red-backed Squirrel Monkey	354

Papua New Guinea

Aproteles bulmeri	Bulmer's Flying Fox Fruit Bat	956
Dorcopsis atrata	Black Dorcopsis Wallaby	803

Paraguay

Blastocerus dichotomus	Marsh Deer	498
Chrysocyon brachyurus	Maned Wolf	758
Felis [=Leopardus] wiedi	Margay	699
Lutra longicaudis	Long-tailed Otter	880
Ozotoceros bezoarticus	Pampas Deer	544

Peru

Ateles geoffroyi	Black-handed Spider Monkey	327
Blastocerus dichotomus	Marsh Deer	498
Cacajao calvus calvus	White Uakari	339
Callimico goeldii	Goeldi's Marmoset	361
Felis jacobita	Andean Cat	667
Hippocamelus antisensis	North Andean Huemul	534
Lagothrix flavicauda	Yellow-tailed Woolly Monkey	352
Lutra felina	Marine Otter	878
Trichechus inunguis	Amazonian Manatee	996
Vicugna vicugna	Vicuna	468

Philippine Islands

Axis porcinus calamianensis	Philippine Deer	494
Bubalus mindorensis	Tamaraw	580
Tarsius syrichta	Philippine Tarsier	315

Philippine Islands: Leyte, Samar, Negros, and Panay islands

Cervus alfredi	Visayan Deer	500

Portugal

Monachus monachus	**Mediterranean Monk Seal**	986

Republic of Congo (formerly Zaire)

Acinonyx jubatus	**Cheetah**	657
Ceratotherium simum cottoni	**Northern White Rhinoceros**	401
Cercopithecus lhoesti	**L'hoest's Guenon**	270
Gorilla gorilla beringei	**Mountain Gorilla**	5
Gorilla gorilla graueri	**Eastern Lowland Gorilla**	14
Kobus leche	**Lechwe**	618
Loxodonta africana	**African Elephant**	394
Pan paniscus	**Pygmy Chimpanzee**	27
Pan troglodytes	**Chimpanzee**	30
Pan troglodytes schweinfurthi	**Eastern Chimpanzee**	33
Panthera pardus	**Leopard**	718
Procolobus badius ellioti	**Elliot's Red Colobus**	122
Procolobus badius oustaleti	**Oustalet's Red Colobus**	124
Procolobus pennantii tholloni	**Thollon's Red Colobus**	142
Procolobus rufomitratus foai	**Foa Red Colobus**	149
Trichechus senegalensis	**West African Manatee**	999

Russia

Capra falconeri	**Markhor Goat**	584
Cervus elaphus bactrianus	**Bactrian Deer**	505
Eschrichtius robustus	**Gray Whale**	980
Panthera tigris	**Tiger**	721
Panthera tigris virgata	**Caspian [=Turanian] Tiger**	747
Ursus arctos beringianus	**Kamchatka Bear**	450
Ursus [=Selenarctos] thibetanus	**Asian Black Bear**	458

Russia: Siberia

Moschus spp.	**Musk Deer**	538
Nemorhaedus goral	**Goral**	621
Panthera tigris altaica	**Siberian Tiger**	724

Rwanda

Cercopithecus lhoesti	**L'hoest's Guenon**	270
Diceros bicornis	**Black Rhinoceros**	405
Gorilla gorilla beringei	**Mountain Gorilla**	5
Loxodonta africana	**African Elephant**	394

South Africa

Acinonyx jubatus	Cheetah	657
Damaliscus dorcas dorcas	Bontebok	596
Diceros bicornis	Black Rhinoceros	405
Equus zebra zebra	Cape Mountain Zebra	487
Felis nigripes	Black-footed Cat	674
Hyaena brunnea	Brown Hyena	769
Manis temmincki	Cape [=Temminck's Ground] Pangolin	948

Spain

Capra pyrenaica pyrenaica	Pyrenean Ibex	587
Felis pardina	Spanish Lynx	681
Monachus monachus	Mediterranean Monk Seal	986

Sri Lanka

Elephas maximus	Asian Elephant	391
Macaca sinica	Toque Macaque	243
Panthera pardus	Leopard	718
Presbytis [=Semnopithecus] entellus	Entellus [=Sacred] Langur	99
Trachypithecus vetulus	Purple-faced Langur	111

Sudan

Acinonyx jubatus	Cheetah	657
Alcelaphus buselaphus tora	Tora Hartebeest	559
Ceratotherium simum cottoni	Northern White Rhinoceros	401
Diceros bicornis	Black Rhinoceros	405
Equus africanus [=asinus]	African Ass	474
Gazella leptoceros	Slender-horned (=Rhim) Gazelle	610
Loxodonta africana	African Elephant	394
Pan troglodytes schweinfurthi	Eastern Chimpanzee	33

Surinam

Tapirus terrestris	Brazilian [=South American] Tapir	430

Syria

Gazella dorcas saudiya	Saudi Arabian Gazelle	606

Tadzhikistan

Panthera uncia	Snow Leopard	749

Taiwan

Cervus nippon taiouanus	Formosan Sika Deer	530
Macaca cyclopis	Formosan Rock [=Taiwan] Macaque	235
Martes flavigula chrysospila	Formosan Yellow-throated Marten	868
Neofelis nebulosa	Clouded Leopard	711

Tanzania

Acinonyx jubatus	Cheetah	657
Diceros bicornis	Black Rhinoceros	405
Loxodonta africana	African Elephant	394
Neotragus moschatus moschatus	Zanzibar Suni	623
Pan troglodytes	Chimpanzee	30
Pan troglodytes schweinfurthi	Eastern Chimpanzee	33
Procolobus pennantii tephrosceles	Uganda Red Colobus	139

Tanzania: Zanzibar Island

Procolobus pennantii kirkii	Zanzibar Red Colobus	136
Procolobus pennantii gordonorum	Uhehe [=Pennant's] Red Colobus	133

Thailand

Axis porcinus annamiticus	Hog Deer	491
Bos gaurus	Seledang [=Gaur]	569
Bos javanicus	Banteng	574
Bos sauveli	Kouprey	576
Cervus eldi	Eld's Brow-antlered Deer	519
Craseonycteris thonglongyai	Bumblebee Bat	958
Cuon alpinus	Dhole [=Asiatic Wild Dog]	760
Felis planiceps	Flat-headed Cat	683
Felis [=Prionailurus] bengalensis bengalensis	Leopard Cat	660
Hylobates lar	Lar Gibbon	67
Hylobates pileatus	Pileated [= Capped] Gibbon	74
Muntiacus feae	Fea's Muntjac	540
Tapirus indicus [=Acrocodia indica]	Asian [=Malayan] Tapir	422

Tibet

Bos grunniens mutus	**Wild Yak**	571
Cervus elaphus wallichi	**Shou [=Sikkim Deer]**	515
Macaca thibetana	**Tibetan Macaque**	245
Moschus spp.	**Musk Deer**	538
Ovis ammon	**Argali**	630
Pygathrix [=Rhinopithecus] bieti	**Yunnan Snub-nosed Monkey**	90
Ursus arctos pruinosus	**Horse[=Brown] Bear**	455

Togo

Loxodonta africana	**African Elephant**	394
Lycaon pictus	**African Wild Dog**	765
Trichechus senegalensis	**West African Manatee**	999

Tunisia

Cervus elaphus barbarus	**Barbary Deer**	507
Gazella cuvieri	**Cuvier's Gazelle**	598
Gazella dorcas massaesyla	**Moroccan (=Dorcas) Gazelle**	602
Gazella leptoceros	**Slender-horned (=Rhim) Gazelle**	610
Hyaena hyaena barbara	**Barbary Hyena**	772

Turkey

Panthera tigris	**Tiger**	721
Panthera tigris virgata	**Caspian [=Turanian] Tiger**	747

Uganda

Cercopithecus lhoesti	**L'hoest's Guenon**	270
Gorilla gorilla beringei	**Mountain Gorilla**	5
Loxodonta africana	**African Elephant**	394
Lycaon pictus	**African Wild Dog**	765
Pan troglodytes	**Chimpanzee**	30
Pan troglodytes schweinfurthi	**Eastern Chimpanzee**	33
Panthera pardus	**Leopard**	718
Procolobus badius ellioti	**Elliot's Red Colobus**	122
Procolobus pennantii tephrosceles	**Uganda Red Colobus**	139

United Arab Emirates

Hemitragus jayakari	**Arabian Tahr**	614

Uruguay

Felis [=Leopardus] wiedi	**Margay**	699
Lutra longicaudis	**Long-tailed Otter**	880
Ozotoceros bezoarticus	**Pampas Deer**	544

Venezuela

Cacajao melanocephalus	**Black-headed Uakari**	345
Tapirus terrestris	**Brazilian [=South American] Tapir**	430

Vietnam

Axis porcinus annamiticus	**Hog Deer**	491
Bos gaurus	**Seledang [=Gaur]**	569
Bos javanicus	**Banteng**	574
Hylobates concolor	**Crested [=Black] Gibbon**	57
Macaca arctoides	**Stump-tailed Macaque**	232
Moschus spp.	**Musk Deer**	538
Nycticebus pygmaeus	**Lesser Slow [=Pgymy] Loris**	311
Prionodon pardicolor	**Spotted Linsang**	870
Pygathrix nemaeus	**Douc [=Red-shanked Douc] Langur**	94
Pygathrix [=Rhinopithecus] avunculus	**Tonkin Snub-nosed Monkey**	88
Tapirus indicus [=Acrocodia indica]	**Asian [=Malayan] Tapir**	422
Trachypithecus [=Presbytis] francoisi	**Francois' Langur**	104

Yeman

Gazella gazella	**Arabian Gazelle**	608

Zaire (now Republic of Congo)

Acinonyx jubatus	**Cheetah**	657
Ceratotherium simum cottoni	**Northern White Rhinoceros**	401
Cercopithecus lhoesti	**L'hoest's Guenon**	270
Gorilla gorilla beringei	**Mountain Gorilla**	5

Master Index

See Contents, page iii, for animals grouped by families/type
See Country Index, page 1031, for animals grouped by regions

A

C

F

R

S

U

V

W